SYSTEMS:

D1543041

RESEARCH AND DESIGN

PUBLICATIONS FROM THE SYSTEMS RESEARCH CENTER,
CASE INSTITUTE OF TECHNOLOGY

Donald P. Eckman, Director
SYSTEMS: RESEARCH AND DESIGN

SYSTEMS:

RESEARCH AND DESIGN

proceedings of The First Systems
Symposium at Case Institute of
Technology

edited by
DONALD P. ECKMAN

Professor of Instrumentation Engineering
and Director of Systems Research Center
Case Institute of Technology

New York • London, John Wiley & Sons, Inc.

FOREWORD

It is becoming evident that we are in a new and different kind of a race today—a race that symposiums such as this can make a significant contribution toward winning. We are all familiar with the current contest between the West and Russia, but this is not the race to which I refer, although the contest with Russia has an important bearing on it.

The race that I want to discuss here has to do with systems engineering itself. There are two contestants in this race: systems engineering *versus* the rapidly increasing complexity of our growing technological civilization. The outcome of the race will be determined, in effect, by whether systems engineering as a discipline is able to grow and develop quickly enough to successfully meet the problems of the future, which we can see will be ever more pressing and difficult.

The systems operations of the world, be they military, production, communications, or transportation, are every day becoming more complex, faster paced, geographically more widespread. Although the increasing complexity of our civilization results in part simply from the growth in population, the major share comes from the increasingly extensive use we are making of science and technology in both our military and nonmilitary activities. As a direct consequence of this situation, and this is most important, we are now reaching the point where the issues of military defense and the standard of living are being joined by a third issue, one that is new to us. This is the hard fact that the complexity of our civilization, with all of its interconnections and interactions, is growing so rapidly that there is a real danger we shall be unable to avoid chaos in our daily operations.

It is obvious that the one chance we have to avoid chaos depends upon even more advanced applications of science and technology to the problems involved. It is also obvious that the systems engineering approach will be mandatory in handling these problems. At this point, it might be well to review some of the characteristics of modern systems engineering.

We might start with the role of science. Not only are many more people at work in the field of science, with many new discoveries resulting, but much more than in the past we are making immediate application of the newest scientific discoveries. In fact, it is not unusual for us to start work on the practical applications before the scientific work itself is completed. Beyond this, many of our newer systems are so complex or so sophisticated that the basic techniques and theoretical approaches common to science must be employed if the systems engineering is to be performed on a sound basis. This intimate involvement with science is an important characteristic of modern systems engineering.

Another factor that makes necessary the use of scientific and quantitative techniques is the increased pace of these times. New systems must be developed and carried through to completion on a much shorter time scale than we have been accustomed to in the past, and the rate of technological obsolescence is likewise much faster. We no longer have time for leisurely cut-and-try methods in many instances, even if we could afford their cost.

Because of the complexity of our civilization, we find much more often in the engineering of new systems that it is important for us to take into account the relationships between the new system and already existing systems and organizations. This matter of interrelationships has a further aspect; namely, that nontechnical factors are coming to play a major role in modern systems engineering. The economic, military, governmental, and even sociologic considerations enter more and more frequently into systems engineering decisions. For a large-scale systems project, the problem of merely making arrangements to get the project under way may be the most difficult to solve of all the problems involved. A part of this is the decision-making problem. Too often these days it takes longer to get, from all of the parties involved, a decision to go ahead on a particular project than it takes to accomplish the project itself.

Another characteristic of modern systems engineering is the fact that the systems engineer has to cope with an exceedingly difficult analysis problem. The mathematical equations that describe a complex system are so complicated and so numerous that it would be futile to attempt to solve them by hand. Such analysis can be accomplished only by using large-scale computers and simulators. In fact, it could be said that systems engineering in today's sense became possible only with the introduction of the large digital computer. Simulators are equally necessary for solving certain problems that cannot be handled efficiently on digital computers or that are not understood well enough for satisfactory mathematical formulation (trial-and-error techniques, of course, are still practical tools for many subsystem and component problems).

A further factor in the modern systems approach is the recognition given to the human element in the system. We attempt to design a system not only so that we do not ask too much of the human beings in the system but so that we do not ask too little. We have had long experience with the extension and replacement of man's muscles by the machine. Now we are engaged in a similar substitution with respect to man's senses and his brain. Of course, no computer that is in existence or that is foreseeable has more than a tiny fraction of the ability of man's brain. But there are many narrow functions—particularly those involving large quantities of data, high speeds, and simple decisions—where a computer can far excel man. We can expect that systems which will relieve man of routine mental effort will become the greatest growth industry of the coming generation, making it possible to reserve man for the higher intellectual tasks to which he is uniquely suited.

It is now generally accepted that we are in transition today toward a new, highly technological age. As has already been pointed out, the systems operations of our civilization are every day becoming more complex, more interrelated, faster paced, more geographically widespread. These systems encompass not only the military defense systems required for our national survival, but the systems that are necessary to handle our everyday peacetime pursuits, be they production, communications, transportation, or tax collection. It is clear that there will be an increasing dependence on systems engineering in order to achieve a more secure world and a more orderly one that will be able to provide for the needs of the earth's rapidly growing populations. It is equally clear that systems engineering itself will have to develop and grow rapidly as a scientific, quantitative discipline if it is to be able to meet successfully these challenges of the future.

SIMON RAMO
Executive Vice President
Thompson Ramo Wooldridge Inc.

Canoga Park, Calif.
July, 1961

PREFACE

Systems Research and Systems Design are composed of something old, something new, and something borrowed. Many disciplines have been concerned with analysis and synthesis in complex situations and problems; the engineer, the biologist, the medical scientist, and the manager, each in his own particular field of endeavor, has made many advances in the study of complex systems. New in the last few years is the rapid growth of the abilities of the scientist and engineer to apply advanced computational techniques to problems having many variables and parameters with statistical and nonlinear characteristics. New also is the greater ability of scientists to understand the general implications of the structure of complex systems. Borrowed are the methodologies of the analysis of complex problems from the operations researcher, the industrial engineer, the computer analyst, the mathematical statistician, and the automatic control engineer.

The study of systems must be characterized by objectivity, that is, the analysis and synthesis must be directed toward the ultimate utility or purpose of the system to man. This automatically implies an ultimate sociological objective and further implies that the ultimate system embraces the universe. It is obvious that any real systems study can only encompass a portion of the ultimate system, and, therefore, that every system being studied is but a portion of a larger system. This, in turn, causes almost all systems studies to be directed toward an intermediate objective, such as an economic value, political worth, purely technical performance, or some understandable combination of these. The role of the environment of a system, which is everything outside the system under study, is exceedingly important in the influence on the behavior of the system itself.

The complete accomplishment of the study of any problem involves three specific and well-defined but interrelated tasks.

1. The *systems* analysis is directed toward an over-all objective, must be related to environment, and will involve analysis, modeling, communication, control, optimization, and evaluation.

2. The *design* synthesis must achieve the various directed objectives,

should be introspective in order to evaluate physical realizability, and must be based unpon practical knowledge of the physical world.

3. The *scientific* study provides a behavioral and phenomenological base for the various activities of design and, ultimately therefore, systems analysis. The interplay of these three disciplines must be promoted to the greatest extent because without this interplay no systems study will be successful. Systems analysis leads to the directed objectives of design, which, in turn, must call upon the various sciences for better understanding; thence returning through the interplay from scientific phenomena to the design synthesis to the systems re-evaluation. The result of this interplay is like an equilibrium equation in which every part is vital and important:

$$\text{Sys} \rightleftharpoons \text{Des} \rightleftharpoons \text{Sci}$$

Like an equilibrium equation, the final state of the system will be a composite of the interrelations and can be considered completed only when the final objectives are attained.

The systems analyst is not a know-all, see-all, hear-all omnipotent but rather a legitimate expert in the methodology and techniques applicable to the study of complex systems. Hence it is concluded that every worthwhile and purposeful systems analysis must be accomplished by more than one person. Call this group a team if you like, but regardless of whether the team interplay is formalized or not, the interchange is a necessary activity.

A word must be said about engineering. The traditional concept of the engineer is that of a person who deals primarily with physical systems in which the role of living matter is a minor one. Thus a systems engineer is an engineer who deals with the analysis of physical systems. This traditional concept is rapidly changing so that at the present time the engineer is delving into areas that heretofore would have been considered outside the normal sphere of engineering activity. This broadening of the scope of engineering activity is everywhere causing a reassessment of the role of technological education.

The history of the growth of a systems philosophy is probably rooted in the very substantial developments in industrial engineering, and in automatic control engineering, followed by operations research and automatic computation. At Case Institute of Technology from 1955 to 1958 there existed a strong group in Operations Research under the leadership of Dr. Russell L. Ackoff, an active development in digital computation under Dr. Raymond J. Nelson, and a growing activity in automatic control engineering under my direction. Meeting occasionally, this group realized that the underlying philosophy of each of these three activities was strikingly similar and that each employed almost identical methodologies and techniques in developing performance criteria, modeling, analysis, and evaluation.

From these discussions the Systems Research Center at Case Institute of Technology developed gradually with the considerable support of Dr. John A. Hrones, Vice President of Academic Affairs at Case, and the ultimate support of the Ford Foundation. Substantial progress was made through the active support of Dr. E. W. Abrahamson, Dr. R. J. Adler, Dr. R. E. Bolz, Dr. B. V. Dean, Dr. H. R. Nara, Dr. I. Lefkowitz, Dr. M. Mesarovic, Dr. R. Plonsey, Dr. C. Saltzer, Dr. J. D. Schoeffler, Dr. S. Seely, and Dr. L. W. Weinberger.

The papers of the first systems symposium at Case Institute of Technology form the collection in this textbook. The symposium served to orient the systems group at Case toward a variety of problems and the need for the widest viewpoint and objectives in the systems study of such problems. It is hoped that the future will unfold the tangled facets of systems study and make it possible for mankind to face the more complex problems of life with more confidence than has been possible in the past.

I wish to thank my wife for reading the proof, a great assistance when the burden of initial organization of the Systems Research Center was already immense.

DONALD P. ECKMAN

Cleveland, Ohio
July, 1961

CONTENTS

SYSTEMS:
RESEARCH AND DESIGN

CHAPTER 1

BELOW THE TWILIGHT ARCH— A MYTHOLOGY OF SYSTEMS

S. BEER

You honor me too much by your readiness to hear me speak tonight.* I was frankly overwhelmed when your invitation came. So often I have sat at home in the evening twilight watching the sun set on England, and thought of the new dawn it would bring to the New World—and many friends. And I have long wished to visit you. Here, at last, I am: with thanks on my lips, inquiry in my head, excitement in the blood, and "cybernetician" on my passport.

In coming, I have followed the sun. I have had to fly below the twilight arch. My assignment is to place before you some thoughts on systems research, the subject over which this conference presides. It is a *new* field, rich in promise—or so we tend to say. And yet mankind has always been conscious of system: on the face of the earth and in the firmament; in the behavior of the body; in seasons and societies; in numbers and machines. Nor has mankind been slow to describe and codify the system he detected all around.

Thus there is much on which we can draw today in undertaking systems research. There is an opulent heritage of thought which it would be both brash and wasteful to ignore. Unfortunately, there is also much from the past which is not helpful—unless correctly interpreted. Much of what we think, and above all our *habit* of thought, is implanted in us by history. For we have, after all, been *taught* to think; thinking is not some great free spiritual afflatus of the human soul. It is more accurately called cerebration: an activity of the brain: a highly conditioned form of cerebral behavior. We are not usually aware of the extent to which the past is imported into our thinking. But, genetically speaking, we are our own parents. No one can say to what extent the inherited machinery in his head is structurally capable of the novel activities he intends. Secondly, and psychologically speaking, we are our own teachers and mentors. Who can be

* At the banquet, First Systems Symposium, April 27, 1960.

sure that he has freed his thoughts of lumber from the propaedeutic years?

All this strikes me as singularly appropriate to our subject. For system above all things is—ourselves. In every conceivable way *we are* system: extrapolated from the past, oriented to the present, projected towards the future. So for those engaged on research into the nature of systems there comes a warning: we research into ourselves; and our research is bounded by ourselves—and all we ever were or hope to be. Now what becomes of the objectivity of science? How can we separate ourselves from the subject of our studies? In physics we have learned this danger long ago; and nowadays we handle the dynamite of Indeterminacy with practised hands—and measure it in megatons. But outside physics, scientists too often forget their Heisenberg and all that follows; they are content with Bacon and Descartes.

My case is this: we still stand in the twilight of our subject, a twilight inhabited by shadowy concepts from the past. There gods and giants battle still, to typify the dualism which haunts all human thought. It is possible, however, that we are on the margin of full daylight. The work of recent years has done a tremendous amount to explode the old mythology of systems. But let us consciously confront our myths, before we press too far ahead, and see them for what they are. I told you that to come here I had to fly below the twilight arch. That was to move into the evening sun. But in our work we now move out into the light of morning. My invitation is to turn momentarily back, to where the myths still writhe: let us fly back—below the twilight arch of dawn.

ON MYTHS OF ORDER AND CHAOS

System is one of the names of order, the antonym of chaos. The basic myth of which I will speak first is made up of four propositions: that the raw state of nature is chaotic; that order is something introduced into chaos and imposed therein as a monolithic structure to be weathered by random noise; that within this structure a second-order chaos lies invisible; and that once the energy necessary to maintain this order ceases to be available all reverts to chaos once again. You may be thinking that in calling this outlook a myth I am proposing unilaterally to repeal the laws of thermodynamics. Not so: I am proposing merely to examine critically the conventions under which we view these things. And, as befits mythology, I shall start a long way back.

The Origins and Maintenance of the Mythology

The Ionian philosophers of ancient Greece, such as Leucippus and Democritus, concerned themselves with the existence of supposedly elementary particles of matter which they called "atomic," meaning indivisible. A century later, their celebrated successor Epicurus conceived of the atoms as possessing the power of movement; and from their chaotic (or random) atomic entanglements he envisaged the generation of life itself. According to this doctrine of "hylozoism," an invisible material chaos begat all that is systematic, which it continued to inform—in continued atomic action below the threshold of visible action; in the appearance of life; and in the evidence of moral choice.

The emergence of these doctrines in the great age of Greece was profoundly backed by yet more ancient literature. Of this the Hesiodic poets are the most relevant, for they dealt essentially with the emergence of order out of chaos. We are now back in the eighth century B.C. Ἦ τοι μὲν πρώτιστα χάος γένετ', αὐτὰρ ἔπειτα Γαῖ' εὐρύστεργος, thundered Hesiod in his *Theogony*: "At the very first chaos was created, and thereafter the broad-bosomed earth." And this is perhaps as far back as the myth can be traced. It is the background clue to the Epicurean philosophy of the fourth century B.C., whence we pass directly to the Roman poet Lucretius who, writing 250 years later, expounded Epicurus in didactic and rapturous verse. When a great poet talks philosophy, he tends to enshrine the thought in lapidary style. Five centuries after Epicurus, his ideas were still being regurgitated word for word. And this was sad; "a clear symptom of decadence," in the eyes of that great Hellenist, Gilbert Murray.

If this was decadence then, where are we now? For the myth of prior chaos is with us still. In his biological outlook, contemporary and educated man seems to embrace a neo-Darwinism. According to this, there was once a chaos (usually thought of nowadays as the ocean). In this the atoms of the Greeks still intertwined; they were perturbed, through aeons of time and random permutations, to become organic molecules. These polymerized. So macromolecules, above all proteins, would be formed—there would as yet be no bacteria to bring about decomposition. The ordering process, driven by the random movements of chaos, marches on: small parcels of enzymes next emerge, enclosed in handy membranes. Then, ultimately, and by the same fortuitous process comes the organism. But chaos still informs this organism in its unseen genetic depths. Random mutations occur, and evolution can progress; for natural selection filters the adventitiously patterned offerings of chaos, building yet more order amid the environmental noise. Finally, for each metastable organism comes the stability of death: the ordering is disordered, and chaos supervenes. Here is the hylozoism of the educated twentieth century man.

Take next the physical outlook of this same man. This too begins with the assumption of chaos. We may build from chaotic atomic components a regular cubic lattice of copper, and another of zinc. By the interpenetration of these cubic lattices, a further ordering process is carried out. Each cube of the copper lattice now has at its center a zinc atom, and vice versa. A metallurgical ordering has taken place, to yield a body-centered cubic lattice named β-brass. But if we heat this alloy, the atoms migrate, and chaos returns. Significantly, we call this an *order-disorder* transition. Note again the Epicurean conventions: the initial atomic chaos; the order imposed as structure builds on structure; the hidden atomic chaos which goes on beneath the lattice model; the reversion to chaos when the conditions of order are withdrawn.

Thus we could easily continue for a long time. But let us take three quick examples from our own field of study. A logical system has been constructed, an organization. This might equally well be an electronic model of a learning process, a logical flow system portraying an industrial works, or a chart depicting the managerial structure of a company or other society. These models have been, in our eyes as model builders, constructed by an ordering process out of chaos. We have observed the learning going on, and have seen it as the imposition of structure, a network of connectivity between elements and subsets of a set in which relationships were originally chaotic. In like manner we have imposed an order on the otherwise chaotic industrial works, giving it a structure, showing how material flows and where the system is uncoupled by its stocks. And in the third case, the social chaos of a mass of human beings has been ordered too: the responsibilities of leaders have been defined, the dependence of subordinates, the interdependence of groups, of committees, etc. Next we observe these models are too static; they are not viable systems at all. Order has been *frozen* out of chaos: and this will not do. Beneath the semblance of rest, Lucretius tells us, the chaos must go on.

And so we insert black boxes in the model of the learning process: random noise is pumped into the system and marshaled into stochastic patterns. The model of the works is turned into a simulation and put onto a computer, in which pseudo-random numbers are generated by the thousand to bring the thing to life. Thirdly, the managerial structure is contemplated under chance and moral choice: the "human element" is introduced, whereby people do not do as they are told, they make mistakes, they die and cannot be equivalently replaced. All is now well; the chaos works within the order like yeast in bread. Then finally: observe the last result, whispers the ghost of Epicurus in our ears. Let the system run, let the entropy increase; remove the "ordering principle," or the group dynamic, or free energy, or management. In all three models the probabilities begin to equate. The learning machine is deconditioned, learns everything and nothing. The works accepts its rules and succumbs to its constraints: its stocks steadily rise, its queues lengthen, its processes grind to a halt, and everything is equiprobable. The social structure, too, is denatured, until "when everyone is somebody, then no one's anybody." Chaos, which the Greeks taught us is more natural than order, is back again. The thermodynamic heat-death is upon us.

This is our myth. This is the understanding we have been handed down from Hesiod onwards, which is built into our thinking. We may not visualize it in the way I have unfolded it; that I must concede. But we all *behave* as if it were true.

The Attack on the Mythology

Through these examples, the myth may be examined and exploded. For the myth is not *what* we know; but *how* we know it. It is with the expression, the conventions of viewpoint, that I quarrel. And the quarrel is not pedantic; I contend, and hope to show, that we misdirect ourselves quite seriously.

First, a new track must be chosen from the start. Not "chaos was created" is the theme, but another account of creation must be chosen. Let us pick on St. John as our alternative. Ἐν ἀρχη ἦν ὁ Λόγος: "In the beginning was the Word." Here at once is the idea we need: the idea that I will call *immanent organization.*

Man has for long flirted with this idea. In theology, he was safe: St. John had, after all, gone on to identify the Word, and indeed the immanence, as God. "The Word was God . . . . All things were made by Him." There is no difficulty about organization if an omnipotent Organizer is presupposed. In philosophy, too, various devices were available for handling this idea. For example, Spinoza (pre-eminently the philosopher of immanence) described a thoroughgoing monism in which nature itself and its own organizational effects were both aspects of the same thing. They were to be distinguished only by a neat piece of syntax: *natura naturans* as the creating, organizing aspect; *natura naturata* as the organized effects.

But in science the idea of immanent organization was in difficulties from the start. For science had neither God nor "substance" in which this immanence could inhere. Science until recently was about *things*, and so we trace our thought to postulated all-pervasive things which might have carried a "principle of organization" in themselves. The ether was one such thing: it does not seem to be altogether forgotten even now. Phlogiston was another. I sometimes think that Eddington was always on the verge of inventing yet one more: a kind of existence principle masquerading as a set of eigenvalues. Of course, his model was intended as a conceptual construct; and yet it sounds so often like a *thing* spread-eagled throughout the universe, measurable in its physical constants, and essentially extended in its modalities. How else but in extension can we understand what Eddington could possibly have meant when he spoke of a measurable as having "fifteen different ways of not existing"?

Now the answer to this problem which can be deduced from our latest scientific insights seems to be this. *We can actually start with a nonchaos;* and we do not need a "thing" in which to contain this "principle" of immanent organization. All we need is a non-Hesiodic language in which to talk about it. Let us begin with physics, in which this conclusion can be most readily exemplified. There is no need to question the account I gave just now of the atomic-level behavior of a β-brass. No doubt all happens so. What I suggest we ask ourselves is why the process then described should be known as an order-disorder transition when it is much more simple to think of it the opposite way round.

If we consider a system in the light of thermodynamics, the language employed has in general the Epicurean cast. There is the assumption of molecular chaos, the idea of ordering the system so that it is no longer chaotic, etc. To achieve this ordering, there has to be (familiarly, by now) a mechanism capable of instituting order. This is personified in the Maxwell demon who does the selecting of particles which produce the ordered state. Again (also familiarly) this mechanism turns out in the light of later knowledge, in this case information theory, to be a long-term impossibility, as Wiener has pointed out. For the information on which the demon requires to act is a negative entropy, which means that the demon is coupled to the energy system itself, and in the long run subject to random motion determined by temperature changes.

Moreover, and here is another of our familiar signposts, the laws of classical thermodynamics, as given in the so-called "geometric" proof, turn out to be too static: everything is fixed, and the account only holds for statistical averages of molecules. Where has the subthreshold chaos gone? Drop to a small enough system, and it is there—in the Brownian motion. But now the rigid laws no longer hold.

Then let us turn to more convenient terms, a better model within which to talk. Now we say: all free-running processes in the world are moving from states of disequilibrium towards states of equilibrium. Disbalance the equilibrium, and they will return. From statistical mechanics we observe that the equilibrial states are more likely, and will eventually predominate. Entropy has now become a measure of the probability of the universe. Very well: in these terms, again, it seems we have the movement from chaos to order that we expect— disbalance is superseded by balance, etc. But just a minute: the sign seems to have changed. What used to be chaos is now an equilibrium, and what used to be order is now disbalance. Epicurus is standing on his head.

And very rightly so. Why should we not insist that what is most probable counts as being most ordered? Could anything be more ordered than a perfectly even distribution of molecules, heat, energy, or any other commodity, over a given adiabatic space? And if the system is not an isolated one, but part of an assembly of systems, then surely the most ordered state is that in which the whole is equilibrial—which is again most probable in the end. According to my language, then, I now assert: *order is more natural than chaos*. This is, I infer, a startling statement; for when I recently published it a number of people wrote to indicate the "printer's error." What is more, I find that the statement is actually important to me: it represents a break with the descriptive conventions of Hesiod which have lain heavy on my head with the weight of 2700 years. It has given me a completely new outlook on systems.

The Replacement of the Mythology

What after all *is* order, or something systematic? I suppose it is a pattern, and a pattern has no objective existence anyway. A pattern is a pattern because some*one* declares a concatenation of items to be meaningful or cohesive. The onus for detecting systems, and for deciding how to describe them, is very much on ourselves. I do not think we can adequately regard a system as a fact of nature, truths about which can be gradually revealed by patient analytical research. A viable system is something we detect and understand when it is mapped into our brains, and I suppose the inevitable result is that our brains themselves actually impose a structure on reality. I have already spent some time on a key example, which may be epitomized thus.

If we structure reality as a chaos-order-chaos transition, then this is what reality *is*, and our systems will have to include massive control units capable of constructing and sustaining the ordered phase. But if we structure reality as an order-chaos-order transition, then this is reality instead, and our systems will be largely *self*-organizing. The chaotic phase here is disturbance to the system from outside; and control units are merely required to filter this noise as far as possible, and to provide a matching store of variety in which disturbance can be absorbed as by a sponge—so that order returns. (Ashby has given us the formal mechanism for this in his work on homeostasis.)

We have already used the example from physics to make the change of viewpoint clear. Let us now look at the other instances cited. In biology, the old hylozoism was traced down to an outlook described as neo-Darwinism. The difficulties of this outlook are tremendous, and center on the point that there is no room in it for the emergence of immanent organization: mutations are thrown up *by* chaos in the nucleoproteins of the chromosomes, *into* the environmental chaos; order is achieved by a ruthless and crude vetoing procedure. How order manages to survive in the presence of quite so much noise, both within and without, is not at all clear.

The new language compels us to begin with the supposition of order, and therefore presupposes a natural and intimate collaboration between the organism and its environment. Some modern biologists, such as W. R. Ashby and J. Z. Young in Britain as well as many Americans, are themselves cybernetic pioneers. Let me draw especially at this point, however, on the geneticist Waddington. He regards this natural orderliness (in my sense) of the whole organism-environment system as exerting a causal influence on embryological development, the study of which is called epigenetics. Adaptation, then, is explained by the gradual building up of an "epigenetic landscape" which "*guides* the phenotypic effects of the mutations available." Waddington goes on to say that, in the light of this, the conventional statement that the raw materials of evolution are provided by *random* mutation "appears hollow."

Hollow indeed; and any cybernetician who has carried out experiments in which hylozoistic rules for the creation of order out of chaos operate *without* any such guide will confirm my own experience that the process is far too slow and too precarious to satisfy the demand for an explanation of any evolutionary process which actually succeeds in adaptation. (So, too, would any manager capable of transferring all this to his own experience of evolution in a business or a works.) Here, then, is a convention for looking at biology as including immanent organization which certainly pays off. It is highly analogous, I would further suggest, to the neurophysiological conception of facilitated pathways in the brain.

Next we may return to the set of examples concerned with learning machines, operational research, and the organizational structure of companies. Taking the first two together, there is just one central point to make; and if I seem to castigate, then let it be clear that I accept these strictures for myself. It really is ludicrous that we should have gone so far with Epicurus as to manufacture chaos where none exists in order to provide ourselves with the properly certificated raw material for system building. Take my own case. There are random number tables on my bookshelf; there are computer tapes for producing pseudo-random numbers next door; there is a large electronic machine for generating noise upstairs; down the road there is a roomful of equipment designed to hurl thousands of little metal balls about in a random way; and I use ten-sided dice as paperweights. The upkeep of this armory is considerable: think of all the time we spend trying to insure that all these artifacts produce results which are "genuinely random"—whatever that may mean. This tremendous practical problem of guaranteeing disorderliness ought to be enough to satisfy any systems man that nothing is more *un*natural than chaos. We are never even confident we have got it.

Why should we want it? The answer is just this. In any study of a real system we meet *indeterminacy,* and this has to be modeled and understood. Our way of thinking leads us to produce the artifact of indeterminacy by injecting absolute order with absolute chaos, although (as I have tried to show) both concepts are meaningless in the real world. But to do anything else, we say, would "introduce bias." This is true, but only in the Hesiodic language I am seeking to replace. And I will give this pointer to a possible solution. The biological model with the epigenetic landscape is precisely a machine for introducing bias into the abstract notion of random mutation. There is nothing wrong with this *provided* that it does not constrain adaptability and therefore survival opportunity. If this condition is to be met, then (it seems to me) there must be a multiplexing of whichever transformations themselves beg questions about the future. This is to take up von Neumann's ideas about error-free though defective systems, and to adapt them. For it is not exactly "error" with which we have to deal. Quasi decisions have to be taken about the future (in arranging for the emergence of an epigenetic landscape) which may or may not prove suitable later on; what is important is that the system should be robust when proved wrong. By this I mean that its sensitivity to the biases it will introduce should be inversely proportional to the probability of their being falsified as forecasts.

My proposition is that by multiplexing the set of input transformations which produce the epigenetic landscape a mapping of environment into organism will give rise to invariant points as key features of the landscape. This invariance is with respect to a poorly chosen transform somewhere in the multiplex: the system will learn to facilitate pathways to the landscape which are equifinal. This is an extension of Waddington's theory, based on what I hopefully take to be a cerebral mechanism. (A paper about a machine to act as a brain artifact for an industrial company, which is based on this thinking, will be put forward at the Urbana symposium on self-organizing systems in June 1960.*)

In concluding this section, there is something to be said about the example from organizational structure. I will not go through the argument about chaos and order again, trusting it is sufficiently clear. But the inference to be drawn from the reversal of the linguistic convention is worth stating. An existing system of human relationships in a large and complex society is to be regarded as self-organizing, as ordered already: homeostatic, equilibrial.

Many people dimly realize that this is a fair description; for instance, they incline to say about a new project: "We must carry everyone with us." By this they mean that they ought not to fight the system. But I will risk being quite emphatic about this. When they say "the system," they almost certainly do not mean the naturally ordered system I am talking about; they mean the *official* system, the one constructed as an artificial order—out of the alleged "chaos" which is in fact the *real* system. This official system is the one set down on charts, the one crystallized in titles, the one imitated by many doomed automatic control systems. If these people were talking about the real system, they would say instead: "Let us use the system to amplify this project into effect."

The Mythology and Management

I can well imagine managers declaring what has just been said to be naïve, and adding that they know it all, and more, already. But I am unrepentant, and will face this out. We may be as subtle as we like in discussing human relationships and unofficial channels as

*Editor's note: "Towards the Cybernetic Factory."

addenda to the official organization chart. But the system all this is supposed to control can always go one better. There is always far more variety in the whole society than the official (Epicurean) order can cope with. For not only must that order be constructed by effort and sanction from the "chaos" but the order (which is exiguous) has then to attempt the organic control of what is left over (which is extensive). This is in flat contradiction to Ashby's law of requisite variety, and quite certainly an impossibility. A false dichotomy has been drawn by this orthodox model, and the scientific consequences are inescapable.

In short, the only acceptable evidence that people really do know already what these arguments have educed would be the existence somewhere of a managerial structure which could permute its own variety into continuous correspondence with the natural driving energies of the rest of the system under disturbance. This would probably look quite different from anything we have today. For example, it would be unlikely to happen that a business would be permanently demarcated *at the top* into such fixed areas as "production," "sales," and "finance," for this would constrain the available directorial variety far too much. All right, you may say, how is it that businesses run successfully like this at present? The answer is that they do not run like this; that the official demarcations are overrun at the social level (which is why all great businesses pay so much attention to "acceptability"), and that, despite their titles, jobs continuously change their character. Then what am I complaining about? The answer is that I am not complaining; the self-organizing system has organized itself, and all is well. The whole discussion seems to have vanished. But it has not. The point was whether people who (naturally enough) know perfectly well *how* the whole society runs in fact have a real understanding of *why*. This is to say that an understanding of politics does not imply an understanding of cybernetics. And if politics is "the art of the possible" in a system, cybernetics is the science of the actual. If this science is understood, then management becomes more effective and less painful.

Now this is not intended as an indictment, but as a constructive insight. If we changed our model and accepted the proposed language reversal, thereby obtaining a more appropriate account of the system concerned, I think many things would change. Titles, definitions of responsibility, the actual treatment of people as opposed to the "personnel policy" (particularly with regard to succession), the structure of committees, etc., would all change. In a first-rate concern, the descriptive changes would not lead to any actual changes of behavior, because the system is self-organizing anyway. But in a less satisfactory company (if there are perchance less satisfactory companies) the new correspondence of description with fact would produce real changes, because the ostensible system would no longer impede and retard the natural tendency towards an equilibrial state on the part of the real system. As to the individual and first-rate manager, to change his title from a function- or technique-oriented name ("Sales Manager") to a succession of problem-oriented names ("Manager of Project 6") would involve no alternation in his work at all, because he is already tackling problems and is leading "Project 6" without naming it. But a poor manager (if there should perchance be one) would suddenly find that his title to intervention in other people's work, and his capacity to frustrate them, had gone. He would also find that to "own" a department or policy like a landlord, who prosecutes trespassers and charges rent, would no longer of itself justify his existence.

There are in fact many indications in the way people behave which reveal that they do not after all understand the "why" of the system according to the model I have advanced. These indications are strong enough to defend this analysis against the familiar charge of triviality; the logically valid objection can be only that the analysis is wrong.

Management is the restoring of natural order to a system which has been disturbed, and which is trying to regain its equilibrium. This does not of course exclude progress: by equilibrium I do not mean a stationary balance. The system is fed with a reward function, which is the payoff of the society concerned, and which had better be as much concerned with survival value as with immediate satisfactions. This drives the system on, and itself disturbs the equilibrial state. The new equilibrium will have a higher payoff than the last. The reactions which restore this state are natural laws: management is catalytic.

Thus I picture the cybernetic managerial structure as the *focus* of the natural order; a structure that flows to fit the changing "response surface" of the situation; a structure that is integral with the system and exemplifies its natural orderliness. And I contrast with this the structure that sees its own order as bred from and imposed on chaos; a structure that is rigid; a structure that is concerned with divisions and functions, instead of unities and problems; a structure that actually *hates* the remainder of the system, which it sees as chaotic, and by which it must therefore feel threatened. The first understands the nature of systems, and seeks to remedy its own deficiencies by mapping the changing state of the world into its own epigenetic landscape —which will in turn modify its nature gradually towards increasingly effective control. This is management by cybernetics. The second understands only its own needs, and tries to adapt itself to change by plugging gaps with new titles and committees, and by balancing responsibilities instead of dynamic trends—which will in turn modify it in clumsy steps towards the goal of increasingly tidy organization charts. This is management by aesthetics.

Perhaps most actual social systems lie somewhere on a scale determined by these extremes. To evaluate whereabouts on the scale a particular system falls, we might examine the behavior of the people in authority. For those who do not understand the system's "why" betray themselves by hatred and fear of the chaos they assume to lie outside the door; by a failure to amplify themselves and their policies by coupling each to the natural order; and by acting instead as if their job were to lay about them in the chaos with the jawbone of an ass. Such men are supported by a Hesiodic scripture some twenty-seven centuries old. May I outdo them in the authority of antiquity by quoting cybernetics from one of the Upanishads, the Hindu scripture. The book is called the Bhagavad-Gita, and goes back 5000 years. In it the Lord Krishna declares to man:

Action is the product of the qualities inherent in nature. It is only the ignorant man who, misled by personal egotism, says: "I am the doer."

ON MYTHS OF PARTS AND WHOLES

The Mythology of Division and Composition

So far we have been discussing systems in a particular but vital dimension: the dimension of *orderliness*. But there are many other dimensions of systems, some of which are equally important, and equally difficult to examine. One of these is the dimension of *completeness*, to which I shall now turn. For just as every real system expresses more or less order, so every real system expresses more or less integration.

"The part is greater than the whole" is an aphorism everyone has heard, and there are occasions when people think they discern a meaning in the paradox. When something is labeled "a system," the whole intention would seem to be to assert that a collection of separate things is in an important sense a whole. But no one imagines that this debars him from dividing the system into parts for the sake of description; indeed, any arbitrary division is logically admissible, and the criterion of suitability is that of convenience alone. The would-be divider of systems must, however, be careful: he may succeed in making a division which destroys the sense in which the system is a whole. A surgeon who treated migraine by amputating the patient's head (cephalectomy?) would be doing this. And the patient, on discharge from the hospital, might posthumously reflect on the sense in which this part of him had proved greater than the whole.

At the very least, there is more to say about part of a system than that it is contained in the whole. Leibnitz said that it *expresses* the whole, and this was because he saw parts not as divisions of space or divisions of function but as *dynamically involved* in the whole: a "systems" outlook. Hegel went further: every relation by which terms are related is an integral part of the terms it relates. And Whitehead went further still, by making Hegel's indivisible but passive system of relatedness *active*. His doctrine of "prehension" saw things as formulating their own natures out of other things, by seizing on relationships with them. In other fields than philosophy, too, the same insights may be found: they are there in relativity physics; they are there in Gestalt psychology; they are there in the best operational research.

For this is not mythology. The myth is the contrary idea that a system can sustain arbitrary division without ceasing to be the system that it is. And judging by many practical observations, this myth is very strong. We divide what we have no business to divide; the old logicians entered this operation on their list of fallacies, and called it *divisio*. Consider two examples from systems research.

The first is formal. Open any textbook, any paper, in our field, and consult the diagrams. There are rectangles representing activities, or processes, or operations, or even people. In information theory terms, the amount of variety denoted by each box may be colossal. The boxes are solemnly connected by attenuated, solitary lines with arrowheads on the ends. (What channel capacity those lines must have!) Now, three questions: How many vital features of the organic wholeness of the system have been utterly obliterated by this particular division? How many essential relationships between each *bit* in each box with every bit in every other box are depicted by the connections shown, and (given that this is a well-understood convention) have we any means of recognizing the conditions in which one of those *not* shown will turn this version of the system into another and quite different version? Can the passage of information (in however subtle an interpretation) really account for the wholeness of the whole, or is there something yet to learn from Hegel about other modes of relatedness? These are sobering questions. And when one contemplates some of the diagrammatic automation schemes, economic models, organization charts, maps of the brain, and many more, that are riddled with this mythological *divisio* the blood runs cold. Bear in mind, also, that systems fallacies of this nature are not committed in diagrams alone. Some forms of mathematical reasoning, particularly in operational research, might be open to this objection. At the risk of sounding quite heretical, I will admit that I have always been nervous of linear programming for this reason.

The second example is industrial. A company is an integrated whole in at least these ways: it is an indivisible legal entity; it is an indivisible financial entity as to its solvency (despite the fact that both its assets and its liabilities are eminently divisible); it is a virtually indivisible commercial entity, because the business confidence it inspires tends to disseminate uniformly over its activities; it is a virtually indivisible social entity, because its reputation as employer, subsidizer, patron, or menace is also disseminated throughout the locality. But to run this company, it simply must be divided, and divided in a way which will not murder it. Thus law, finance, sales, and labor became examples of suitable divisions of administration. But remember what was said earlier about such demarcation *at the top:* would this be a safe division, or is it perhaps a dangerous *divisio?*

Now consider production. Here again there are important senses in which the company is an integral whole. There is the pressure of throughput, which determines an indivisible rate of metabolism—particularly in such places as steelworks where heat is the driving force: to uncouple the system anywhere involves the cost of either conserving or wasting heat. Is the uncoupling the best that can be devised in terms of the organic whole, or has this desideratum disappeared in too local an evaluation of technological convenience? As a second instance, there is the "growth" of the product, which involves monotonic measures of size, complexity, cost, and risk. To write in "monotonic increasing" there may appear pedantic, but it is certainly not. It is the very fact ignored by the division fallacy when it appears in cost control. For when division has been accomplished, we may find these measures treated as departmental plateaus, each on its own merits, and without regard to the various threads of growth which integrate the whole. The outcome is that consequences for the cost of foregone opportunities elsewhere in the system, or for the differential adjustment by departments of standards of inspection, are rarely drawn.

The Relevance of the Mythology

There are many more ways in which production is naturally integral, yet divided it must be. And so a group of departments is formed, developed, and extended by accretion. The myth says this is all right; it does not matter; only let the division be convenient. But systems research must look out for *divisio*. Wherever there is geographical or technological or administrative division, the system has been uncoupled. Wherever the system has been uncoupled there will be found a collection of such things as queues, dams, reservoirs, buffer stocks, feedbacks, triggers, valves, controllers, surge hoppers, paperwork, reserves, voids, idle times, defectives, closed loops, oscillations, more men, hunting punched cards, indicators, negentropy, the company's capital, and obscene language. This is a formidable price to pay for interfering in the natural system, but it is absolutely unavoidable. It is also absolutely right that much effort and *expertise* should go into the task of organizing the system at this point, and it is worth a good deal of money to reach the least fallible control system, the optimal levels of stock, etc. Assume that absolute optima for everything have now been found: there is no possibility of improvement. Then can we not say that the job is done and all is well? Given the mythology, yes; for the optimization is based on one of an arbitrary set of convenient divisions—the one that exists. But take away the comfort of the myth, and division may become *divisio*. Let me offer you this maxim: *the most profitable control system for the parts does not exclude the bankruptcy of the whole.*

This readily emerges from what has already been said. If a division is chosen which is in the long run lethal to the mode of integration that makes the whole system viable, then the profitability of any or every *part* is irrelevant to survival. Worse: what was once a fairly satisfactory division may *become* a lethal one as technological and economic changes occur. Ecologically speaking, the long history of the extinction of species by the self-same mechanism is a serious warning. For the adaptability of animals is far greater than that of artificial organisms like companies: species are self-organizing systems which on the whole find equilibrial states. Their final extinction is due to a particular biological form of *divisio:* overspecialization—in which irreversible divisions of the whole occur which turn out to be inappropriate in the long run. It is certainly interesting that primitive and unspecialized organisms fail, because of their absence of advanced internal organization, to attain ecological dominance. Whereas by not involving themselves in the division of the whole that this would entail, they do not run the risk of making an inappropriate *divisio*, and their survival value is much higher than that of organisms which have run this risk. Perhaps there is something to learn from the individual insect which maximizes its chance of survival in infancy by remaining unspecialized in the larva, and then attains to dominance by metamorphosis to a higher specialized structure after pupation.

This question of the fallacious division of structure is put forward as a very serious matter, and an obvious target for profound systems research. In expounding the point, I have naturally considered the ultimate outcomes of bankruptcy and extinction. But because a particular company is not at all likely to be threatened with imminent destruction the point is not robbed of its impact. A company can suffer from hardening of the divisions to its detriment without actually dying of thrombosis. The systems diagnosis here is likely to be made by a study of flow. In the coarsest sense, it is often possible to find that the same firm undertakes contrary operations on the same product (as, e.g., when long pieces of steel are cut up for ease of handling and later welded together again; or where a geographical separation involving a long transit time is covered repeatedly in opposite directions by the same product). There were once remarkably cogent reasons for doing this; are there still?

But in a more sophisticated sense, it is the flow of specifying information that ought to be studied. An order for a product that is still in the mails has infinite variety: it may be a request for anything, even something the company does not make. When the order is booked, the specification may not yet be complete; and anyway it is still an open question as to which precise resources will be used to discharge the order; but some variety has by now been lost. At the planning stage, more of this variety is shorn away; and as production proceeds more and more degrees of freedom are assimilated into decisions taken. When the finished product is ready to leave the factory, there is just one bit of information left in it: the answer to the question whether it will be dispatched or not. Now this diminution of variety from infinity to zero is by no means linear and by no means continuous. Moreover, each product or product group has its own curve against time. The whole process of manufacture, which is customarily regarded as the growth of organization of parts (materials) into wholes (products) from raw material to output (entropy falling), is alternatively regarded as the destruction of an equal amount of information (negentropy falling). The factory is thus equivalently a machine for making products or a machine for destroying variety. Technology will say what is the best arrangement for the factory as product maker;

cybernetics will say what is the best arrangement for the factory as variety destroyer. Each will have its own optimum set of divisions. It is an operational research problem in systems to find the break-even point between the two answers, and the commensurable factor is entropy (the positive and negative entropies being continually in balance). I will hazard this guess: if this study is undertaken in a sizable factory more than 10 years old, a *fallacia divisionis* will somewhere be uncovered. What should have been kept together has been uncoupled. If the division is then altered (something which normally is very rarely done), cycle times, stocks, inventories, and overheads will all decrease; deliveries will improve; profits will rise.

In considering this myth that any system can be arbitrarily split into components without altering its nature, consider briefly its complementary form: that it is admissible to put parts together into arbitrary wholes. This complementary fallacy to *divisio* is known as *compositio*. The one example to be mentioned is this. Suppose seven policy problems arise in different areas of administration, and the decisions are taken: a, b, c, d, e, f, g. If these decisions are all implemented, the whole policy compounded of these parts will be a + b + c + d + e + f + g. It could well be that this is a *compositio*. In the context of the whole system, some of these fortuitous conjunctions should possibly be disjunctions, and the total picture should read: a + c + (b or f) + (d or e or g). This risk, which looks so obvious as to be easily avoidable, is made serious by two facts. The divisions already discussed may turn some area of the whole system into a relatively isolated system on its own. And the differential and uncertain rates at which all the decisions which have been taken in mortgaging the future mature in facts make it easy to misconstrue under what conditions any one decision is likely to mature. It is a problem of a complex time-dependent system. Probably this is an entirely trivial thought; one just wonders then why the mistake occurs so often—in national as well as institutional policy making.

But it is un-British to be disingenuous. The whole of this discussion comes down to this final point. We have shown that the organic integration of a system is a vital concept, and that there are myths about the division of its whole and the composition of its parts to be eschewed. But earlier it was contended that the boundaries of a system are subjective; and this is strongly supported at the philosophical level by the Hegelian axiom of internal relations—which of course makes it logically possible to equate every system with the universe itself. So the crucial scientific problem for systems research is this: how to separate a particular viable system for study from the rest of the universe without committing an annihilating *divisio*. And the crucial practical problem for systems research is this: how to stop someone else specifying the system for you, and "killing it off" himself. (If there is an operational research man who cannot endorse this, he surely cannot have done any real-life operations research.) Most seriously: these are problems of desperate urgency for every nontrivial systems study, and I commend them to the attention of this first symposium.

Towards the Replacement of the Mythology

Throughout this discourse criticisms have been made of the way we have been doing things in systems research. This was to be expected in a piece about mythology: I invited you to join me in a conscious confrontation of our myths. But matters are improving, and we may end by considering in what way. There is perhaps a key idea in this work which helps to avoid the myths of orderliness, with their dependence on chimerical concepts like "genuine randomness," and their consequences in *overmassive* control devices; an idea which will blow away the myths of integration, with their paradoxes about wholes and parts and "convenient divisions," and their consequences in the *wrong* control devices.

I propose that this idea is the primacy among systems of the brain. The brain is itself the most resplendent system of them all: the most highly organized, the most effective, the most robust, the most adaptive. And the brain is also ourself, the system into which research is really done, and which entirely conditions our ability to understand at all. Why, for instance, do we encounter these great and paradoxical dichotomies of chaos and order, parts and wholes? Why is the whole history of human thought littered with the remains of great dichotomies of the past: matter and form; *res extensa* and *res cogitans;* life and death; good and evil; organism and environment; etc., forever? And why, above all, why is it that these paradoxes are never actually resolved? After centuries of discussion they prove to be "unreal"; they are eventually purged from the human intellect by the catharsis of argument, and the hard attainment of a glimmer of understanding. To return once more to Hegel, the thesis and the antithesis finally dissolve inside a higher synthesis. This is indeed, for intellect, the very analog of evolution. (The most recent completed example of this process has perhaps been the resolution for physics of the particle-wave dichotomy in the complementarity principle of Bohr.)

Surely the answer to all these questions lies in the brain. Surely the answer is that our machine for viewing reality is a network of two-state neurons; and surely it might be possible to show that the operations of such a machine inevitably dichotomize the output. If so, there will be yet one more problem in dichotomy to resolve: the perfect, ultimate, elegant mystery—to be answered only in a metalanguage we cannot know. Here is the question: is reality like this because the brain is limited by its fundamentally binary structure, or is the brain like this the better to perceive the essentially binary structure of reality? Descartes, himself the uncompromising dualist, rejected the concept of *Deus deceptor:* God cannot deceive. But it seems less impious to suppose that God might well enjoy a joke.

A full empirical demonstration of the utility of the brain as a model in systems research, which I have just tried to establish on a priori grounds, would be very lengthy and highly neurophysiological. Here are just a few disorderly comments on aspects which are important. For the structure and organization of the brain are extremely subtle. If we do not understand either very well, and probably we do not, at least intensive study of the brain provides an insight into problems of the kind with which we have been dealing. The insights seem to take the form expected by the last few paragraphs: they are awarenesses of higher synthesis, of complementarity between contrary propositions.

Firstly, consider the argument from chaos. We cannot question the orderliness of the brain in its achievement of results. Nor on the other hand can we question the neurological muddle: the endless array of fibers and cells which are certainly not assembled according to a circuit diagram. Dendrites wander about fortuitously, forming synaptic connections with anything they happen to encounter. Axons branch and ramify, wandering away to the cortical surface when everything suggests they should descend to lower levels. But the general design is always there, and the indeterminate connectivity is not "perfectly random" by any means. The idea of an *immanent organization* takes shape and begins to mean something. What it means above all is *redundancy,* which is most surely a shock absorber for all the ills the brain is heir to. (We discussed this matter briefly before in terms of multiplexing.)

But secondly, as we said when talking of managerial structure, there has to be a certain paradoxical fluidity in the order which controls, to enable the requisite variety to be generated that will absorb the high variety of disturbance in the system to be controlled. And as we said more recently, there has to be "at the same time" division tending to specialization and an absence of *divisio* implying undifferentiation: another paradox. Some insight into these difficulties may be found by learning about localization in the cerebral cortex, particularly in the frontal lobes and cerebellum. We may not understand how it *is*, but we do find out how to *say*, that "this activity goes on just here, but it does not necessarily matter if just here is destroyed or isolated": it is a question of redundancy again. Now McCulloch has a splendid name for the facility we want. He calls it "the redundancy of potential command." (And it is not to the cortex that he turns to find the best cerebral exemplification, but to the reticular formation of the brain stem.) Without going too far into this, it may be possible to relate the answer given by these neurophysiological inquiries into "potential command" to the question about how to isolate the system under study without flouting all the rules concerning parts and wholes. The system is defined by where the command is now and the trajectory on which it is (probabilistically) moving. (Obtaining an insight into this was suddenly to discern some meaning, though probably not the forensic one, in the legal maxim: *ubi major pars est, ibi est totum.*)

Thirdly, the brain so well manifests all the features of self-organizing systems—it is their archetype. Again, there is no time now to say much. But we really ought to reflect on a mechanism which does not need a blueprint of detailed circuitry, and which works perfectly well at the highest levels of intellect with an incredible tangle of low-tension wires that have fritted themselves together. Here Pask's work on chemical cells is tremendously relevant. I consider that the race of ever more gargantuan computers, with their tremendous specialization (in the morphological, not applicatory, sense), and with their frenetic struggle to impose yet more categorical order on a chaos of flying bits, will eventually go like the dinosaurs. Something more brainlike will have been found; something more cheap; something self-organizing; something that will begin operations with the printout "order is more natural than chaos." It is to the development of such a system that most of my private research is devoted. On the strength of that, let me make this observation: it is not likely to be done with orthodox electronics. We need a better analog of the *fabric* of the brain than wire and glass.

The Rational Consequences of Irrational Action

From the dawn of scientific thinking, anyone who *was* anyone in science has been at pains to emphasize the role of measurement. Physical science is "the systematization of knowledge obtained by measurement," said Eddington, and Kelvin had his famous dictum too. Let us agree that quantification is paramount in science. But it is high time that we advanced beyond the crude concepts of "objective" measuring rods and clocks (the quotes have had to go on since Einstein's work), and looked to the brain for advice. How often does the brain produce an output in numerical form when not actually asked to do arithmetic? And when it does, how accurate is the answer? "Half a mile down the road," "7 inches long, dear," "he was in there a good hour," says the brain when asked "how much further?" (2 miles), "how long is this knitting?" (5.9 inches), "how long did you wait?" (42 minutes precisely). And yet we pick our way across fast-moving traffic streams without getting killed. Conclusion: *there is more to quantification than numeration.*

It may be thought that we know about this already. A continuous error-correcting feedback system does not print out the amplitude of the oscillations it has damped. The point is that "if it were asked to" it could and would. The brain on being asked to allot such numbers cannot—although clearly these quantities are available to it in some form. Consider this illustration. In the next room, which contains an alcove, a cupboard stands against the wall. You are asking yourself whether the cupboard will fit into the alcove. I suggest that you try to map the visual image of the cupboard onto the visual image of the alcove. Unless you are a craftsman used to measuring tapes, in which case the answer may be different, you do not attempt to map first the image of the alcove and secondly the image of the cupboard on to an image of the measuring tape, and then sit back to contemplate a numerical inequality.

Now this is a psychological inquiry. The brain as a machine may (for all I know) use some *tertium quid* onto which to map the two quantities. If so, however, I would doubt whether it is such a simple construct as a measuring rod: perhaps it would be best to regard the brain structure itself as the *tertium quid*. The point is that, in any case, this mechanism for very close correspondence does not succeed in making itself known in numerical form. It also seems probable that numeration (which is itself a set of mappings of some rather elementary measuring rods) is grossly inadequate as a model of quantification in both the brain and the outside world, and also of the relations which subsist inside each and between the two. This argument seems entirely consistent with the earlier considerations from the mythology of parts and wholes. Straightforward numeration methods first of all commit *divisio* by the special way they divide whatever is quantifiable into too simple an arrangement of uniform quantities, and then commit *compositio* by assembling these units and their more obvious relationships (such as square measure) into elementary "numeration machines" by the rules of schoolboy arithmetic. The result is that if someone were about to draw a picture of a road that included a line of telegraph poles receding into the distance, and were asked to estimate, in inches, the decreasing intervals between the poles, he would certainly not be able to do it. Let him draw the picture "by eye," however, and he will manage most creditably. The inference is that the brain "can do" projective geometry (of which consciousness knows nothing): i.e., it can bring the actual lines of poles and the drawing into very close correspondence. But, as with the earlier example, it cannot give an account of this process in numerical terms.

When we build a control system, the object is always to induce a form of behavior in a relatively uncontrolled state of affairs which is recognizable as corresponding to a form of behavior regarded as satisfactory or desirable. This may be either an actual situation (such as a winding road with which a car's behavior must be made to correspond) or an idealized model (such as an approved sales policy). Thus the control system is a machine for mapping one world picture onto another; and we know that the control must be capable of handling the requisite variety involved. This is clearly a process of quantification, and indeed measurement. We mislead ourselves, however, if we go on to say that therefore the subtle measures in the system must be numerically available. We assume that this follows because we are trapped in mythological thoughts.

If a computer control is envisaged, then its contents can be printed out: its mappings are numerically accessible. If the full numeration cannot be given, it means that the control is inadequate—there is not enough variety in the system. But consider a colloidal cell into which inputs from the situation to be controlled are transduced as low voltages across platinum electrodes, and which is then allowed to "solve the problem" represented to it by precipitating a growth of metallic iron on the floor of the cell. This solution to the problem is quantified; the precise shape of this growth at the molecular level is a measurement. Because this machine does operate at the molecular level it has ample variety to provide a control. But its measurements are inaccessible: they cannot be printed out. Since, however, these measurements are not required for any purpose whatever (just as they are not required in the examples given from the brain) this does not matter. What is needed is a means of focusing the control device, with its high-variety solution to the problem, back onto the problem. And this of course can also be done for this sample machine by electrical responses to the changing state of the cell.

Thus a more advanced concept of quantification is available than the mythological one that measurements are by their nature able to be perused. This leads straight to the idea that more advanced control machines are available than those which make their own "calculations" available in numerical form. Not only "more advanced," interestingly enough, but "very much cheaper" too. For most of the cost of orthodox control equipment lies in its *accessible measurements*, whether digital or analog. Inaccessible measurements are cheaper, because molecules are assembled free by nature.

Finally, then, systems freed of at least some mythological thinking can be envisaged which implicitly recognize the brain as an archetype. They have no order-chaos dimension; they have no parts and wholes. They are fluidly organized for potential command, and are essentially variety absorbers. Disturbance, noise, or irrational action is perceived by them as interfering with a natural but evolving pattern in the system under surveillance. They preside over the restoration of an equilibrial state, and use the energy made available by the disturbance to make evolutionary advances according to the epigenetic landscape of the moment. The outcome is control: the order of the system that is more natural than chaos. Disturbance is used to amplify pattern; noise is transformed by learning into signal; above all, irrational action results in consequences that are rational for the survival of the system.

We may thank the real, not mythological, gods of system that systems in real life do work like this; that immanent organization is forever emergent to absorb the risks of everyday mischance. For natural systems accommodate themselves to "malice in the object," or bad luck, and are robust against disturbance. And they accommodate themselves to stupidity in men, or bad management, so that rational consequences ensue from irrational action.

Artificial controls, in political, social, and economic affairs, and in industrial and commercial systems too, have not perhaps learned these lessons from the brain. Many still grind on with infinitely too little variety, infinitely too much effort and expense, to relatively nugatory results. The metal cupboards in which they are encased gleam refulgently with dials and switches, yet rattle with the skeletons of gods and giants from the twilight of the mythological dawn.

I thank you for accompanying me on this retrospective trip. We now move forward into a new era in the handling of systems; an era in which man will base his understanding of control on the archetypal viable system of cerebral behavior, as he has already learned to base his knowledge of power on the archetypal energy system of hydrogen-helium fusion. I believe the outcome may be just as far-reaching and much more constructive. Let us hope that we can play our own parts with sufficient insight and sensitivity that we do not annihilate the very equilibria we seek to reinforce.

CHAPTER 2

SYSTEMS, ORGANIZATIONS, AND INTERDISCIPLINARY RESEARCH

R. L. ACKOFF

"Speak English!" said the Eaglet, "I don't know the meaning of half those long words, and, what's more, I don't believe you do either!" And the Eaglet bent down its head to hide a smile: some of the other birds tittered audibly.

From *Alice's Adventures in Wonderland* by Lewis Carroll

When the announcement was made of the establishment of a Systems Research Center at Case, a number of my associates in operations research asked me how the activity of the Center was to differ from that of the Operations Research Group at Case. My colleagues in the Control (or Systems) Engineering Group at Case were asked similar questions concerning the relationship of their group to the Center. The question could be answered by saying that the Center is designed to facilitate cooperative research and educational activities among the Operations Research Group, the Control Engineering Group, and other systems-oriented activities at Case, particularly the Computing Center.

This answer may satisfy the curiosity of some and discourage probing by others. It is not enough, however, to satisfy or discourage probing by those of us who have some responsibility for the development of this Center. Much more than good will among men is required to make this Center play a significant role in research and education. Part of what is required is a philosophy and a program. A philosophy and program for the Center cannot be expected to spring into existence in a mature state; it must evolve out of proposals, discussion, reformulations, and experience. I should like here to formulate an initial philosophy and program which I hope will lead to constructive discussion, not only at this conference, but afterwards in other cells in which the systems movement is taking shape. There is no doubt in my mind that centers such as we are forming here at Case will develop in profusion in other academic institutions and in industrial and governmental organizations.

I will use my own interdiscipline, operations research, as my springboard. But before I take the leap I would like to make some general observations about the systems movement.*

First, I believe the systems movement will reach its fruition in an interdiscipline of wider scope and greater significance than has yet been attained. I should like to emphasize that my concern is not with what systems research is, but rather with what we can make of it. I consider operations research an intermediate step toward this fruition, a step away from traditional science. Correspondingly, I take systems engineering to be an intermediate step toward the same objective, a step away from traditional engineering. I believe systems engineering and operations research are rapidly converging. What more fitting title for the convergence than systems research.

Operations research is concerned with increasing the effectiveness of operations of organized man-machine systems. A complete understanding of the significance of this too brief characterization requires at least definitions of *systems, operations,* and *organization.* I shall deal with the first two very lightly, only enough for my immediate purposes.† I shall, however, deal with the concept of organization in more detail because I shall use it as the key to the philosophy and program which I hope to develop. It is in the context of organized man-machine systems, I believe, that we find the most comprehensive demands for departure from the existing content and structure of science and technology. Now, to the task.

SYSTEMS AND OPERATIONS

The term "system" is used to cover a wide range of phenomena. We speak, for example, of philosophical systems, number systems, communication systems, control systems, educational systems, political systems, and weapon systems. Some of these are conceptual constructs and others are physical entities. Initially we can define a system broadly and crudely as *any entity, conceptual or physical,*

* I am deeply indebted to Vernon C. Mickelson for the use of his mind and ears in the preparation of this chapter.

† For a more detailed discussion of "systems" and "operations" see "The Meaning, Scope, and Methods of Operations Research," Chap. 1 in *Progress in Operations Research,* Vol. I, edited by R. L. Ackoff, John Wiley & Sons, New York, 1961.

which consists of interdependent parts. Even without further refinement of this definition it is clear that in systems research we are interested only in those systems which can display activity, i.e., *behavioral* systems.

It is also apparent that systems research is only concerned with behavioral systems which are subject to control by human beings. Consequently, the solar system—although it may be on the verge of becoming so—is not yet a part of the subject matter of systems research. The relevant domain of such research, then, is controllable behavioral systems.

The essential characteristics of a behavioral system is that it consists of parts each of which displays behavior. Whether or not an entity with parts is considered as a system depends on whether or not we are concerned with the behavior of the parts and their interactions.

A behavioral system, then, is a conceptual construct as well as a physical entity since such a system may or may not be treated as a system, depending on the way it is conceptualized by the person treating it. For example, we would not normally think of a man who starts a car as a system because we do not distinguish the parts of the man involved in the component acts. We may, however, consider man as a biological system when studying the metabolic process. A physical entity is considered a system if the outcome of its behavior is conceptualized as the product of the interactions of its parts. Therefore, many entities may be studied either as elements or as systems; it is a matter of the researcher's choice.

The behavior displayed by a system consists of a set of interdependent acts which constitute an *operation.* An operation is a complex concept which I do not want to deal with in detail here. Loosely put, a set of acts can be said to constitute an operation if each act is necessary for the occurrence of a desired outcome and if these acts are interdependent. The nature of this interdependence can be precisely defined. Both the relevant outcome and acts involved in an operation may be defined by a set of properties which can be treated as variables. The acts are interdependent relative to the outcome if the rate of change of any outcome variable affected by change in any variable describing one of the acts depends on (i.e., is a function of) all the other relevant act variables. Therefore, if all the variables can be represented by continuous quantities, the derivative of an outcome variable with respect to any act variable (if it exists) is a function of all other act variables. In ordinary language, then, an outcome is the product of a set of interdependent acts if it is more than the sum of (or difference between) these acts.

ORGANIZATION

An organization can be defined as an at least partially self-controlled system which has four essential characteristics:

1. *Some of its components are animals.* Of particular interest to us, however, are those systems in which the animals are human beings. Wires, poles, switchboards, and telephones may constitute a communication system, but they do not constitute an organization. The employees of a telephone company make up the organization that operates the communication system. Men and equipment together constitute a more inclusive (man-machine) system that we can refer to as organized. Since most organizations utilize machines in a significant way in order to achieve their objectives, the discussion here will be directed to organized man-machine systems.

2. *Responsibility for choices from the sets of possible acts in any specific situation is divided among two or more individuals or groups of individuals.* Each subgroup (consisting of one or more individuals) is responsible for one or more choices of action and the set of choices is divided among two or more subgroups. The classes of action and thus the subgroups may be individuated by a variety of types of characteristics, for instance:

(a) *by function* (e.g., the departments of production, marketing, research, finance, and personnel of an industrial organization),
(b) *by geography* (e.g., areas of responsibility of the Army), and
(c) *by time* (e.g., waves of an invading force).

The classes of action may, of course, also be defined by combinations of these and other characteristics.

It should be noted that the individuals or groups need not carry out the actions they select; other human beings or machines may perform the actions, which are programmed or controlled in order that the desired objective is accomplished. It should also be noted that the equipment involved and the subgroups may also be considered as systems, i.e., as subsystems.

3. *The functionally distinct subgroups are aware of each other's behavior either through communication or observation.* In many laboratory experiments, for example, subjects are given interrelated tasks to perform and are rewarded on the basis of an outcome which is determined by their collective choices. The subjects, however, are

not permitted to observe or communicate with each other. In such cases the subjects are unorganized. Allow them to observe each other or communicate and they may become an organization. Put another way, in an organization the human subgroups must be capable of responding to each other either directly or indirectly.

4. *The system has some freedom of choice of both means (courses of action) and ends (desired outcomes).* This implies that at least some parts have alternative courses of action under at least some possible sets of conditions. The simplest type of system, the *binary* type, has only two possible states: "off" and "on" (e.g., a heating system in a home). More complex *adaptive* systems can behave differently under different conditions, but only in one way under any particular set of conditions (e.g., a ship operated by automatic pilot). Still others are free to choose their means to an end but have no choice of this end (e.g., a computer programmed to play chess). Finally, there are those which are free to choose *how* they will act in any situation (means-free) and *why* (ends-free). To be sure, such systems are usually constrained in their choices by larger systems which contain them (e.g., government restrictions on a company's behavior). Their efficiency is also affected by either the behavior of other systems (e.g., competition in industry) or natural conditions (e.g., weather).

The four essential characteristics of an organization, then, can be briefly identified as content, structure, communication, and decision-making (choice) procedures.

DESIGN AND OPERATION OF ORGANIZED MAN-MACHINE SYSTEMS

Now we want to consider the significance of these characteristics to one who wants either to create an effective organized system or to improve the operation of an existing one. He has four basic types of approach to organizational effectiveness and combinations thereof. The basic types of approach correspond to the four essential characteristics of organizations.

Content

The content (men and machines) of an organization can be changed. The study of organizational personnel—their selection, training, and utilization—has come to be the domain of *industrial psychology.** Three fundamentally different approaches to personnel problems have developed within industrial psychology. The first, *personnel psychology*, is primarily concerned with selecting the right man for a specified job. Its principal activity, therefore, is directed toward specifying the relevant characteristics of a job, determining which individual properties are related to its performance, and selecting those individuals who are best equipped for the job. The personnel psychologist, therefore, takes the task to be done as fixed and varies the men.

The personnel psychologist is also interested in modifying man so that he is better capable of performing the task. He attempts such modification through education and training. Here he partially overlaps with the *industrial engineer,* who tries to modify the behavior of man more directly. On the basis of time and motion studies the industrial engineer attempts to find those movements which optimize the individual's operations. The industrial engineer, therefore, is preoccupied with manual operations, whereas the personnel psychologist tends to concentrate on communication and decision making.

The second psychological approach is that of the *human engineer.* The human engineer tries to modify the job to be done so that it can be done better by the people available to do it. Here the men are taken to be fixed and the task is taken to be variable. Hence, human engineers, like industrial engineers, are concerned with the acts to be performed, but they try to modify them through the design of the equipment involved in these tasks. It is only natural, therefore, that there has been an increasing convergence of these two approaches.

A third psychological approach takes both the man and the job to be fixed, but the psychological and social environment to be variable. This type of approach yields studies of motivation, incentive systems, interpersonal relationships, group identification or alienation, and the like and the effect of such variables on human productivity, job satisfaction, and morale. These studies are essentially *social-psychological* in nature and are epitomized by the early work of Mayo and Roethlisberger and Dickson. Studies of the social environment frequently consider the effect of the noncontent aspects of organization (structure, communication, and control) on human performance. For example,

* For a very penetrating review of this field see Mason Haire's "Psychology and the Study of Business: Joint Behavioral Sciences," in *Social Science Research on Business: Product and Potential,* Robert A. Dahl, Mason Haire, and Paul F. Lazarsfeld, Columbia University Press, New York, 1959.

the effect of various types of communication networks on the performance of an individual in the network has been extensively explored. Clearly, such studies are related to those directed at structure, communication, and control, but the emphasis of most of them is on the *individual's* performance rather than on the performance of the organization as a whole.

The other part of the content of man-machine systems is equipment. We have already observed that human engineers are concerned with modifying equipment so that it can be better operated by available personnel. They seldom, however, completely design this equipment. Normally they collaborate with representatives of the traditional branches of engineering in design activity so that the latter can take the capabilities of the operators into account more effectively. Human engineers, therefore, do not replace, they supplement, the traditional engineer in his design function.

The individual piece of equipment can frequently be studied as a system. Engineers have increasingly tended to so regard the machine and the weapon. In equipment incorporating automatic controls the systems approach is almost inescapable. In addition, engineers have become increasingly concerned with the interactions of equipment in machine and weapon complexes and so they have become concerned with larger and larger equipment systems. Out of this concern the interdiscipline of *systems engineering* has emerged. The engineer, of course, can no more ignore the human operator than the personnel psychologist can ignore the machine to be operated. The variables which they manipulate, however, remain distinct.

Structure

The second major approach to organizational effectiveness is through its structure, i.e., to the way that the necessary physical and mental labor is divided. Although political scientists, economists, and sociologists have concerned themselves with organizational structure, there is as yet no organized body of theory or doctrine of practice on which a unified disciplinary or interdisciplinary applied-research activity can be based. As a consequence most studies of organizational structure, such as those leading to reorganization of a system, are generally done by managers or management consultants whose approach involves more art and common sense than science.

Within the last few decades there has been increasing experimental study of organizational structure. More recently, there has begun to appear a body of mathematical theory of organizational structure. Haire has pointed out, however, that as yet

We do not have much in the way of systematic behavioral data collected for the purpose of testing hypotheses or quantifying variables used in models. For example, we have models dealing with the cost of decentralized decision-making in abstract terms, but we know nothing about the information and decision load that can be supported, or how individuals vary along this dimension. . . . We know little about the effect of various communication structures and practices on alternative forms of organizations and their cohesiveness. . . . We should be just on the brink of a period of exciting systematic data collection. (1959, p. 72)

We may have reached that brink in a provocative new development: operational gaming.* In operational gaming organized groups are given problems analogous to real ones, usually with a collapse of the time dimension, and are observed under controlled conditions. We appear to be developing a way of experimenting quantitatively with at least small organizations under conditions which appear to be relevant to actual operations.† Difficult problems remain concerning inferences from the game to the real situation, but there is little doubt that within the next few years a significant reduction of these difficulties will occur.

Communication

The effectiveness of an organization depends in part on its having "the right information at the right place at the right time." The study of organizational communication is in much the same stage of development as the study of organizational structure. It has no organized body of theory, but it has been developing a doctrine of practice. *Systems and procedures analysts,* stimulated by the numerous installations of automatic data-processing systems, have been perfecting techniques of qualitative analysis of information and its flow. It may seem peculiar that this work is predominantly qualitative in light of the highly developed mathematical theory of communication, based to a large extent on the work of Claude Shannon,[1] and its pervasive application to the design of physical communication and information-processing systems.

This theory, however, concerns itself exclusively with the physical aspects of communication and has no relevance to problems involving

---

*For a detailed discussion of the product and potential of this technique see Clayton J. Thomas and Walter L. Deemer, Jr., The Role of Operational Gaming in Operations Research, *Operations Research,* Vol. 5, Feb. 1957, pp. 1–27. For illustrative applications see Harold Guetzkow, The Development of Organizations in a Laboratory, *Management Science,* Vol. 3, July 1957, pp. 380–402.

† For some work along these lines performed at Case see D. F. Clark and R. L. Ackoff, A Report on Some Organizational Experiments, *Operations Research,* Vol. 7, May–June, 1959, pp. 279–293.

the meaning of the communication. In Shannon's theory, for example, the measure of information contained in a message is a function of the number of distinct physical messages that could have been sent and the probability associated with the selection of each. The measure makes no reference to the content or significance of the message.

The same thing has been said very well by Haire in his discussion of an article by Rapoport:

> He [Rapoport] points out that in dealing with communication among linked individuals we have tended to use the information theory developed by the communications engineer. Such a formulation is useful for determining channel capacity . . . but it is not maximally useful for studying decision-making in groups. Here one needs a model of the cognitive aspects of communication theory—a way to indicate the potential of bits for reducing uncertainty about a real state of affairs. Such an approach contrasts with the definition of information in terms of the probabilities of selecting a certain class of messages from a source with given statistical characteristics. (1959, p. 7)

There is a growing body of experimental work on the effect of different types of communication networks on organizational (rather than individual) performance, particularly on small groups. Such experimentation has been stimulated to a large extent by the pioneering work of Alex Bavelas.[2] In addition, the body of special theories is rapidly expanding so that we may well be on the verge of a major breakthrough in this area. This work is very effectively summarized in the recent work of Colin Cherry.[3]

Beginnings toward the construction of a behavioral theory of communication have been made at Case.[4] This theory has two essential characteristics. First, it does not equate the transmission of information with communication but recognizes three types of message content: information, instruction, and motivation. Information is defined and measured in terms of the effect on the receiver's possibilities and probabilities of choice. Instruction is defined and measured in terms of the effect on the efficiency of the receiver's action, and motivation in terms of the effect of the message on the values which the receiver places on possible outcomes of his choices. A single message may combine all three types of content.

The second essential aspect of this theory is that it provides separate measures of the amount and value of information, instruction, and motivation contained in a message. It therefore distinguishes between information and misinformation, effective and ineffective instruction, and motivation.

A theory with these characteristics, whether the ones developed at

Case or another, increases the possibility of useful quantitative treatment of organizational communication problems.

Decision-Making Procedures

The last type of approach to organizational problems involves its decision-making procedures. An organization with good personnel and equipment, and an effective structure and communication system, may still be inefficient because it does not make effective use of its resources. That is, the operations of the organization may not be efficiently controlled. Control is a matter of setting objectives and directing the organization toward them. It is obtained by efficient decision making by those who manage the operation.

Study of the effective utilization of economic resources in industrial and public organizations is a well-established domain of interest to that splinter group in economics which concerns itself with *microeconomics* and *econometrics*. In the last decade it has produced a rapidly expanding body of theory and research techniques. Concurrent with this development there has been another which deals with a broader class of resources than do the economists alone and, consequently, with a wider variety of organizational decision problems. This broader interdisciplinary approach to organizational control has come to be known as *operations research*.

The essential characteristics of this interdisciplinary activity lie in its methodology. Out of an analysis of the desired outcomes, objectives of the organization, it develops a measure of performance (P) of the system. It then seeks to model the organization's behavior in the form of an equation in which the measure of performance is equated to some function of those aspects of the system which are subject to management's control (C_i) and which affect the desired outcome, and to those uncontrolled aspects of the system (U_j) which also affect the outcome.

Thus the model takes the form:

$$P = f(C_i, U_j)$$

From the model, values of the control variables are found which maximize (or minimize) the measure of the system's performance:

$$C_i = g(U_j)$$

The solution, therefore, consists of a set of rules, one for each control variable, which establishes the value at which that variable should be set for any possible set of values of the uncontrolled variables. In order to employ these rules it is necessary to set up procedures for determining or forecasting the values of the uncontrolled variables.

It will be recognized that this procedure is one by which equipment systems should be ideally designed. In design one should also develop a consolidated measure of system performance, and identify the variables which the designer can control as well as those uncontrolled aspects of the system or its environment which will affect its performance. Unfortunately, in many cases such a model of a desired equipment system cannot be constructed because of our ignorance. For example, I have not yet seen a good single consolidated measure proposed for the performance of an aircraft. Nor is there sufficient knowledge to relate any of the less perfect available measures of performance to the large number of design variables of such craft. As a consequence, design is currently accomplished by a combination of scientific analysis, intuition, and aesthetic considerations. It should be recognized, however, that current design procedures are only an evolutionary stage which will be replaced as rapidly as possible by effective modeling and the extraction of solutions from the resulting models.

INTEGRATED RESEARCH INTO ORGANIZED MAN-MACHINE SYSTEMS

As we have seen, there is a large group of disciplines and interdisciplines dedicated to studying various aspects of organized man-machine systems. The fact that the subject is so dissected leads to several residual problems. Suppose that an organizational problem is completely solvable by one of the disciplines we have considered. How is the manager who controls the system to know which one? Or, for that matter, how is a practitioner of any one discipline to know in a particular case if another discipline is better equipped to handle the problem than his is? It would be rare indeed if a representative of any one of these disciplines did not feel that his approach to a particular organizational problem would be very fruitful, if not the most fruitful. The danger that results can perhaps be best illustrated by a report that may be apocryphal but which makes the point very well.

The manager of a large office building received an increasing number of complaints about the elevator service in the building. He engaged a group of engineers to study the situation and to make recommendations for improvements if they were necessary. The engineers found that the tenants were indeed receiving poor service and considered three possible ways of decreasing the average waiting time. They considered adding elevators, replacing the existing ones by faster ones, and assigning elevators to serve specific floors. The latter turned out to be inadequate and the first two were prohibitively expensive to the manager. He called together his staff to consider the report by the engineers. Among those present was his personnel director, a psychologist.

This young man was struck by the fact that people became impatient with a wait which seemed so short to him. On reflection he became convinced that their annoyance was due to the fact that they had to stand inactive in a crowded lobby for this period. This suggested a solution to him which he offered to the manager, and because it was so inexpensive the manager decided to try it. Complaints stopped immediately. The psychologist had suggested installing large mirrors on the walls of the lobbies where the people waited for the elevators.

Those who have worked with systems can recall many such incidents, i.e., many except those in which they played a role similar to that of the engineers in the one just recounted. There is undoubtedly a considerable waste of research effort and a considerable failure to obtain successful solutions to system problems just because the wrong discipline was involved. How can this be avoided? We shall return to this question in a moment, but now let us look at the second residual problem.

In most problems involving organized man-machine systems each of the disciplines we have mentioned might make a significant improvement in the operations. But as systems analysts know, few of the problems that arise can be adequately handled within any one discipline. Such systems are not fundamentally mechanical, chemical, biological, psychological, social, economic, political, or ethical. These are merely different ways of looking at such systems. Complete understanding of such systems requires an integration of these perspectives. By integration I do not mean a synthesis of results obtained by independently conducted undisciplinary studies, but rather results obtained from studies in the process of which disciplinary perspectives have been synthesized. The integration must come during, not after, the performance of the research.

We must stop acting as though nature were organized into disciplines in the same way that universities are. The division of labor along disciplinary lines is no longer an efficient one. In fact, it has become so inefficient that even some academic institutions have begun to acknowledge the fact. What can be done about it?

If the various disciplines involved in studying systems were to be brought together organizationally, this would help solve the first type of problem because it would then be possible to have each discipline examine each problem that arises. Presumably, the interdisciplinary group could by discussion determine which of the disciplines is best suited to handle a particular problem if it can be handled exclusively by one discipline.

This type of proximity between the disciplines is not enough, however, to effect a truly interdisciplinary approach to systems. The various disciplines must be able to work together effectively on the problem, not merely before and after the problem is studied. To accomplish this some specific steps should be taken.

First, it will be necessary to construct mathematical models of systems in which content, structure, communication, and decision variables all appear. For example, several cost variables are usually included in a typical operations research model. These are either taken as uncontrollable or as controllable only by manipulating such other variables as quantity purchased or produced, time of purchase or production, number and type of facilities, and allocation of jobs to these facilities. These costs, however, are always dependent on human performance, but the relevant variables dealing with personnel, structure, and communication seldom appear in such models. To a large extent this is due to the lack of operational definitions of many of these variables and, consequently, to the absence of suitable measures in terms of which they can be characterized.

In order to be able to construct truly interdisciplinary models of systems, then, it will be necessary to relate conceptually the variables dealt with in each of the disciplines which should be involved in systems research. This is a formidable task, but a beginning has been made. At the Institute of Experimental Method (which operated at the University of Pennsylvania in 1946 and 1947) a monograph was produced which attempted an interdisciplinary conceptual system.[5] More recently, Rudner and Wolfson have been extending this work, particularly as it applies to organizations.[6]

The second requirement is for the self-conscious development of a sound methodology for systems research. This can be accomplished by turning systems research in on itself since systems research is itself an operation performed by man-machine systems. The methods and techniques of the traditional sciences and technologies are not good enough for the job which must be done. Let me illustrate this point briefly by reference to only one of many methodological problems that might be discussed.

The performance objectives of most systems can be stated in terms of a number of variables. For example, in a truck we seek such characteristics as speed, rapid rate of acceleration, long range, large pay load, and low cost of operation. We cannot really optimize the design of an aircraft unless we can in some way amalgamate these performance considerations into a single measure of performance. In a production system, for example, we may have to amalgamate a measure of cost, a measure of the length of time required to fill orders, and a measure of the frequency and duration of shortages. In order to accomplish such an amalgamation of measures we must be able to transform all the scales involved into some common (standard) scale. We have much to learn about how to find the appropriate transformations or "trade-off" functions.

The criterion of "best performance" can be shown to depend further on our ability to find the relative value (or utility) of increments along the scales used to measure performance. For example, to a man who is destitute, the value of $20 is clearly not twice that of $10. If it were he would prefer a 51% chance of getting $20 to the certainty of getting $10. We have experimental evidence that this is not the case. It is important, therefore, to increase our ability to measure the value of increments of performance along whatever scale(s) they are measured.

The third requirement for effective systems research is effective education and organization of representatives from practically all the scientific and technological disciplines. Systems research will not be the only beneficiary of such education and organization. The contributing disciplines will be significantly benefited. It is not accidental that so much of the important work currently going on in many disciplines is being done by persons trained in other disciplines. For example, the most important work being done in the behavioral sciences, in my opinion, is that being reported in two new journals, *Behavioral Science* and *Conflict Resolution*. Most of the contributors to these journals were not trained in the behavioral sciences. Major work in learning theory, for example, is being done by Merrill M. Flood,[7] a mathematician at the University of Michigan, and Frederick Mosteller,[8] a statistician at Harvard. On the other hand, measurement theory, which has been thought of as the domain of physics since the work of Norman Campbell,[9] has been significantly extended by psychologists such as S. S. Stevens[10] and Clyde Coombs[11] and a philosopher of science such as C. West Churchman.[12] The implications of these observations to the educational process are important.

No single individual can be educated so as to be expert in all the disciplinary approaches to systems. It is difficult enough to make him expert in one. We can, however, educate him to an awareness of what others know and can do in systems work and motivate him to desire to work collaboratively with them. Scientific snobbery must go. Systems research cannot thrive where it prevails.

It is my feeling that the two most important steps that can be taken to break down barriers to effective interdisciplinary collaboration are

1. to elevate those trained in each discipline to a uniformly high level of competence in mathematics and statistics, and

2. to educate all students in science and technology to a thorough understanding of the scientific method in its most general sense.

Mathematics is the language of science and, like all languages, it molds the concepts and thinking processes of those who are familiar with it. In my opinion, the behavioral sciences are less mathematically oriented than are the physical sciences not so much because of the difference between the types of phenomena they study as because of the difference of language in which their practitioners think about these types of phenomena. On the other hand, existing mathematics is not adequate to provide a complete basis for quantification in the behavioral sciences because it was developed as a handmaiden of the physical sciences. The greatest challenges to mathematics, it seems to me, are increasingly to be found in the behavioral rather than the physical sciences.

Through an exposure to the accomplishments and problems of scientific method the student can best come to understand the underlying unity of science and thus of its disciplines. Only by a thorough analysis of research procedures in each of the sciences can one come to an appreciation of the interdependence of the sciences. In this way a student can come to realize that progress in physical science involves (among other things) continuous reduction of observer errors and that perceptual psychology and human engineering have a great deal to contribute to such error reduction. He can also come to understand that the social environment of a physical laboratory affects the reliability of measurements of even simple physical quantities. Through the study of scientific method, then, he can begin to see the scientific crusade for the reduction of error as one that is necessarily interdisciplinary in character.

For the systems researcher methodological self-consciousness has an added importance because, as already observed, research itself is frequently an operation performed by an organized system. As such it is susceptible to the same kind of analysis as are other systems. The possibility of so studying research holds great promise for future increases in research effectiveness in all areas of science and technology.

In summary, then, if systems research is to develop the capacity to conduct effective research on complex as well as simple types of systems, we must do the following:

1. Develop a conceptual system which relates the concepts applied to systems by various disciplines and reduce them to quantities which are measurable along compatible scales.

2. Develop methodology better adapted to unique aspects of systems research.

3. Design and put in operation an educational program which produces the kind of researcher who can conduct systems research in an interdisciplinary context.

The era of systems research—and I think this is an era—can become one in which not only science is effectively reorganized but in which the educational process is similarly reorganized. The exciting and challenging character of systems research, then, is not to be found so much in what it is but in what can be made of it and the research and educational institutions that house it.

REFERENCES

1. Claude E. Shannon and Warren Weaver, *The Mathematical Theory of Communication*, University of Illinois Press, Urbana, 1949.
2. See, e.g., A. Bavelas, Communication Patterns in Task-oriented Groups, *Journal of Acoustical Society of America*, Vol. 22, 1950, pp. 725–730.
3. Colin Cherry, *On Human Communication*, Technology Press and John Wiley & Sons, New York, 1957.
4. R. L. Ackoff, Toward a Behavioral Theory of Communication, *Management Science*, Vol. 4, Apr. 1958, pp. 218–234.
5. C. West Churchman and Russell L. Ackoff, *Psychologistics* (mimeographed), University of Pennsylvania Research Fund, 1947.
6. Richard S. Rudner and Robert J. Wolfson, Notes on a Constructional Framework for a Theory of Organizational Decision Making, *Working Paper No. 3*, Management Science Nucleus, Institute of Industrial Relations, University of California, Berkeley, 1958.
7. Merrill M. Flood, "On Game-Learning Theory and Some Decision-Making Experiments," Chap. X, in *Decision Processes*, edited by R. M. Thrall, C. H. Coombs, and R. L. Davis, John Wiley & Sons, New York, 1954.
8. See, e.g., R. R. Bush, Frederick Mosteller, and G. L. Thompson, "A Formal Structure for Multiple-Choice Situations," Chap. VIII, *ibid.*

9. Norman Robert Campbell, *Foundations of Science* (formerly titled *Physics. The Elements*), Dover Publications, New York, 1957.
10. "Mathematics, Measurements, and Psychophysics," Chap. 1 in *Handbook of Experimental Psychology*, edited by S. S. Stevens, John Wiley & Sons, New York, 1951.
11. C. H. Coombs, H. Raiffa, and R. M. Thrall, "Some Views on Mathematical Models and Measurement Theory," Chap. II in *Decision Processes, op. cit.*
12. *Measurement: Definitions and Theories*, edited by C. West Churchman and Philburn Ratoosh, John Wiley & Sons, New York, 1959.

CHAPTER 3

ON THE CHOICE OF OBJECTIVES IN SYSTEMS STUDIES

C. J. HITCH

One of the more tiresome bromides to which operations researchers or systems analysts are subjected is the injunction to *first* choose the right objectives. Now I would be the last to urge you to choose the *wrong* objectives. Nothing is more important in systems studies than to define the right ones. Working out solutions, however elegantly, with the wrong objectives is equivalent to answering the wrong question, seldom a useful exercise.

It might appear then that it would make sense to *begin* with some broad "given" or accepted objectives; to derive from them appropriate local or subobjectives for the systems problem in hand; and then to design the analysis to maximize, in some sense, the proximate objectives. In the special case of national security problems, with which I am most familiar and from which I will therefore select most of my examples, this means beginning with given national objectives and deriving from them the appropriate proximate military subobjectives. In industrial operations research it usually means starting with company objectives, and deriving appropriate departmental or lower subobjectives.

Not only is this a plausible approach, but it is in some special cases an acceptable one; it is usually (not always) better than making no systems study at all; and it is frequently, given limitations on available time or manpower, the only feasible approach. I think I was the first to use the term "suboptimization" to describe this style of operations research (in 1952), and I am no implacable or dogmatic foe of its use. Some of the most rewarding systems studies have in fact been low-level suboptimizations.

But in general suboptimizing is not good enough; moreover, it foregoes some of the greatest potential gains from the application of our craft. I am concerned that suboptimizing has such great appeal to many physical scientists and mathematicians engaged in operations research and systems studies. Their interest is concentrated on technical aspects of their problems and on the design of appropriate models. "Objectives" appear to come from a different sort of world, and hopefully someone else's world. They are tainted with "value judgments" —anathema to any true scientist. They involve economics and other social sciences. Many—by no means all, but many—physical scientists are happy to accept authority for inputs so uncongenial to their accustomed modes of thinking. And they do not much care whether the authority is a general, the president of a company, or a social scientist. A definition—the clearer and less ambiguous the better— will permit them to get on with the fascinating, if sometimes relatively unimportant, task of designing models.

Unfortunately, escape is not so easy. The principal theme of this chapter is that in many of the most important problems objectives cannot be taken as given; that ends and means interact in complex ways that the systems analyst must master; and that he can, indeed, and should as one of *his* major objectives, help clarify and define the objectives that he strives to maximize.

Why does not the plausible and superficially attractive device of getting the best qualified person to "give" you the objectives work? There are many reasons, some important in some cases, others in other cases. I am going to try to sort them out systematically, taking my examples mainly from the field of national security.

First, it is impossible to define *appropriate* objectives without knowing a great deal about the *feasibility* and *cost* of achieving them. And this knowledge must be derived *from* the analysis.

Is deterrence of attack by the threat of nuclear retaliation a feasible military objective, assuming current technology and a more or less rational enemy? We are highly confident that the answer is yes, given the geography and Gross National Product of the United States. Pretty obviously the answer is no, given the geography and Gross National Product of Liechtenstein. But what of the interesting intermediate cases like Great Britain, France, Japan, India? The answer is not obvious to me. The important role for military systems analysts in these countries is to help them decide what their strategic objectives should be, what kinds of objectives are feasible in terms of resource costs. If we shift our attention from retaliatory forces to active air defense during the next decade, the answer to the feasibility question is unclear even for the United States—or so it seems to me.

In fact, cost is *always* relevant in defining insurance objectives. Air defense, like many other national activities, has only a contingent value. Its value may be nil or very great, depending upon what happens in the future. Providing it is equivalent to buying insurance at the national level. Now insurance is a nice thing to have, at either the national or the personal level, but one does not necessarily buy it for that reason. Whether one buys it depends upon how disastrous the contingency would be, how likely one thinks it is to happen, and the cost of the insurance, as well as upon the basic objectives or character of the person making the choice. Some people, in their personal lives as in making decisions for the nation, play for safety, whereas others take risks and live dangerously. I am inclined to be cautious in such matters. I carry a great deal of insurance of various kinds. But you cannot deduce from that that I buy any and all insurance against all unfavorable contingencies irrespective of cost. Even I draw the line.

Several years ago we lived on the beach in Malibu and I of course insured my house against fire (even though that was very expensive), wind damage, earthquake, and falling airplanes (because that was very cheap and I cannot resist a bargain). I seriously thought about insuring it against a tidal wave, the effects of which would have been catastrophic (but probably for me and my family as well as for the property, which *reduced* my incentive; note the analogy to air defense). I did a little research on the risk and the cost (I will not dignify it by the name systems analysis, but it was that sort of thing) and learned that there had not been a tidal wave on our coast in nearly 200 years of recorded history, and that the only insurance company interested in assuming the risk demanded premiums of 10% per annum. I had little trouble deciding to take my chances. Rigorous, systematic analysis of the risks and costs in analogous national security problems can be equally helpful—even if we cannot insert at the beginning of the analysis some neat formula defining the nation's propensity to avoid risks. (I could not do that explicitly in solving my personal problems.)

Which leads into my second difficulty with this approach: there frequently is no national or other high-level objective that can be taken as "given." For all sorts of good reasons that are not about to change, official statements of national objectives (or company objectives) tend to be nonexistent or so vague and literary as to be nonoperational. It is easy, but not helpful to the systems analyst, to say that the objective of the military establishment is to prevent war if possible and to win one if it occurs.

So how and from whom does the analyst obtain his high-level

objective? To whom does he appeal? Can the president (of the United States or of the company) give a sufficiently definitive and precise answer? And even if he can in some theoretical sense, what if he is inaccessible or inarticulate?

Actually, ours is a democratic and plural society, with a government distinguished by division rather than concentration of power. There is no single authority, neither the Joint Chiefs nor the National Science Council nor the President, that can say "These are our national objectives." There are many important influences on national decisions: high officials, assorted low officials, Congress as a body and many individual congressmen, the judiciary, public opinion, and the opinions of many influential private persons.

And the views of these bodies and these persons differ. Some are risk takers, others risk avoiders. Some are conservative, others liberal. Some emphasize and others de-emphasize military solutions. When objectives conflict, they will assign different weights to the alternatives, and sometimes different signs to their values.

This would not matter, of course, if we could construct from all these individual objectives functions some appropriately weighted national objectives function. But this is a practical absurdity, and even theoretically it has been demonstrated that there is no unique or even plausibly satisfying way to derive social preference functions from individual preference functions.

In more authoritarian countries or organizations these difficulties would be less than in the United States Government. But I am acquainted with no country or company so authoritarian and monolithic that it is less than formidable.

There is an added difficulty if the systems study relates to a future time period (as it usually does). The relevant objectives when the system is operational are future objectives, the relevant circumstances are future and uncertainly predictable circumstances, and the relevant officials and influential personages unknown. The only thing you may know is that the incumbents will not still be around.

Even in the best of circumstances, ignorance and uncertainty about high-level objectives make reliance on official definitions a precarious procedure. We know little enough about our own personal objectives. There are doubts about the therapeutic value of psychoanalysis, but no doubt at all that it has revealed to surprised patient after patient that his *real* motives for action bear little relation to what he believed were his motives. National objectives can only be some combination or distillation of the objectives of people who comprise (or rule) the nation; and we should learn to be as skeptical and critical of the verbalizations and rationalizations that pass for national objectives as we have learned to be of apparent or claimed personal objectives. No lower order of caution and sophistication gives promise of success.

Of course, there is another and lazier way for the analyst, perplexed by such problems, to get on with his suboptimizing, namely, by accepting a proximate objective from his local commander or department head. This is sometimes worth doing, lacking anything better, and sometimes obligatory. But we should not deceive ourselves that there is any scientific justification for this procedure. Officials in a bureaucratic hierarchy have no special competence in deriving appropriate low-level objectives consistent with higher level objectives. In fact, there are built-in biases in any bureaucratic organization which make it likely that proximate objectives defined by an official at one level will give inappropriate weight to important interactions with objectives for which other officials are responsible.

This brings me to the third and greatest difficulty in starting with given objectives: the fact that objectives are multiple and conflicting, and that alternative means of satisfying any one are likely to produce substantial and differential "spillover" effects on others. Ends and means do not fit into neat compartments side by side.

The illusion that there is broad agreement on national objectives stems from the practice of listing, with no exchange rates indicated, nice things for the nation to have. We are all (or almost all) in favor of God, motherhood, peace (and therefore deterrence), winning a war if deterrence fails, protection against nuclear blast and fallout, the containment and rollback of our enemies, better education, more superhighways, a higher standard of living, a balanced budget, lower taxes, more rapid economic growth, etc., etc., etc. But lists of this kind are almost useless for the analyst. In addition to being imprecise, they ignore the all-important questions of choice among nice things when having more of one means having less of another.

Take a hard look at the protection of the population against nuclear blast and fallout. This would be nice to have, and at first glance some combination of air defense and civil defense would seem to be the means of achieving it. But two sorts of conflicts will plague us as we proceed: (1) How much shall we spend on air defense and civil defense? Saying that protection is nice to have does not help us here a bit. We know that other things are nice to have too, and the more protection we buy the less we have to spend on offensive forces, on schools and highways, and on personal satisfaction out of incomes before taxes. As we have already seen, we cannot decide whether to spend *anything* until the analyst has given us some notion of feasibility and cost. And (2), there will be complex interactions and conflicts with other objectives—direct conflicts, not merely indirect ones through competition for budget and resources.

It is possible, for example, that some of the extreme forms of civil defense would change, for the worse, our whole mode of life; that concentration on air and civil defense would weaken our alliances by appearing to commit us to a fortress America concept; and that air defense and civil defense, by making it more credible that we would, in some circumstances, strike first, might actually weaken deterrence of an enemy's first strike on us. Some forms of active defense might even be perilous to our own offensive weapon systems.

Of course, the sign of the effect on other objectives is not necessarily negative. Civil defense shelters might help solve the urban parking problem, or in homes do double duty as wine cellars. Some forms of active defense, especially their warning components, can protect our offensive force as well as our cities, and thereby contribute to deterrence.

Nor is this the whole story. The objective of protecting cities can be profoundly influenced, for good or ill, by means usually associated with the achievement of other objectives—like a strong, well-protected, offensive force that deters any attack; or an offensive force deployed well away from centers of population that draws fire away from cities; or an offensive force capable of killing the enemy's offensive force; or, to take a negative example, an accident-prone offensive force that triggers a thermonuclear war desired by no one.

Enough of this example, which is illustrative, but fairly typical both of military and industrial problems. All these interactions, positive and negative, have one thing in common: they make it impossible to deal adequately and honestly with the problem of protecting the population against nuclear attack by taking that as the given objective and optimizing the means usually associated with it.

Let me spend just a minute on a slightly different and more subtle form of conflict. We have spoken of deterrence of the enemy as an objective, perhaps the primary objective, of our military forces. But we learn, after only a little study, that there are many different forms of deterrence—many different sorts of action by an enemy that it would be *nice* to deter. There is the usual question: how far down the deterrence road is it desirable to go? We know we want the military capability to deter the enemy from striking us directly, and that, at the other extreme, it is probably silly to try to deter him by military means from frowning at us. But where in between do we draw the line?

So far, this sounds familiar. But as we dig deeper we discover conflicts within the general objective of deterrence—cases where strengthening one kind of deterrence weakens (or may weaken, if we choose certain means) another kind of deterrence.

One of my colleagues, a sophisticated systems analyst, once tried to solve a personal problem by a rigorous maximization of an objectives function supplied by his doctor. He needed to lose weight, so he determined by consulting the experts his minimum requirements for proteins, carbohydrates, fats, vitamins, minerals, etc. He also obtained the quantities of each of these food elements in the 500 or 600 foods on the Bureau of Labor Statistics list. Then, on the plausible theory that mass is filling and that most dieting attempts fail because the subject feels hungry, he maximized, subject to various constraints, the weight (not counting water content) of the diet that would give him his minimum caloric requirements. The answer, ignoring minor quantities of various foods, was that he should drink 80 gallons of vinegar per day (vinegar is a weak acid, and its weight per calorie is remarkably high). Since his own taste buds and digestive tract were to be the victims of this experiment, he knew intuitively that the answer was crazy, and informed his machine that it should recalculate, ignoring vinegar. The second answer, incidentally, proved to be as unacceptable as the first, so he introduced still other conditions.

Now my colleague was proceeding very sensibly with his problem, starting with an oversimplified formulation and adding complications as their necessity became apparent. But it is slightly worrisome that the method he used is very similar to the one so many of us use: to take some plausible objective as given, and calculate like mad to maximize it. But we are using it in areas where our intuition does not reach very powerfully, and it therefore is not so easy to recognize vinegary answers for what they are. This does not keep them from being just that.

So what does the analyst do? If he cannot find anyone to give him acceptable objectives, where does he obtain them? The only answer I have is that learning about objectives is one of the chief objects of this kind of analysis. We must learn to look at objectives as critically and as professionally as we look at our models and our other inputs. We may, of course, begin with tentative objectives, but we must expect to modify or replace them as we learn about the systems we are studying—and related systems. The feedback on objectives may in some cases be the most important result of our study. We have never undertaken a major systems study at RAND in which we were able to define satisfactory objectives at the beginning of the study.

In spite of some provocative remarks near the beginning of this talk, I am not really afraid that American analysts will neglect the study of objectives. It is a national trait to be fascinated by higher level problems. A friend of mine, an economist, recently returned from a visit to Russia, where he had interviewed a large number of industrial officials in the hinterland. He was reporting to a group of us his impressions from these interviews. He found that the officials, almost without exception, talked interestedly and intelligently about their own problems and the problems of officials *below* them in the hierarchy. They received (from on high) a plan or target, and exercised all their ingenuity in carrying it out. But my friend was completely unsuccessful when he probed for information about decisions at higher levels. The officials did not know how such decisions were made. It was none of their business. They were not interested. They would not even speculate. They had nothing intelligent to say.

A voice spoke up from the audience: "In the United States it's precisely the opposite."

If the Russian is an incorrigible suboptimizer, presumably for reasons of health, the American is unwilling to be just that. I think we all understand that we cannot hope to suboptimize appropriately without knowing a good deal about the problems of at least the next higher level, and that we may have to go higher than that, as well as to collateral levels. The question is not really whether we should be concerned with higher level objectives, but how we should concern ourselves with them.

One snare, I have tried to say, is to assume that someone else can supply the answer. Another is to look for something too pat and neat —some function to be passively maximized. The higher level world is seldom like that.

Nothing but rigorous, quantitative analysis can tell us whether some objective makes sense or not—whether it is feasible, how much it will cost. Nothing but rigorous analysis can reveal the conflicts between objectives. Nothing but inventive and ingenious analysis can uncover means or systems that contribute to several objectives, or that function in a wide variety of relevant circumstances, or that satisfy influential people or organizations with quite different views about higher objectives.

This is a lot messier than maximizing given objective functions. But it can also be a lot more fruitful. We know this intuitively in our personal and family life, and act accordingly. If I love vacations in the mountains and hate the seashore, and my wife is just the opposite, we do not devote all our effort to analyzing which of the two is preferable; we spend some of it seeking a third alternative that we both like. National life and company life are not too different from family life in this respect.

To conclude: we must broaden our horizons and ambitions. In the hierarchy of ends and means there is no essential difference among levels, or between means and ends. The systems analyst may be able to make contributions at high levels as well as low; and may frequently be unable to contribute at low unless he also contributes at high. This is a challenge and opportunity. If there is to be any clarification of objectives for systems studies, any gain in their concreteness, detail, and operational usefulness, we are going to have to do the clarifying. No one else can help much. And we have tools to use if we can rid ourselves of dogma and false hopes for tidy, authoritarian, or external solutions.

CHAPTER 4

THE USE OF OPERATIONS RESEARCH IN THE STUDY OF VERY LARGE SYSTEMS

E. A. JOHNSON

One of the most fascinating and intriguing aspects of operations research is the fact that, as a new science, it pioneered in its approach to creativity and synthesis, and has continued this pioneering. In the beginning, however, it was more concerned with analysis than synthesis. This chapter is concerned with the problems of synthesis as contrasted with analysis and with the important distinctions between them. I will define operations analysis as that part of operations research in which the operational problem is studied as though the constants of the operation and the laws governing it are essentially fixed, like the operations and laws of nature. The problem of the operations researcher, then, is to understand the system he is studying, discover the laws that govern its behavior, construct a model describing the operation, and then manipulate the variables of the model so that the objective desired in the actual operation can be optimized.

Of course, all of the early operations researchers understood as well as we do today that in such operations there is no immutable system, there are no immutable laws. These exist only transiently for a few months or a few years. On the other hand the "constants" remain "constants" and the "laws" remain "laws" long enough for practical purposes and permit the description and subsequent manipulation of the operational situation to the advantage of the executives concerned with optimizing the operations of the near future. The kind of operations research that has become increasingly, if not primarily, important, however, is that concerned with the operations which will not actually occur until 10 or 20 years in the future, but in which the preparatory actions must be taken between the present time and the time at which operations actually occur. To handle this problem, we have to deal with the possible operational situation which can only be *forecast,* in which the operational situations envisaged do not as yet exist, and have only a *probability* of actually existing. Thus the operational "laws" do not as yet actually exist, but must be brought into being by proper prior manipulation of the operational environment. The operational system must be invented, the operational "laws" must be invented, and the means for making these inventions must be imagined and brought into being. This requires a synthesis, not only of means already existing which might be gainfully preserved for use in the future operation, but also of many new means which must be constructed and which aim to win in a competitive situation that does not as yet exist, but must exist if the future synthesis is to be truly creative. Competitors, of course, are trying to bring other systems and "laws" into being.

The other important problem in synthesis is not only that all aspects of systems are probabilistic in nature but also that alternative future systems must be studied. Thus, not only must we optimize each system, but we must also consider how to optimize the future by comparing the values and objectives associated with a set of alternative optimized future systems.

In the primitive beginnings of operations research, 20 years ago, when the idea that future operations implied only a few weeks or a few months ahead in time, and where the system and laws were regarded as analogous to the system and laws of nature, these problems and uncertainties were not critical, and creativity in synthesis and *invention* was not the important problem but rather analysis and discovery of the true nature of the system and the laws governing it.

THE PROBLEM OF SYNTHESIS

There are four difficulties in synthesis: the first and inevitable difficulty in dealing with a choice between a set of future systems, each one created by the operations researcher or the planner, is that it becomes necessary more and more to concern oneself with the dependence and success of the synthesis on the long-range operational forecast, on the results of future research and development, and on the politics and finances involved in the generation of a new operational environment. With continuing technological uncertainty it is necessary to deal with very big systems, because as operations research concerns itself with the very long range future, concentration on a small part of the system is most unprofitable. The forecast of the future operational environment surely improves, at least in a general way, with the size of the system considered, i.e., with the size of the system involved in the future operation which the planner and executive propose to bring into being. This is illustrated in military situations where gross errors have been made by using the outdated World War II philosophy of fixed operational "laws" and a technologically fixed environment. The efforts produced military systems, based on excellent concepts if the assumptions had been right, such as the Bomarc system, of extremely high cost and negligible value in spite of good design.

The trend nowadays in the military establishment is to be increasingly concerned with the entire nature of future armed conflicts, and the "suboptimizations" are concerned with problems such as the entire air war, or the entire ground war, or the entire sea war, and even this suboptimization is regarded as unsatisfactory because of interactions and overlap. The effort is to understand the larger suboptimization of armed conflict in its relation to world politics.

The second difficulty is connected with the rate of technical progress. Such progress is many orders of magnitudes greater in its effect since 1950 than ever before,[1] primarily because the number of choices resulting from an increase in knowledge has become so great that major innovations occur with such rapidity that systems capable of an order of magnitude improvement in performance are possible every five years or less. The rate of introduction of such new systems is no longer limited by the appearance of new knowledge, but rather by the difficulty in processing with understanding the great amount of new knowledge available and the difficulty of inventing new systems, together with long lead times connected with development, production, capital investment and its amortization, and the limited funds available in each particular area of innovation.

The third difficulty is the existence, in the capitalistic world and the communistic world equally, of both internal and external competition that drives all of the participants of the competitive system to exploit fully any possible innovation that would give a competitive advantage. This is true in business, in the affairs of government, and in the conflict between nations.

The fourth difficulty is that because (1) lead times are so long, (2) the uncertainty in the effectiveness of future systems is so great, (3) the forecast of the future environment is so large, and (4) competition is so keen the value of system effectiveness must have as high an accuracy as possible if organizational survival is to be assured.

However, it is because of the very existence of these four great difficulties that operations research is becoming one of the most valuable management tools in the world.

OPERATIONS RESEARCH METHODS
IN SYSTEMS RESEARCH

Since systems research is still in its infancy, it is worthwhile for an individual to clarify his particular semantics, especially when systems research can cover such an extremely wide range of meanings. It is my opinion that the words "systems research" have a meaning only if they are modified in an appropriate way to narrow or specify the scope of the systems involved, as, e.g., "weapons" systems, "tactical" systems, or "strategic" systems, "inventory" systems, etc.

The dictionary says that a system is, among other things, one of the following: (1) an organized or methodologically ordered set of ideas arranged in rational dependence, (2) a formal scheme governing organization, modes of procedure, or definite plans of operations, or (3) an aggregation or assemblage of objects (as in a machine) united by some form of regular interaction or interdependence—an organic or organized whole.

It is in the broad sense that I proposed to discuss systems research, rather than in the very narrow meaning used in the military dictionaries of "the system which encompasses the weapon or weapons and associated materiel employed to bring destructive power of the weapon against the enemy."

In earlier days, technical innovation, which has been the fertilizer of systems growth, was achieved largely on an unorganized basis and usually without any research. This was just as true with respect to systems innovations and design as it was for the invention of particular consumer, military, or other material items. It was a sort of natural growth occurring at a slow and steady rate over long periods of time. It has been during the last 500 years, however, that we have been subject to an increasing organization of innovation, but more especially since World War II, when full appreciation of the importance of systems innovation combined with the great increase in fundamental knowledge has led to our present extremely great rate of change and of innovation—innovation which is rich and fruitful from the very lowest level of consumer and military products to major systems themselves.

In our analogy, the amount of fertilization has become so great that we have to worry about the general health resulting from rank and rapid growth and overcrowding. The important step taken by operations research in World War II was the recognition that the operation of the future could be treated as a formal research problem and therefore could be treated by scientific methods. A full appreciation of this statement (plus five years of practice) and its acceptance as an attitude in dealing with the operational problems is all that is required by skilled scientists to become expert in the science of operations research, because the technique and scientific skills of operations research are the normal skills of science and otherwise are not to be especially distinguished.

There are, however, new techniques that are especially important as far as big systems research is concerned. Traditional techniques which have been successful also apply in the case of research on big systems. The old reliable "first" is the formal formulation of the operational problem, including preliminary evaluation of the objectives and values concerned in the solution of the problems; these as a result of preliminary results to be re-evaluated, and the problem to be restated. A rather nice example of this procedure, one never fully reported, is Thornthwaite's[2] assignment to a study of social unrest which ended instead in a study of and a solution for a queuing problem in agriculture (which solved the social problem).

The next two well-known procedures have about equal value, and neither can be said to dominate. After the formulation of the problem and the initial analysis, the design of a theoretical operational model is sometimes the next step. The actual logical description of such a model can take any of several forms, usually mathematical; sometimes a simulation can be designed which can be carried out using a wide range of techniques now available. These include simulations ranging from the use of digital computers to actual physical simulations. Such models can be designed so that optimum solutions can be found to predict future effectiveness of the system, including average values of the outcomes and the risk associated with each average outcome. The other important approach is to conduct field experiments to obtain data on the parameters needed for the model design or to gain insight. Very often an important part of a design of such an experiment is the subsidiary problem of the design of an index which will provide a way of ranking some operational parameter for which no previous index exists. In the case of Thornthwaite,[2] for example, his determination of the time for growth between two nodes of the pea plant was used by him (and now by many others) as a growth index that could be related to the climatic environment, to the variety of the plant concerned, and other operational factors.

The difficulty with field experiments involving an extrapolation to a long-range future in which a new big system must operate is that it is usually very hard to obtain the kind of operational environment that will be encountered in the future. In very big systems this is of extreme importance, since the environment now implies the rapidly changing cultural, educational, economic, and technological environment in the case of underdeveloped areas, and in the military problem involves strategies (such as deterrence) and tactics, often as yet not invented, or at least extremely uncertain.

From my point of view it is in this situation that the newer techniques of operational gaming and operational simulation are the most important. Operational games can be used as *pseudo* experiments. As pseudo experiments in one case, the forecast of tactical environment but not the technical characteristics of material is postulated, and the actual players on the two sides play against each other in manipulating the systems parameters in the presence of this postulated tactical environment which they are asked to accept. The playing of such a game often extracts from the players a creativeness and inventiveness in innovations expressed in the creation of a new systems design. Often this cannot be achieved in any other way. Furthermore, serious systems deficiencies are brought out which would not otherwise be recognized. These, in turn, lead to examinations of the subsystems, often by the same techniques, and ultimately to a requirement for a research and development program to rectify the deficiency aspects of future materiel of the systems encountered in this pseudo experiment.

The second, more popularized, use of an operational game is to accept the technical performance of future materiel components of the system or of the subsystems, and accepting these, to manipulate the system strategies and tactics that in themselves, as new innovations, lead to better performance and to better systems design. The two uses are different and distinct: one tends to hold tactics constant, the other to hold materiel constant.

The first step in the study of very big systems at the Operations Research Office (ORO) is the use of simulation following successful gaming. Equally necessary is a decision to consider a particular set of possible future systems. One of the characteristics of all operational games, at least up to this time so far as I know, is that the playing time tends to be between 10 to 100 times real time (I am not now discussing simplified *educational* games such as the popular business game). This means that it is impossible to play enough games to determine statistically and in detail the distribution of the outcomes as a function of the various and often many parameters or as a function of scale. It is only by a simulation that we are practically able to determine the average outcome of the operation of the system and the risk associated with each outcome as a function of the operational parameters of the system.

The next step in the study of very big systems at ORO has been to take the simulation results and to use them in an analytical model. The functions involved in this model are almost always nonlinear and are dynamic. The techniques for such programming are not well developed, but we do need to face the fact that in the study of very big future systems we cannot employ simple models using aggregated parameters (as for Lanchester's equation) and we cannot use linear, nondynamic parameters.

At ORO we are making a great effort to solve the nonlinear dynamic programming problem. Some of our early results have been presented elsewhere.[3]

In dealing with very big systems, then, we must use a feed-around procedure, combining all of these techniques in an iterative process. We must formulate the problem, make a gross initial strategic analysis, and in a first iteration reformulate the problem. We must design models for each one of the sets of alternative future systems to be tentatively considered; we must design and conduct field experiments, producing as best we can the environmental conditions forecast for the future. We must calculate the value of parameters involving technical and tactical innovations; we must conduct operational games, both as pseudo experiments and as means for developing the creativeness of the players and stimulating them to design new systems; we must simulate the operation of each future system of the set and calculate the outcomes and the results as a function of systems parameters; and we must then combine all of these results in what will usually be a nonlinear, dynamic program matrix which we can manipulate in order to optimize each system. We can *then* compare the effectiveness, values, and costs in a combined program with an index of value to determine the choice between the proposed systems.

If we accept the foregoing arguments, it is clear that a dilemma arises as to where operations research ends and systems planning begins and what the role of operations research is in connection with research and development on both materiel and personnel, since these will determine in an unknown way the value of systems parameters which will not be fully known until some of the research and development and other preparatory actions have taken place. This is exactly the dilemma that exists in research and development and engineering on materiel problems.

In physical research the question of where basic research stops and applied research begins, applied research stops and development begins, and development stops and engineering begins has never been adequately resolved. Indeed, the question of the management of the materiel innovations process has proponents who argue that all of the aspects should be closely interlocked in a single system, and others who argue for a separation and centralization of the several functions. One difficulty that occurs is that at the basic research end there needs to be a tremendous freedom for exploration; at the engineering end of the specific systems plan involving the design of engineering materiel, the engineering work is very costly and must be very explicit with little freedom for exploration. On the one hand, a minimum of technical discipline is indicated; on the other, a maximum. If the integrated approach is taken, the amount of intellectual discipline required by basic research conflicts with the greater discipline needed by engineering. Similarly, in operations research the freedom at the research end conflicts with the discipline that is essential at the systems design end, and this range of freedom and/or discipline within a single organization cannot be achieved without much compromise. On the other hand, the segregation and centralization of these different functions lead to communications failures and difficulties in the transition from one isolated organization to the next organization in the chain. Whichever is chosen, there are organizational compromises usually involving some procedure of project manager or loan of personnel, first from engineering to research during the early stages, later from research to engineering. The personnel in each case ultimately return to their parent organization. With the right attitude on the part of the organizations concerned, both systems can be made to work.

There is one factor which does need to be firmly understood in the organizations or parts of organizations concerned with each step. At the end of each of the processes there must be specific conclusions and specific recommendations summarizing the results of each step of the work so that the basis for the next step can be transmitted without ambiguity. This fact is often poorly comprehended by the people at the basic research end. It is still their duty to study the ultimate needs of the over-all system and to state their conclusions and recommendations in a firm and unequivocal way.

Nevertheless, the great difficulty that we must cope with in systems design is the fact that we must continuously consider the over-all system and simultaneously the subsystems at a number of levels. Furthermore, since there is an intricate feedback, and necessarily so, in the process of the evolution of a particular system, or of a set of systems, it simply will not do to carry out the operations research and the systems design in series. These kinds of feedback are so powerful and progress is so rapid on subsystems because of technological dynamics that any method which involved a series procedure would inevitably fail owing to the great increase of the lead times in decision making.

It seems clear to me that the first step in any systems research is to start out with the long-range forecast of the future operational environment (the nature of the problem having first been outlined). If the study requires some years of time, it is absolutely essential that the long-range forecast be maintained continuously up to date, so that it can be incorporated in an improved form in each iteration. I would argue that four parallel types of studies must proceed when a very big system is under research.

First, there must be long-range studies on how to use the system. These would be primarily concerned with the values and objectives involved in satisfying the problem that has been posed. I would call these "strategic" studies, and I would state their purpose to be the establishment of the strategic objectives.

The second study, or set of studies, also quite broad in nature, would be concerned in more detail with how specific systems would have to work. It would be concerned with specifying the systems requirements which would have to be satisfied if the system objectives and values are to be met. I would call this a "tactical" study.

The third kind of study, and the one with which we are thoroughly familiar, would be a consideration of the actual physical materiel in its broadest sense. In the case of business or economic systems, this would cover the entire range from consumer products to the equipment used in production, as, e.g., machine tools, and would cover all of the materiel systems involved, such as inventory, transportation, and similar systems. I would consider it the function of the operations research concerned with materiel to specify the technical characteristics of the materiel needed to satisfy the systems requirements.

The fourth kind of study would be concerned with the problems of personnel. In the broadest sense this would cover the cultural and demographic characteristics—the characteristics of the technical labor force, consumer preferences and biases, man-machine relationships, the general psychological problems which affect systems behavior, and problems of education.

This parallel approach is designed to reduce lead times. However, it does more than that, because even with teamwork the tasks of research on the design of big systems require increasing specialization at the materiel and personnel levels of operations research. There simply must be parallel inputs and feedbacks, because we do not know how to proceed fast with very big teams of specialists from many different professions. It has been my own experience that teams of 5 to 10 research people are about the optimum, and that it is better to break the operational problems into pieces that can be handled in teams of about this size. The secret of rapid systems research certainly depends on such a breakdown and increasing synthesis. A hierarchy of groups is needed, i.e., a team of teams with increasing synthesis and aggregation at the top, but with a process of synthesis and aggregation aided by feed-around and carried out in parallel in an iterative process.

The foregoing observations have their parallel in the materiel research with which we are most familiar, where it is now becoming better appreciated that basic research, applied research, component development, and subsystems development must proceed in parallel if the specific materiel end item is to be produced more rapidly. In fact, the higher in the executive hierarchy the parallel problems of basic and applied research are foreseen, the better.

The next problem which is beginning to cause more and more difficulty (although it has always caused difficulty) is that of standardization in making a fit among the four main elements noted above, that is to say, the personnel, materiel, tactical, and strategic aspects of the system. These must all fit and be compatible. This is actually very hard to achieve when the rate of technical innovation is very great and when the system's educational lead times are very short, i.e., short compared to a professional lifetime. In earlier days, when innovations were rare, it was possible to adjust the other elements of the system gradually to technological innovation so that the balanced set would come about without too much difficulty. When the rate of innovation is very great, as it is now (and continually increasing), it becomes very important that the whole set of innovations be continuously compatible. If there is great material progress in one particular kind of product or procedure or tactics, this may have a disadvantageous effect on the whole system, although as a subsystem it may appear to be desirable. For example, in agriculture, the extremely great improvement in per capita productivity of farmers has upset the agriculture system and has required treatment of the symptom of overproduction. This has actually greatly lowered farm income at the same time that it has greatly increased capital investment requirements for the farm. I do not know how this problem will be solved. I do not believe continuous innovation and improvement in farm productivity by itself is likely to be a satisfactory solution.

On the other hand, our entire economy is built on a system of standardization of components of both materiel and cultural aspects. This tends to be true of all tactical and strategic elements of big systems operations as well. Perhaps pseudo stability of subsystems and systems for limited periods should be considered. The range of intervals that might be considered would be 5 to 10 years, and perhaps in those systems where control may be regarded as desirable, some criteria and legal basis can be established with respect to the desirability of jumping at intervals to a new system of increased effectiveness. Thus unreasonable imbalances of the system are not justified

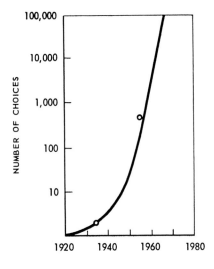

FIG. 1. Number of technical choices.

unless the eventual and worthwhile *jump* in effectiveness is so great that it justifies a temporary imbalance. I am actually arguing against continuous innovation only if it is introduced because it is new—it should be worthwhile as well as new.

All systems research of necessity deals with transient systems, systems usually in the process of violent revolutionary change in all of their parameters. Furthermore, systems research deals primarily with the future of a system and with the uncertainty in the expectation of the particular value of a particular technologically dependent system parameter. I do not mean that it is not worthwhile to do some analysis of existing and perhaps semistable systems, but this is usually done as a springboard to find out how to design better future systems, to change, and thus improve, the existing system, or to help design an orderly transition to a future system.

It is the rate of increase of new technical knowledge that provides the raw material for systems change. This rate of change is well epitomized by the fact that there are now about 60,000 scientific and engineering publications (world-wide)[4] which discharge their monthly quota of new facts into the stockpile of human knowledge. The effect of this knowledge on weapons development is shown in Fig. 1,[1] which illustrates the increase in the number of choices available in the design of an aircraft weapons system with time. This curve is *typical* of

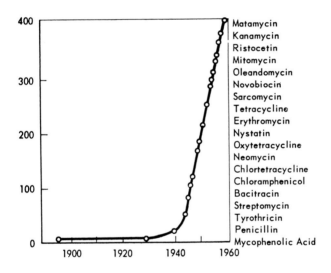

FIG. 2.   Antibiotic compounds.

military weapons and weapons systems. The number of choices is now bewilderingly large in comparison to the past. The increase in the number of choices has occurred primarily in this decade, and there is every sign that the increase in the number of choices is continuing. It is the existence of such a large number of choices that forces systems research upon us.

As an example of rapid change, Fig. 2 shows the increase in new products in the antibiotic industry,[5] an increase that brought a new 300 million dollar-a-year industry into being in only a few years and has revolutionized the entire system and practice of medicine in the United States.

As another example, Fig. 3 shows the change in per capita productivity in farming[6] that has been due to technical improvements, primarily in the application of an enormous increase of automotive power and fertilizer to farming operations. This per capita increase in farm productivity has tremendously perturbed the entire agri-

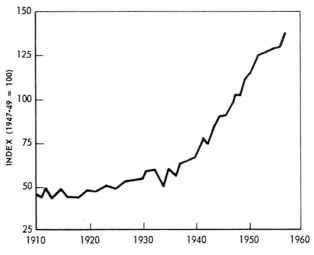

FIG. 3. Per capita productivity of farmers.

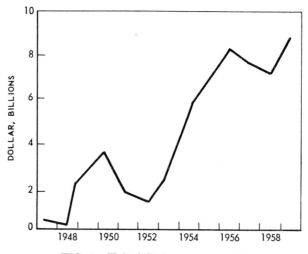

FIG. 4. United States crop support.

business system and has greatly affected the national budget as well. In fact, the inability of farmers to adapt rapidly to their new economic situation has forced heavy farm support as treatment of this symptom of system illness, as shown in Fig. 4,[7] in order to maintain some reasonable sociological stability in the important agricultural areas of the United States.

These situations exemplify the fact that systems research, as an aid to systems planning, is required well ahead of the time that symptoms of system illness appear in order to make it possible to adapt our human, economic, and military systems to the effects of technological change in a reasonable, healthy, and orderly way.

STRATEGIC RESEARCH IN BIG SYSTEMS

The problem of the design of strategies is critical in the world today, whether in government or business. Although a strategy is in itself dependent upon parameters of higher systems, it is affected equally by parameters of lower systems. These ramifications are inherent in the broad procedures necessary in dealing with the research and planning for major military strategic systems that are sketched in the succeeding paragraphs.

With respect to strategic research the "methodologically ordered set of ideas arranged in rational dependence" is shown in Fig. 5 for the problem of United States national strategy. In this figure, for example, for the United States we could state our *national goals* to be "to preserve for ourselves and our posterity freedom and the blessings of liberty." This would not only be a gross oversimplification; it would indicate a unidimensional value system. Actually, ours is a multidimensional value system, with a related and compatible set of goals that were partly written down in condensed form in our constitution and that have been expanded and interpreted over the last two centuries in laws and decisions and other actions taken by the executive and legislative branches and by the Supreme Court. I think that we can assume that these *national goals* change relatively slowly, and, therefore, describe rather stable systems parameters.

Because of the situation in which we find ourselves with respect to the Soviet Union, one possible *national objective* (in a set of objectives) might be "to remove the threat of militant communism to the survival of ourselves and our national goals."

Figure 6 illustrates the typical and slightly more detailed considerations that need to occur at each step of analysis in this system. Let us suppose now that our *national objective* is actually to remove the threat of militant communism to the United States. We need to choose between a policy of annihilation (i.e., to destroy the U.S.S.R. either in the ideological or physical sense) or of attrition (i.e., to wear down slowly or roll back the U.S.S.R. by a technique of conversion). If we chose annihilation as a policy, this might further lead to emphasis

UNITED STATES

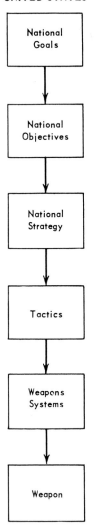

FIG. 5. Flow of analysis from goals to weapons.

on offense, and if the emphasis were in the militant direction, this would then lead to the establishment of very large offensive military forces. On the other hand, we might choose a defensive policy with respect to military actions, in which, on balance, the military forces would be

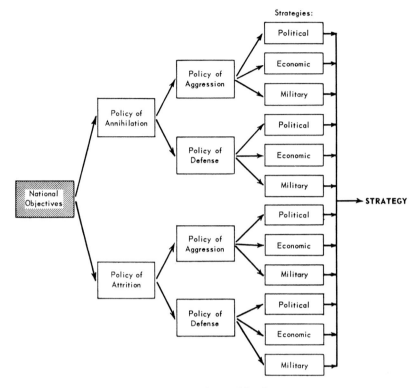

FIG. 6. Flow of choices from objectives to strategy.

designed to deter the Soviet Union from military aggression. We could then emphasize political communications and economic measures to "destroy" the ideology of militant communism (destruction of communist ideology to come, hopefully, from within). If our policy was one of attrition and of defense, we might choose a policy of containment and the establishment of military forces just adequate to hold against Soviet attack, and again restrict aggressive policies to political and economic measures. The choice of a set of related military, political, and economic measures would then constitute, for each particular time frame, the "strategy" of the nation.

It is clear that we can proceed by similar analyses from strategy to tactics, taking into account geopolitics in the theaters where we might have to fight, the problems of transportation, etc., and thus come to weapons systems designed to further the tactics and to weapons designed to optimize the weapons systems.

It is, however, well known that we need to consider the interactions among all elements in our system, and so we need to add the feedback shown in Fig. 7. Certainly if tactical atomic weapons constitute one of the elements, the effect on the rest of the weapons system is

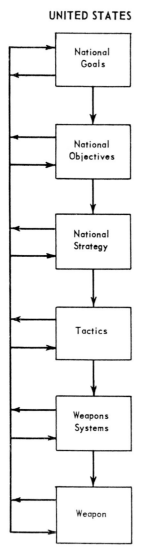

UNITED STATES

FIG. 7. Interactions in national system analysis.

tremendous, with an important interaction on tactics, strategy, and national objectives. For example, this currently has led us to feel that we might be able to substitute, at lower cost, more atomic weapons for fewer soldiers in the employment of atomic tactics empha-

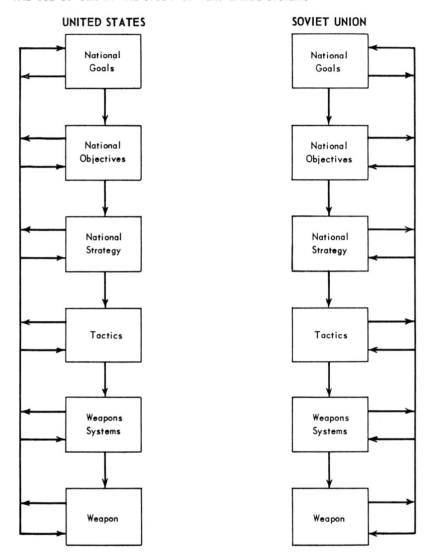

FIG. 8. United States and Soviet national systems.

sizing movement and dispersal, supporting in turn a strategy emphasizing containment and thermonuclear deterrence of the Soviet Union.

Although we are doing this preliminary analysis on our own system, based on certain assumptions with respect to Soviet intentions and capabilities, it is obvious that we must also analyze in detail the Soviet problems, as shown in Fig. 8. Each national system has its

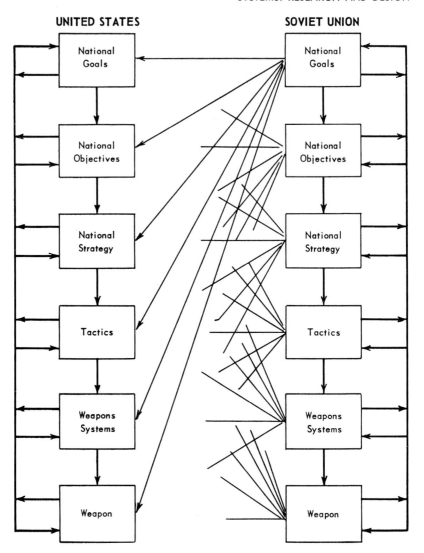

FIG. 9. Interaction of United States-Soviet systems.

own and different respective set of feedbacks. I should emphasize at this time that both systems are, of course, subject to political, economic, and population constraints as well as military ones.

It is further clear that if the analysis is to be complete all of the interactions for each of the main parameters shown must be considered in order that we may find a major strategy that will give us the best chance of meeting our national goals and objectives. One set of these interactions is shown in Fig. 9. You can imagine the intricacy of the double set of 72 interactions among all parameters.

This kind of a diagram is not a foolish concept or theory. We do indeed need to take into account the question of whether the unalterable goal of unidimensional Soviet society is to convert and conquer

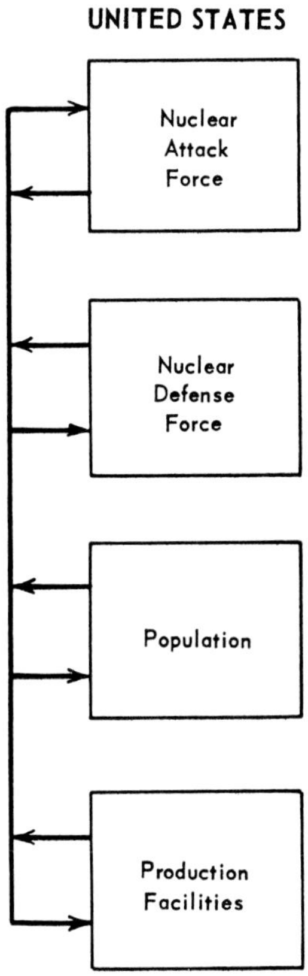

UNITED STATES

Nuclear Attack Force

Nuclear Defense Force

FIG. 10. Interaction in United States nuclear system.

Population

Production Facilities

the world, and whether their present pleasantness may or may not be political deception. Their goal will clearly affect in a practical way our own national budget, strategy, and tactics. Even worse, if the Soviet military strength, as indicated by their weapons system and their stockpiles, becomes tremendous in the future compared to our own, then consideration might even be given by some, as suggested in the December 21, 1959, issue of *US News and World Report,* as to whether we should "fight or surrender." Certainly to surrender would mean that we would abandon our own goals. This seems extremely undesirable and unlikely to me.

In general, the attempt to find solutions for the problem of our national-military system involves a series of difficult and complicated interactions which are at best, at the present time, only semianalytical and semilogical.

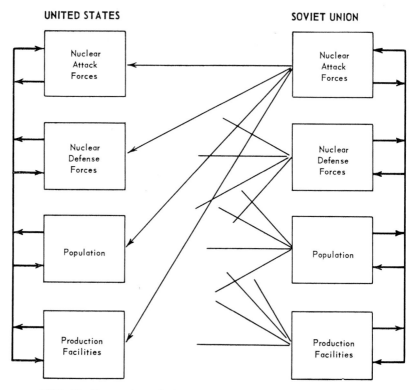

FIG. 11. Interaction of United States and Soviet nuclear systems.

Coming further down toward realities, let us consider one aspect of strategy: thermonuclear deterrence. Figure 10 shows the major parameters to be considered. We can have deterrence only if we can, if we wish, strike heavily against the Soviet Union, but we must be able as well to defend ourselves against a Soviet initial blow. We need to consider as a parameter how we preserve our population, one of the main goals of all of our efforts, if not the principal one. We need also to preserve the production capability that we now use both to achieve national well-being and to provide our own defense. It is clear that the Soviet Union has similar problems.

Figure 11 shows a few of the 32 complicated interactions that must be taken into account if we are to find the minimax solution which will bring about relatively stable thermonuclear deterrence. Also, I want to remind you again through Fig. 12 that the military aspects must operate within the national political, economic, and other ethical constraints. We can consider a range of possible stable systems which at one extreme involve an uncontrolled arms race in which stability

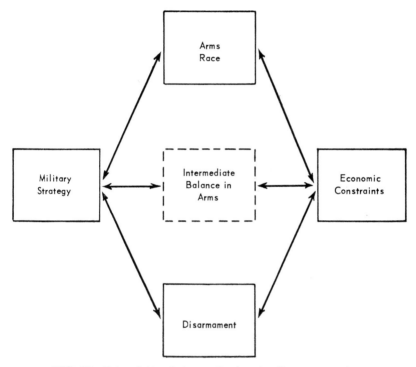

FIG. 12. Interrelation between fiscal and military constraints.

is sought by maximizing military strength on both sides. At the other extreme is disarmament, in which stability is sought by legal and binding agreements and inspection systems with very low levels of military strength. In between we have the remote possibility that both sides might desire *mutual* thermonuclear deterrence to the degree that they would be willing to achieve it with uncertain but implicit agreements and within limited, sensible, economic constraints.

Let us now suppose that we are getting down to the more specific analysis of the weapons system in this problem of thermonuclear deterrence. One-half of the interactions, that is to say, the problem of United States defense, is shown in Fig. 13. Here we must consider the interaction between the Soviet offensive capabilities in aircraft, ICBM's, submarines and submarine-launched missiles and aircraft, and subversive delivery and our defensive capabilities. Our systems analysis must determine the best mix in interceptors, ground-to-air

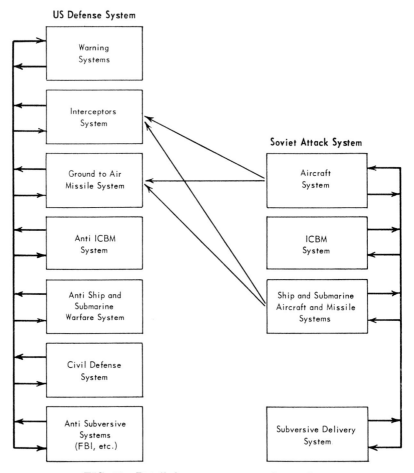

FIG. 13. Detailed weapons systems interactions.

missiles, anti-ICBM's, antiship and antisubmarine warfare, civil defense systems, and antisubversive systems such as the FBI. All of these must of course be served by the appropriate warning and control nets.

At this stage we can at least begin to think more in terms of the engineering of weapons systems, of the actual effectiveness of the weapons in military operations, and of the cost and timeliness of the weapons.

As an example of the number of weapons (each a technical and operational system of its own) that have been considered in one small

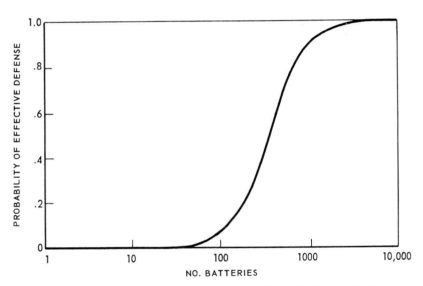

FIG. 14. List of competing missiles.

NIKE AJAX

NIKE HERCULES

NIKE ZEUS

TALOS

HAWK

BOMARC

FIG. 15. Operational effectiveness versus number of missile batteries.

part of the over-all system, I have listed in Fig. 14 the competitors in the ground-to-air missile category. The method usually used to compare such a set of competing or possibly supplementary weapons is to construct a system simulation in which every important technical and operational characteristic of the weapon and weapon system is taken into account. From such a simulation, curves like those given in Fig. 15 can be obtained, which relate the probability of an effective defense to the number of missile batteries, for attacks by a specified number of aircraft, in specified formation, at specified altitudes, with a specified number of decoys, and with a specified number of air-to-surface missiles. It takes literally tens of thousands of such curves from a systems simulation to completely describe the behavior of the system under a variety of attack situations.

The other kind of data that must always be considered is that of availability of a weapon as a function of time, as is illustrated in

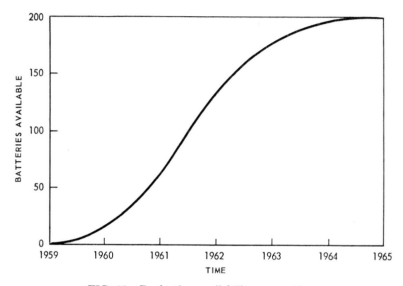

FIG. 16. Production availability versus time.

Fig. 16. In addition, costs of alternative systems investment and systems operations must be determined. The most important skill in complicated systems research is the ability to take the large number of curves usually derived from a simulation describing system behavior (a behavior which is based in detail on such parameters as hit, kill, operational capabilities, etc.) and to transform this mass of descriptive performance information into more manageable analytical equations. With skill, this can be done. One is then sure that the aggregated behavior represented by the analytical equations specifies well enough the comparative effectiveness, cost, and timeliness of the competing weapons in this system. Such analytical expressions are most easily manipulated to find optimum solutions.

It then becomes possible to choose the most favorable schedule for weapons systems evolution to meet the evolving opposed attack system whose effectiveness must also be simulated and calculated. Given such detailed systems analysis for each of the major tactical systems and hopefully a minimax solution, it becomes possible to at least estimate the most favorable choices between the major strategic systems. Finally, it is at least theoretically possible to estimate the choices in national objectives that we may have to consider at the national level in order to achieve the national goals (which I regard as fixed and unalterable).

I think that I have made it obvious that we are always dealing with a set of systems which are in continuous technical change and evolution. Thus the task of systems research in military problems is unending, and is always subject to a very considerable uncertainty because of inadequate intelligence information and its extrapolation to the future.

I have discussed problems that, except for the question of the choice of goals, involve only remotely human choices and a knowledge of human beings in the sense that the goals and other choices usually represent the consensus of a large number of people. Like many others in the United States, I feel that our support of the social sciences has been niggardly indeed. Thus we are only at the beginning of an understanding of man-machine relationships and of systems concerned primarily with the social organization of man. It is appropriate, however, to speculate on both the systematic and the individual reactions of man to weapons systems. The following is an example.

One of the points made by duPicq,[8] discussed by Bernard Brodie[9] in his recent book and by me[10] in my review of Brodie's book, is the fact that man seems to adapt tactically to the design of more and more devastating weapons, and there appears to be reasonable evidence that as weapons have become more effective the rate of killing, or the percentage of casualties per division equivalent per day, appears to remain or come back to an ageless constant. I do not mean to imply that there are no transient departures from the constant because indeed there are, but the transient always dies out and on the average the casualty rate returns to its original lower value. It is as though man will not tolerate too high a casualty rate. One cannot help but be struck by the fact that the percentage casualties for an entire army do not vary much from day to day. Yet the evidence indicates that this is not by design of either higher or lower commanders but rather is an instinctive behavior of the whole system. It seems that if the killing rate is low one attacks and advances; if it is close to the average there is a stalemate; if it becomes too high one retreats.

As a matter of fact, it appears that one of the major military problems at the tactical level is how to take unilateral advantage of the transient increase in killing rates brought about by improved military technology. Such transients occurred, for example, in the Roman infantry weapons system, in the light cavalry weapons system of the Mongols, in the case of the longbow and its tactical use toward the close of medieval times, and in the case of machine guns and tanks in World War I. One now assumes a similar transient with respect to atomic weapons.

AN EXAMPLE OF A NATIONAL SYSTEM

As another example of systems difficulties, I discussed earlier the increase in per capita productivity in United States agriculture and the accompanying increase in government support that became necessary for sociological reasons when farmers' income was greatly reduced because of lowered agricultural prices. We are impressed by the fact that only about 12% of the United States labor force is in agriculture. However, there is the important fact that 40% of all consumer expenditures is made for farm products. It is clear that we need to look at farming in relation to the rest of the American economic system, as Davis and Goldberg of Harvard University have done.[11] We need, in fact, to think of agribusiness instead of agriculture as the pertinent system. When we do this, we need to consider the food industry, farm machinery and automotive power, wholesale trade, transportation, electric and other kinds of power, containers, fertilizer, and many other elements of our economy as a set of inputs to agriculture. Furthermore, the processing of agricultural products is done not only by food industries but by industries producing tobacco products, textiles, wood and paper products, and those manufacturing leather goods, soaps, and paints. Including these, we find that in 1957 36% of the total labor force was concerned with agribusiness.

In the matrix describing agribusiness (illustrated in Fig. 17) agriculture is only the provider of the raw material in one of the biggest subsystems of our whole economy. We are led to quite different conclusions with respect to the importance of farming if we consider it as a source of raw materials, since its end products involve such a big part of our economic well-being. The over-all per capita productivity of agribusiness turns out to be low even though it is high in that small part of agribusiness—agriculture—which is directly concerned with productivity on the farm itself.

THE LEVELS OF SYSTEM RESEARCH

I can summarize my own impressions with respect to the several levels of systems research as follows: I believe that at the present time it is practical to deal by logical analysis with many relatively complicated systems involving men, machines, and economic systems. Analytical analysis, however, becomes difficult when man is introduced as a part of a system and as physiology, psychology, ethics, religion, and cultural attitudes play a dominating part in the choices to be made. However, there is not the slightest question in my mind that greatly improved suboptimization can be achieved if one considers, with the best approach possible, at least the next two largest systems above the system to be analyzed, in order to provide some guidance with respect to the "big picture." It will help one to discard many poor alternatives and poor choices.

I believe that with increased skill and the improvement of analytical methods, and with increased knowledge from the social sciences, we are at the beginning of an era when we will be able to adapt our sociological systems wisely to the changes forced on us by technological progress and at the same time retain both progress and our intuitive and deeply valued national goals. This is more likely to lead to individual happiness and national well-being than an anarchic pursuit of transient economic desiderata or the rigidity of communism.

LONG-RANGE PLANNING

Research on systems is one thing, but planning and design is another. I believe we know how to do research on very big systems, but we do not know how to plan for them or how to design them. This is our next topic—since operations research on very big systems needs a client.

The advantages of planning[12] are self-evident to all who look to future satisfactions and have responsibility for budgeting toward their achievement—in the family, in industry, and in the military. Systematic planning must proceed from a clear concept of objectives and basic policies for achieving those objectives. There are, for example, certain cultural traits that direct us in determining policies: individual rights and dignity, freedom to compete, national survival, etc. What makes planning difficult above all else is the unpredictableness of the future amidst the revolutionary developments resulting from man's able conquest in the fields of science and technology. We cannot plan in any realm on the basis of evolutionary changes when our world is moving forward in revolution. Today, for example, more than at any other time in our history, Americans view our defense program as one that has been too slow in keeping up with the times. The Soviet

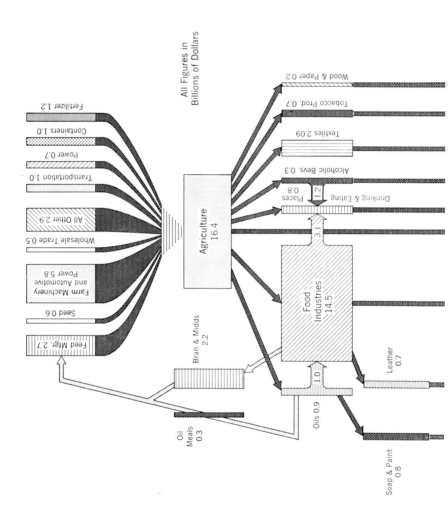

All Figures in
Billions of Dollars

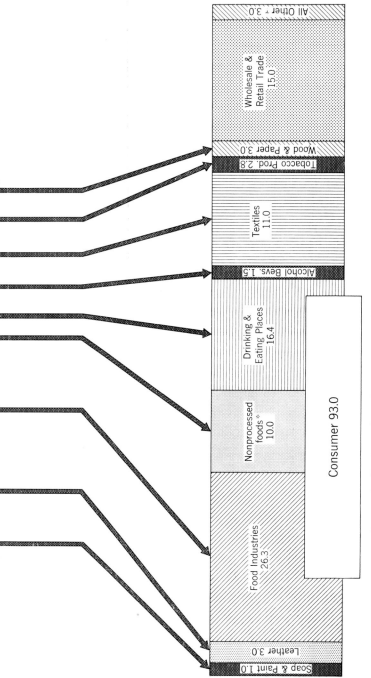

FIG. 17.   Agribusiness flow chart, 1954.   (Adapted from Davis and Goldberg.[11])

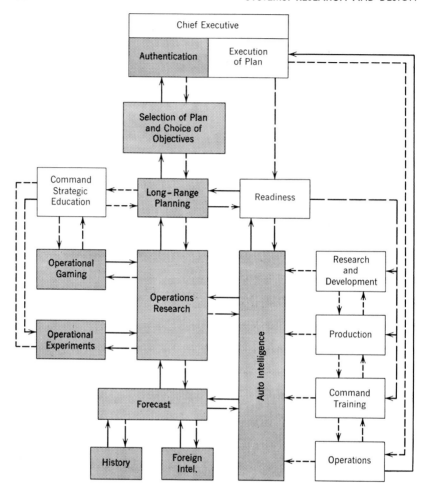

FIG. 18.   Proposed planning system (schematic).

Union's spectacular stride forward in science and development, over the last decade, dramatized for all to see, has alerted our own people to the requirement for more effective planning of the defense of the United States.

In an attempt to identify the requirements of planning, let me outline a philosophy of planning that applies to all parts of our military system and can be translated to cover other large-scale operations. The goal is a planning system that provides in an orderly, logical way for *a continuous and up-to-date* search for solutions based on sound and timely decision making. My proposal is not tied to any specific organization; rather it focuses on the functioning of a logical decision-making system within which long-range plans are developed. Implied is a feed-around of guidance, information, and partial solutions, in a ceaseless search for the flexible, accommodating, over-all solution that adjusts continuously to the new dynamics of technology. Figure 18 shows schematically the sort of system I have in mind.

It is logical to start with the forecast—the basis for rational action. The technical forecast provides the first and fundamental part of a rational basis for future operational planning. The forecast for any particular time frame is based on existing trends in their relation to the values and objectives chosen, and it makes a prognosis of situations that may arise in a future period if these trends continue. It is argued that with skill and experience such formal forecasts can be made with sufficient certainty to provide a far better basis for rational action than the present informal and almost random decision-making system. Without a rather explicit forecast based on the trends, there is no basis, *no rational basis*, for long-range planning.

There are three specific areas of information that provide data for the formulation of a technical forecast: autointelligence, which provides information about ourselves; foreign intelligence, which provides information about our competitors, enemies, and allies; and historical intelligence, which brings together and analyzes the lessons of history. From intelligence studies in these three areas it is possible to develop a probabilistic forecast. On these foundations, the forecast represents a weighed and balanced analysis rather than an intuitive impression of current trends and their possible effect on developments in the future. Such a forecast must not be regarded as a prediction of what will happen in the future, but a prediction of what may or will probably happen if present trends are allowed to continue.

Innovations and Operations Research

In view of the predictions, the focus of the search is to determine possible new technical, tactical, and strategic courses of action that will enhance one's own future operational position. Potential possibilities lie in the area of problem-solving innovations. There is no actual lack of general ideas for such solutions. The practical difficulty is in identifying and gaining support for a truly novel proposal that will provide a more significant advance than that of competitors. It is the role of operations research to identify and compare the most promising alternatives. Wise and timely decisions on the acceptability of proposed innovations are of the utmost importance in the competition for short lead time.

Long-Range Planning Group

The forecast outlines the probable happenings in the continuance of hypothetical futures. Operations research identifies the possible direction to be taken in the attempt to initiate new trends and to manipulate the real world to one's own advantage. Proposed innovations are directed to providing specific ways and means to achieve successful manipulation.

It is the group of highly professional, hard-thinking, imaginative planners who must screen ideas and proposals provided from the forecast-operations research chain. It is their job to select specific and feasible plans to meet those objectives, taking into account many intangibles not susceptible to research at this stage of our knowledge.

Decision Making

The basic problem of management is balance in the programs and choices that will provide readiness in the short-, mid-, and long-range futures. This requires a posture of sufficient flexibility to meet a wide range of possible competitive actions. Good decisions to achieve such a posture are aided in the making and in their implementation by good philosophy and good organizational structure, but they are determined more by that intangible human factor of outstanding and forceful leadership than by any other single factor. The good judgment, strength, and determination of able leadership in the democratic tradition are necessary to engender forward-looking philosophy, efficient organization, and advantageous use of our resources to bring into being the actions necessary to assure the survival of our republic.

The decision maker requires all the aid possible from advanced problem-solving procedures such as operations research that are now available for decision making. As yet, the philosophy of scientific aid for the decision maker has not been too well accepted. Too many decision makers rely fully on the intuitive methods that were sufficient in the past when the problems of an enterprise were comprehensible to a single human being. They have not yet recognized that this is outmoded in truly complex situations and that the utilization of the available tools of science must be *combined* with intuition developed through experience in the different professions.

The executive should have the benefit of the results of all the sophisticated management techniques when individual plans and sets of objectives covering proposed strategies, tactics, and weapons systems are submitted to him. The executive, then, has the responsibility for the final decision that determines whether a proposal is to be subjected to the operational cycle of research, development, production, training, and operations.

There is thus a ceaseless search for a solution, a continuously fresh approach. Figure 19 shows the cycle in more detail.

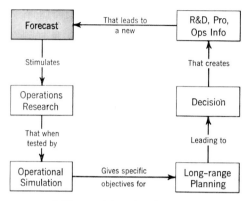

FIG. 19.   The planning cycle.

THE AREAS OF BIG SYSTEMS
OPERATIONS RESEARCH

It is already clear that one area where this problem of the design of a very big system is most acute is in the military systems. This seems natural because of the great amount of operations research expended in the study of military systems and because of the accompanying aggressive, ruthless, and effective research and development programs on military systems which tend to push technical innovations to the limit. The earlier aspect of operations research, that is to say, the greater emphasis on operations analysis as it was conducted in World War II, has become a common technique of every weapons developer and engineer, and is in no sense a specialty of the operations research groups. The real difficulty exists in the fact that it is impossible to design the system of a single service by itself and be sure of even minimum acceptability in effectiveness.

We have noted in the air war, for example, that the roles and missions of the Army, Navy, Air Force, and Office of Civil Defense and Mobilization in both offense and defense are so interwoven that it is absolutely essential to study the over-all system. However, this cannot be done without a tremendous amount of work in the subsystems aspects. So far as I know, the ORO has made the first, and so far only, serious integrated attempt to study in detail the entire air war problem in all of its defensive, offensive, economical, and cultural aspects. There is now actually reasonable agreement among the operations research groups and gradually of the executives concerned with the air war. Indeed, there are indications that the executive branch is being influenced by this consensus to take actions favorable to systems improvement.

The situation in ground warfare and sea warfare is far less satisfactory, primarily because the systems problems involved are so incredibly complex and because these problems have had much less study than the air war problem.

The military-political problem, which is probably the most critical to the United States at the present time (1960), is that concerned with disarmament. At the interface between the military and political arts, there is almost a complete lack of communications. The objectives and values of the United States political and military systems are often inexplicable to members of the other professions. The U. S. Department of State, which appears to have the primary responsibility and cognizance for disarmament, lost the effectiveness of its Research and Intelligence Department at the beginning of the Eisenhower administration, and thus is most inadequately prepared to understand the technical aspects of disarmament, which is so critical to the physical security of the United States. We must, therefore, do our utmost to improve and reinforce our studies of the military-political system which involves disarmament. Here again it is clear that no suboptimization will be of the slightest value.

Thus operational research is badly needed in the State Department. The State Department is faced on the one hand by a population, industry, Congress, Senate, and Administration primarily engrossed with domestic affairs, and on the other by a set of world societies, many in the process of national revolution, and all in a most vigorous sociological interaction. All aspects of this sociological interaction—political, economic, military, and cultural value system—are in a state of violent and revolutionary change. This change in each sociological element has either been brought about by technological advance or has been made possible by it.

Our domestic situation is also in the midst of explosive change for technological reasons, which are world-wide in origin. The State Department is now deeply concerned with the interrelated problems of international aid, diplomacy, atomic tests, as well as disarmament, and with many other problems in which intricate technologies are an intrinsic aspect of the problem. This is a far, far cry from the traditional nontechnical role and philosophy of the nineteenth-century diplomacy in which the State Department has had the most operational experience. The State Department is as yet unprepared for the modern technical aspects of diplomacy, either by education or by prior studies by operational research. This makes it very difficult for its traditionally trained executives to understand and always bear in mind the great twentieth-century interdependence between technology and diplomacy when political policy is being established or political decisions are being made. In these aspects of international negotiation the Russians surpass us because of their prolonged research and prior preparation on the technical aspects of politics. The State Department recognizes its needs, but has not had congressional support for the necessary research.

I believe that it is in the State Department and in politics that the greatest possible advances in operational research can be made in the future, and that here there can be a tremendous use of symbolic logic and computers to provide for all of the interrelations in a way that is presently beyond the comprehension of any single human being or of any group of diplomats of reasonable size.

There are other government systems that are clearly in trouble because of suboptimization. One of these is the agriculture-business system, already mentioned, which has been so well described by Davis and Goldberg. This system is composed of industries such as the farm tool and fertilizer industries and the tremendous research and development programs of the Department of Agriculture and the commercial seed companies. These provide inputs to agriculture itself, which must be regarded primarily as the source of the raw materials of the industries, just as iron and coal mines provide the raw materials for the steel industry. The food and fiber raw materials feed into another set of manufacturing industries that manufacture out of the raw materials a wide range of products from oils and paints to textiles, leathers, and food. These in turn are transported and distributed by an intricate merchandizing complex. All of the foregoing are tied together by an intricate set of feedbacks. At the present time there are serious symptoms of systems difficulty, and a grave disparity between the great per capita productivity in the farming areas as compared with other areas of this system. There is a serious maldistribution in profits and therefore in motivations, and, in general, the symptoms including overproduction of raw materials are treated by *ad hoc* methods. The treatment of symptoms, indeed, of such system diseases is like the attempts of hunting clubs to manage the rabbit-fox cycle by introducing an excess of rabbits at the minimum of the rabbit cycle. This procedure always results in a most violent oscillation of the rabbit-fox population because of course the more rabbits, the more foxes, and later the *less* rabbits.

Another category of important problems which defy suboptimization are joint community problems, such as charity. The recipients of charity exist in a complex of government, local, and state welfare agencies and a host of private charitable organizations. Some of these agencies derive their funds from government and therefore taxation, some from public charity campaigns, and others from private charity campaigns. The various agencies compete with each other to serve the recipients of charity and compete as well for funds. In this complex, the taxpayer, the donor of funds to charity, and the recipient of charity are always helpless actors in the drama. Indeed, the multitude of organizations, all eager to serve the unfortunate, are engaged in a competition they are helpless to control at the present time. Furthermore, no single community can afford the necessary study required to outline the over-all charity system and the ways in which it might be optimized in the future to the benefit of all participants. We need a mechanism to study such systems, since the problem is nation-wide, and a reasonable solution, once found, could be applied repetitively. Indeed, it is the nature of community problems, which include the problems of public health, that they cannot usually be studied adequately with the support of only one community, but once studied and solved, the solution can be applied elsewhere at small additional cost.

There are two kinds of problems connected with business systems which are also increasingly important. These are the problems connected with consumer product stability and with the interactions connected with changes in the geographical area environment, that is to say, in the growth, demographic composition, character of industrialization, etc., with time and with the effect of research and development on the industry.

Clearly, the same problem exists for international business systems. In this respect the kinds of operations research studies that are good prototypes are the studies carried out under Sir Charles Goodeve for the British steel industry. The study considered the raw materials system, the interaction of this with a world transportation system, the design of loading and unloading facilities and ports, the geographic distribution of and the design of steel plants, and the system for distribution. This study, involving a world-wide business system, has, I believe, been to some extent put into effect with profit.

Another example is the somewhat similar French study of a French petroleum system. This considered the raw materials system (which included the problems of geophysical prospecting for oil), transportation systems, the locating of the refining plants, and a study of the distribution system and retail outlets for the end products. Again, this involved an international business system and its relations and optimization in connection with the internal business systems of France and its colonies. In this case, too, the study has been successfully applied.

It is clear that it is in the study of such large systems that operations research will be of increasing importance. Perhaps the most important new application of operations research is in area development problems, especially in underdeveloped countries. There have been various studies with practical applications in these areas, which always involve the most difficult of extrapolations, often the absence of the means to achieve the eventual goals swiftly, and therefore, the comparison of the various paths to be taken in achieving the desired goals and often, as well, the delineation of the goals themselves. The studies of Striner et al. with respect to economic disaster areas in the United States are noteworthy,[13] as are those of Arthur D. Little on the development of Puerto Rico[14] (which has had such excellent results) and of Ackoff and others in India.[15]

I could continue to enumerate the many examples of such major systems, most or many of them in difficulty because of the rapidity of technical and cultural innovations.

PHILOSOPHY AND OPERATIONS RESEARCH

In essence, operations research may be regarded as the application of a theory of the reasoning process at all group levels from worldwide (the "biggest" system) and national down to that of the individual.[16] Operations research has stimulated basic research in this field because it has forced an attempt, on a scientific basis, to include all possible factors affecting given decision problems. It has thus brought persons of scientific training away from their narrow specialized fields into the broad all-inclusive field of decision processes.

Our present literature is filled with some of the more mechanical problems dealing with the decision process, such as those of allocation of resources (linear and dynamic programming) or decision in competition with other decision makers (game theory, etc.). A theory of reasoning necessarily brings together the basic constructs of philosophy, psychology, neurophysiology, and the physical sciences. Indeed, it begins to appear that philosophy is a function of psychology and science in the sense that these provide the raw materials whereby philosophy can be a useful enterprise. Conversely, these latter are dependent upon philosophy. These formal dependencies and congruences are indicated in the study of value theory. The indication is strong enough to lead one to suspect that a development of the theory of reasoning has more promise in the development of advancement of human knowledge than any of the more narrow specialized subjects.

In World War I the technology of chemistry was a major contribution to the progress of civilization (before that, mechanics). In World War II the major contributions were made in the new fields of physics (microwaves and nuclear physics). One might be led to predict that future areas will similarly be dependent upon basic studies on reasoning in decision making and therefore to operational research as the practical outlet of these sciences.

Some specific problems that are basic to reasoning, which I find of interest at present, have to do with a more general mode for rational behavior. We have become sufficiently sophisticated to turn away from deterministic models to base our analyses on *stochastic definite* models—i.e., on models in which it is assumed that we know all the possible states of the system described by the model and also all the transition probabilities involved in changes of state. More realistic models will have to allow for the fact that we are never sure we know all the possible states of the system—particularly when projected into the future—nor do we know the transition probabilities. In other words, we must build decision procedures based on *stochastic indefinite* models. One of the simple constructs that arises in such a model is in the nature of open-ended strategies. These are the means which through usage become sacred in their own right and have values associated with their adoption. In industry, such open-ended strategies have to do with the amortization of capital equipment and with the amount of money spent in research and development. In a society these open-minded strategies are embodied in such words as justice, freedom, etc. At the level of individuals they are expressed by such word as honesty, integrity, etc. There is apparently no a priori way of judging the soundness of these strategies. They appear to be judged a posteriori.

A problem of a practical nature is the question of the size of the operations research effort compared to the problem involved. We have seen how high-level syntheses require up to hundreds of man-years of effort for their completion. A decision process by the methods of operations research can become exceedingly complicated, and many groups will find themselves too small to invest the necessary resources to apply this type of analysis to their decision problem. Charity as a part of Community Services, already noted, is an example. Means must be provided for the routine application of decision principles on a much broader base than those afforded by the direct customer, so that by application of general principles the research is directly useful to the entire class of customers.

SUMMARY

I have outlined the still acceptable effect of the increase in physical knowledge on our peacetime society, and the most unacceptable, crucial, and decisive effect on our military competition with the Soviet Union. I have demonstrated that this crisis in technology has produced a crisis in management. The crisis is becoming equally severe for all of the rest of humanity and has increased the tempo of the second industrial revolution now sweeping the world. I have suggested that this tempo, which has been rising for centuries, rose above a threshold toward a crisis in this decade, i.e., about 1950, that it will become increasingly severe, and that our primary problem is to find a way to manage our very big systems affairs in this new situation. Solutions must be found by far more conscious long-range planning and very big systems engineering and this should be aided by a very great increase in our support of the social sciences.

If the increase in physical knowledge has made the future so uncertain, then we must plan much further ahead in a way that will provide much greater flexibility, whether this be in peaceful or military affairs, whether it be for the individual or for the country. We will need to adapt our culture to more rapid change, and accept such adapting much more readily than in the past, instead of running our lives, our actions, and our affairs as though there continued to be a stable and known way of doing new things. We will need to estimate well ahead of time the cost and values of doing things in new and different ways so that when the time comes to make a decision we already will have thought the problem through. We will have to examine our individual, group, and national values to see what it is we want to do in a rapidly changing world, and to see what we can do consciously to manipulate in our favor the real and perhaps hostile physical and world environment so that it will serve us better. This is a problem of big systems.

It is clear to me that operations research dealing with very big systems is much more difficult than the operations analysis of early years. To be effective the operations research dealing with big systems must operate in a formal relationship to the systems planner and designer. The elements of the research (and design) must be carried out in a planning system that has formal provision for iteration and feed-around of information and solutions. The work must be organized in a hierarchy of a team of teams. The work must be done in parallel. The new techniques show promise of meeting the needs of this difficult kind of operations research, to the profit of systems designers and planners.

As for the older forms of operations research, I believe they are being adopted so rapidly by the engineering and management professions that they have become a common and highly desirable part of our technological skills, and are no longer unique to operations research.

In summary, then, we have a national capability to meet the situations facing us. It is mandatory that we direct our abilities to use this existing capability in fulfilling the obligations inherent in our national goal: ". . . to preserve for ourselves and our posterity, freedom and the blessings of liberty."

REFERENCES

1. Ellis A. Johnson, The Crisis in Science and Technology and its Effect on Military Development, *Operations Research*, vol. 6, no. 1, Jan.–Feb. 1958, pp. 11–34.
2. Joseph F. McCloskey, *ed.*, *Operations Research for Management*, vol. 1, The Johns Hopkins University Press, Baltimore, 1954, pp. 262–264.
3. D. Blackwell, A. Fiacco, and N. Smith, A General Method for Non-Linear Programming, Operations Research Society of America, New York, May 1960.
4. D. J. Price, The Exponential Curve of Science, *Discovery*, vol. 17, no. 6, June 1956, pp. 240–243.
5. Paul R. Burkholder, Antibiotics, *Science*, vol. 129, May 29, 1959, p. 1458.
6. U. S. Congressional Joint Committee on the Economic Report, *Hearings on the January 1959 Economic Report of the President* (86th Congress, 1st Session), Jan.–Feb. 1959, U. S. Government Printing Office, Washington, 1959, p. 112.
7. U. S. Department of Agriculture, Commodity Credit Corporation, *Charts* . . . Nov., 1958, Table no. 7, and Oct. 1959, Table no. 2, U. S. Government Printing Office, Washington.
8. Ardant DuPicq, *Battle Studies*, translated by Col. J. N. Greely and Maj. R. C. Cotton, Military Service Publishing Co., Harrisburg, 1947.
9. Bernard Brodie, *Strategy in the Missile Age*, Princeton University Press, Princeton, 1959.
10. Ellis A. Johnson, Thoughts on Strategy in the Missile Age, *Army*, vol. 10, no. 5, Dec. 1959, p. 46. (Review of Brodie, ref. 9.)

11. John H. Davis and Ray H. Goldberg, *A Concept of Agribusiness,* Division of Research, Graduate School of Business Administration, Harvard University, Boston, 1957.

12. Mary E. Murphy, The Role of Management Sciences in Underdeveloped Countries, paper presented to the Third Annual International Meeting of the Institute of Management Sciences, Oct. 18–19, 1956. (Abstract in *Management Science,* vol. 3, no. 2, Jan. 1957, pp. 210–211.)

13. W. Hochwald, S. Sonenblum, and H. E. Striner, *Local Impacts of Foreign Trade,* National Planning Association, Washington, 1960.

14. Arthur D. Little, Inc., Report on New Industries for Puerto Rico to the Puerto Rico Development Corporation (*Report C 57889*), Arthur D. Little, Inc., Cambridge, Mass., Aug. 1952.

15. Russell L. Ackoff, Operations Research and National Planning, *Operations Research,* vol. 5, no. 4, Aug. 1957, pp. 457–468.

16. Ellis A. Johnson, The Long-Range Future of Operational Research, *Operations Research,* vol. 8, no. 1, Jan.–Feb. 1960, pp. 1–23.

CHAPTER 5

A PROBLEM IN THE DESIGN
OF LARGE-SCALE DIGITAL
COMPUTER SYSTEMS

R. J. NELSON

This discussion is concerned with the problem of nonarithmetic computations on stored program digital computers. In particular, I shall discuss a wide class of pervasive computational operations, essentially those involving scanning of data, or, alternatively, depending on properties of the data, which do not seem to lend themselves to very efficient realization on existing machines. I shall also attempt an analysis of such operations and suggest some principles that might underlie a modified central computer system design.

STANDARD MACHINES

By a *standard machine* I mean the central system of a stored program computer having the following characteristics: a high-speed addressable memory with a capacity for several thousands of words; an arithmetic unit with at least three registers—an accumulator, a multiplier-quotient register, and a third register for holding addends, multiplicands, and divisors, which may or may not be distinct from the memory register normally associated with the high-speed memory; and a control unit consisting of at least a control counter, an instruction register, and instruction-decoding registers and circuitry. The system may also have indexing or "B" registers, and certain concurrency properties achieved either by partitioning the memory into several independent units or by adding extra instruction registers and/or sequencing counters.* We shall also specify that such machines,

* An excellent detailed account of large-scale systems can be found in C. V. L. Smith, *Electronic Digital Computers,* McGraw-Hill Book Co., New York, 1959. See especially Chapters 10–15 and 17.

94

including some recent ones with multiple memories operating on independent cycles or capable of partially overlapping instruction execution, are sequential in operation. This implies that standard machines normally execute the $(k + 1)$st instruction after the kth, where k is a memory location, and execute one instruction at a time with at most partial overlap. A common characteristic of standard machines is that all work on operands (data or instructions) proceeds by bringing one operand at a time into the arithmetic unit.

A standard machine, if synchronous, runs on a fixed-length cycle consisting of two half-cycles, one during which an instruction is obtained from memory and analyzed, and the other during which a datum is selected from memory and operated upon in the arithmetic unit.

As is well known, the decision as to what kinds of operations shall be built into the circuitry of a machine and which left to programmed fabrication is theoretically arbitrary. A very basic practical design principle, however, is that a built-in circuit must save time; otherwise the operation to be realized should be constructed by a programmed algorithm. For example, addition can be realized on a machine limited to a built-in unary successor operation $[f(x) = x + 1]$, a unary predecessor operation $[g(x) = x - 1]$, means for transfer to and from memory, and conditional transfer operations. However, a computer thus limited would be too slow. On the other hand, a built-in square root has little, if any, speed advantage over a programmed subroutine, and thus is not provided for in most standard machines. I shall argue later that certain nonarithmetical operations might well be built in, but in a nonstandard subsystem of the central computer system, because of the need for greater speeds.

BEHAVIOR VERSUS EFFICIENCY

Having briefly characterized standard machines, it is now important to distinguish between what they can do and what they can do well. Such a distinction is already implied in the example of built-in versus programmed addition, and the criterion of efficiency used there was simply speed. This will continue to be our main explicitly used criterion.

Concerning possible behaviors, we expect computers to be able to perform an amazingly wide variety of tasks: evaluate functions, solve large sets of equations, write payrolls, translate Russian into English, translate problem-oriented languages into machine language codes, design logic circuits for new computers, search scientific literature, simulate business enterprises, simulate other computers, play chess, learn to play chess, prove theorems, make business decisions, etc. It is comforting to know that standard machines can do many, if not all, of these things. In the case of purely arithmetical calculations standard machines—given an indefinitely enlargeable memory—can calculate any partial recursive function, or, equivalently, can calculate any arithmetical problem any special-purpose machine can calculate. This fact represents the solution of an existence problem, and covers all the territory one could rationally wish it to. The question whether computers are adequate beyond arithmetic, e.g., for language translation or theorem proving, can be answered in specific cases by showing the computability of certain associated arithmetical problems. This clearly defines another class of possible behaviors. Finally, problems suggested by the terms "artificial intelligence," "learning," and "adaptive behavior" have not to date been clearly stated, although this fact has not served to repress a good deal of very interesting experimentation.*

On the other hand, efficiency problems, which are concerned with the (vaguely conceived) interacting factors of order code sophistication, accuracy, speed, reliability, and low cost, are far more complicated. It should not have to be pointed out that the behavioral adequacy of standard computers implies nothing whatsoever about their efficiency, even given reasonable criteria, or about the worth of attempting certain types of computation on them. This truth is obscured by the fact that standard machines are in some cases extremely efficient on the grounds that without them obviously important scientific problems could not be solved at all, even at great expense. However, save in such clear-cut cases, the objective inquirer does not find it a simple matter to determine whether a standard machine in a given installation (also given a well-defined class of computations for it) is justified by low cost, high speed, by actually doing the work, by the prestige of its being on the premises, or, happily, by all four.

* Some "intellectual" problems may be characterized arithmetically: the problem to design a machine (or write a program) for inverting partial recursive functions; i.e., given such a function $f_m(n)$ with algorithm m, find an algorithm for computing $g(m, r)$ so that $f_m(g(m, r)) = r$. If $g(m, r)$ exists, an algorithm also exists for finding it. Cf. J. McCarthy, "The Inversion of Functions Defined by Turing Machines," in *Automata Studies*, edited by Shannon and McCarthy, Annals of Mathematics Studies No. 34, Princeton University Press, 1956.

The efficiency problem is further obscured by the programmer's artisan-like pride in turning out very sophisticated programs, which greatly enhance the usability of a computer, with nothing but a handful of built-in primitive operations. A most curious development in recent years has been the almost total separation of the activities of the really expert programmer and the central system designer. Yet, it is in this so far almost null intersection of interests that one might reasonably expect to find emerging a broad systems approach to the efficiency problem. In particular, since the programmer's problems arise in the context of symbol manipulation rather than in arithmetic, it seems strange that he has not had more to ask of the designer. The designer, on the other hand, has concentrated on bigger and faster memories, a certain element of "concurrency" (which is again in the interests of arithmetical speed), and has made but few concessions to the manipulation problem, e.g., in the form of character rather than word addressability and in some memory "swapping" improvements. The relative speeds of nonarithmetic operations still, however, remain prohibitively low, as I shall now argue with an example.

AN EXAMPLE

It is well to recall at this point some of the facts concerning large computational problems. A large problem might involve many computations over a 100,000-point lattice and thus solutions to an equivalent number of linear algebraic equations in the same number of unknowns. On a hypothetical 100-microsecond multiply standard machine, assuming an adequate high-speed memory, a single computation would take on the order of 10^4 hours. In the light of these facts it is not very difficult to understand the current interest in the development of ultrahigh-speed computers. Several such machines are being designed, all of which will have memories in the 10^5 word range operating on a cycle of less than 5 microseconds and with multiply times under 10 microseconds.

To further fix the discussion we shall consider just the one question of solving large sets of linear equations, such as arise in the kind of problem mentioned earlier, by iterative methods. In this way it will be possible in a somewhat oversimplified form to examine some of the interrelationships between central computer design and certain numerical procedures, with particular reference to the nonarithmetical aspects of the computations.

In an iterative procedure for solving a set of equations

$$a_{11}x_1 + a_{12}x_2 + \cdots + a_{1n}x_n = b_1$$
$$a_{21}x_1 + a_{22}x_2 + \cdots + a_{2n}x_n = b_2 \qquad (1)$$
$$\cdots\cdots\cdots\cdots\cdots\cdots\cdots\cdots\cdots$$
$$a_{n1}x_1 + a_{n2}x_2 + \cdots + a_{nn}x_n = b_n$$

an initial guess $x_1^{(0)}$, $x_2^{(0)}$, $\cdots$, $x_n^{(0)}$ of the x's is made, and this leads to the approximate solution $x_1^{(1)}$, $x_2^{(1)}$, $\cdots$, $x_n^{(1)}$, etc., successively. In the Jacobi method one obtains $x_1^{(k+1)}$ by substituting $x_2^{(k)}$, $x_3^{(k)}$, $\cdots$, $x_n^{(k)}$ in the first equation, $x_2^{(k+1)}$ by substituting $x_1^{(k)}$, $x_3^{(k)}$, $\cdots$, $x_n^{(k)}$ in the second, etc. In the Gauss-Seidel iteration the latest values obtained are used n the solution of each equation. Thus, again, $x_1^{(k+1)}$ is found using $x_2^{(k)}$, $x_3^{(k)}$, $\cdots$, $x_n^{(k)}$; but $x_2^{(k+1)}$ is found using $x_1^{(k+1)}$, $x_3^{(k)}$, $\cdots$, $x_n^{(k)}$; $x_3^{(k+1)}$ using $x_1^{(k+1)}$, $x_2^{(k+1)}$, $x_4^{(k)}$, $\cdots$, $x_n^{(k)}$, etc. Necessary and sufficient conditions are known for the convergence of both processes. Both of these schemes, which are known as *systematic* iterative methods, in general converge quite slowly, and it is therefore of considerable interest to look for other methods.

In the nonsystematic relaxation methods, one proceeds with the latest values as in the Gauss-Seidel iteration but instead of successively computing each $x_i^{(k+1)}$, one evaluates each linear expression of Eqs. 1, obtaining the *residual*, r_i (e.g., $r_1 = a_{11}x_1^{(0)} + a_{12}x_2^{(0)} + \cdots + a_{1n}x_n^{(0)} - b_1$); then the largest in absolute value of the r_i's is picked and a next value of x_i is chosen in such a way as to reduce the residual to zero or almost so. The residuals are calculated again and the process repeated.*

Not very much is known about the convergence of nonsystematic relaxation.† It seems to be generally agreed, however, that for hand computation the method is much better than those mentioned earlier because of the rapid convergence obtainable by improving the x_i's, at each step, associated with the largest residual. Admittedly this opinion is based on empirical observation of the behavior of the process and not on theory, but for the sake of argument we shall assume that the method is worth serious consideration as one to which *digital computers* might be applied.

In this connection it should be pointed out at once that it is cus-

---

* In this account no mention is made of many heuristic techniques which can be used in relaxation. Our interest here is in the problem of picking the largest residual.

† A sufficient condition is that the matrix A of coefficients of Eqs. 1 be symmetric and positive definite. But if A is symmetric and nonpositive definite with the entries a_{ii} all positive, then the method may still converge for certain initial guesses $x_1^{(0)}$, $x_2^{(0)}$, $\cdots$, $x_n^{(0)}$. Cf. A. M. Ostrowski, On the Linear Iteration Procedures for Symmetric Matrices, *National Bureau of Standards Report*, 1952.

tomary in recent discussions to rule out nonsystematic relaxation as impractical for standard machines. Thus Kunz says that although relaxation is "far superior" to other methods for hand computation, "it is extremely difficult to adapt to an automatic electronic computer . . . . It is not too difficult in hand computing to look back over as many as several hundred residues and pick out the largest . . . . For an automatic calculator, however, this process involves a large number of comparisons, each of which requires time."*

For a 10,000-point problem arising in the solution of Laplace's equation, a computer would have to make 9999 comparisons each time a residual is to be selected. On existing single-address standard machines this means going through an approximately 20 program-step loop 9999 times, each time a single point x_i is to be improved! Not counting the trivial calculation of the new value of the x_i associated with the selected residual, computation of the next set of residuals would take at most half the time of selection, and this would be about the same as computation of each $x_i^{(k+1)}$ in the Seidel iteration. In other words, on standard machines we would tend to adopt a more slowly converging process over one involving many comparisons, given no other choice.

In the face of this situation scientists who have to cope with large problems have turned to the numerical analyst for development of techniques which go between the horns of the dilemma. Indeed, much of the most significant research in iterative methods during the past decade has been motivated by the search for *systematic* relaxation schemes enjoying the accelerating properties of flexible relaxation while at the same time skirting the inefficient nonarithmetic properties of a standard machine.

The example of residue selection is but one among many that could be cited as evidence of the severely limited character of present-day machines in performing certain nonarithmetical or "logical" operations. Anyone familiar with the use of computers in language manipulation problems (automatic programming, prooffinding, language translation) and in data processing can easily produce further examples.

We may summarize the discussion thus far in the following two points:

1. Behavior and efficiency problems in computer design must be distinguished; in particular, efficiency is not always to be gained with a faster standard machine (even at constant cost) alone, since some operations would still be relatively too time-consuming.

* Kaiser S. Kunz, *Numerical Analysis*, McGraw-Hill Book Company, New York, 1957, p. 315; see also F. B. Hildebrand, *Introduction to Numerical Analysis*, McGraw-Hill Book Company, New York, 1956, pp. 440–441; George E. Forsythe, "What are Relaxation Methods?" in *Modern Mathematics for Engineers*, Edwin S. Beckenbach, McGraw-Hill Book Company, New York, 1956, p. 438.

2. Nonarithmetical operations, which we may somewhat incompletely list as selection, matching, collection, insertion, sorting, merging, etc., pervade many "scientific" calculations as well as symbol manipulations.

Also, we assert the following two theses which are implied in the foregoing discussion but which we cannot take space to further argue here:

3. The operations listed in item 2 are not well understood.

4. These operations are neither peripheral nor special, but contrasted with the relatively well-understood and trivial arithmetical operations (*including* operations such as logical AND and logical OR) define the most important efficiency problems in computer system design.

ANALYSIS

All of the operations mentioned in item 2 ultimately boil down to (repetitively) scanning large collections of data (characters, words, or records) for certain order properties, followed by many memory-to-memory data transfers. More specifically, these computations are sequences of subcomputations of the following kind:

(a) scanning (or reading) words
(b) comparing—which is decomposable into
    i. a calculation
    ii. a decision
(c) permuting the words scanned
(d) writing

Thus sorting is a kind of computation requiring an algorithm (or a special machine) composing sequences of sequences of the above kind. At least two words (or a word and an archetype) are compared and then swapped or not, depending on the condition determined by the comparison. In compilation, matching against a symbol n-tuple (e.g., of alphabetical characters) and selecting a subroutine or generating routine again require scanning, a comparison (based on an *ad hoc* ordering), and depending on the result, a selection—a trivial permutation. A little reflection will show that all of the types of computation mentioned in item 2 depend solely on operations of this kind.

On a single-address standard machine the selection of a largest number of a set, as in the residual problem, requires a program of essentially the kind shown in Table 1 (an instruction has only an operation and an address part). Here the α_i are instruction locations,

TABLE 1. PROGRAM FOR SINGLE-ADDRESS MACHINE

	Operation	Address	Explanation
	Clear add	ZERO	
	Store	SELECTEE	Set SELECTEE
	Clear add	SUBTRACT A1	to 000 ....
	Store	α_2	Initialize α_2 and α_5
	Clear add	CLEAR ADD A1	
	Store	α_5	
α_1	Clear add	SELECTEE	
α_2	Subtract	a_i	Compare
	Transfer $(-)$	α_5	
α_3	Clear add	α_2	
	Subtract	SUBTRACT A100	Exit test
	Transfer $(-)$	α_4	
	Stop		
α_4	Clear add	α_2	
	Add	ONE	
	Store	α_2	
	Clear add	α_5	$a_i \rightarrow a_{i+1}$
	Add	ONE	
	Store	α_5	
	Transfer	α_1	
α_5	Clear add	a_i	
	Store	SELECTEE	Permute
	Transfer	α_3	

SELECTED is the address of the destination of the largest number of the collection, which is stored in a_1–a_{100}. SUBTRACT A1 is the address of the (coded) instruction "Subtract a_1"; and similarly for SUBTRACT A100 and CLEAR ADD A1. ZERO and ONE are locations of 000 ... 000, and 000 ... 01.

If it is necessary, as in the residual problem, to remember the location (equivalently, the index of r_i) of the largest number, the program requires several more steps and a "SELECTEE address" location.

Such a program might be considerably shorter (in steps) on a machine with index registers, addressable arithmetic registers, or special instructions like "compare" and "table look-up"; but the time of execution would be only slightly altered, say halved, and we are interested in *time*, not order code novelties.

This is the simplest and in a sense the *core* of all the types of computation in question. Either an insertion or a sort requires much more data transfer since the data at the end of the computation would normally be required to be locations a_1-a_{101} or a_1-a_{100} respectively, and not merely pulled out as in the selection operation. A merge would require, following two or more sorts, an enormous number of transfers.

We may call the foregoing process *internal* selection. In *external* selection a word is picked from a collection by matching against an archetype. The program for this operation is simpler than the previous one, though similar; a table look-up feature on a cyclic memory serves quite admirably. An external sort (analogous to a punched card sort, i.e., a *radix* sort) also preserves the scan-comparison-permute characteristics of selection.

This specific example and its more complicated associates illustrate the type of calculation which, as is widely maintained, a standard computer is unsuited for. It is in fact the program from α_1 et seq. that would have to be traversed 9999 times to select max (r_i) in the 100 by 100 problem previously discussed.

We now note the following properties of the subject class of computations:

1. Only a few of the steps actually effect the reading, comparison, and the (trivial) permutation.

2. In all the types of computation (item 2 of the preceding section) being considered these operations *alone* are involved, with the exception that in some cases more program steps are needed to obtain the permutations.

3. All other steps accomplish either initializing, address modification, or exiting.

These properties are fairly typical of *all* computations. However, the extreme flexibility and elegance contributed by property 3, which almost itself characterizes the remarkable features of a standard machine, suggest that a tack is being driven with the sledge hammer. But to say that the process of selection on a standard machine is both too slow (which we are saying) and too elegant, and therefore very inefficient, is to imply that some central system addition or redesign might be considered. Clearly, the problem is neither one of programming nor of numerical procedure. Equally clearly, the problem is not to be resolved by adding a *selection* (and a *sort*, etc.) operation to the instruction code of a standard machine. Such an instruction would merely set up a sequence of steps about as time-consuming as that established by the core program.

A POSSIBLE SYSTEM DESIGN*

An alternative is to consider the possibility of a symbol-manipulating computer, especially designed to effect the core computation programmed above, which can be incorporated into the central system design and put into communication with a standard machine under the control of certain additional instructions. This is indeed a drastic measure, but is perhaps worth investigation under our hypothesis that selection and the like are truly fundamental operations.

It is obvious that an adequate system, in order to achieve the required speeds, has certain indispensable properties:

1. The system must not have the one-step-at-a-time property of a standard machine. For if it did we would only gain a variation on the core program scheme. This implies that the system should include a simultaneous multiple-access (at least two read and two write points) memory.

2. Such a memory need not be addressable since in scanning-comparing the system can profitably operate on any datum that comes along: the postreading operations of comparison and permutation depend solely on order properties of the data and not on their syntactical depth or nestedness in an algorithm, as, e.g., in an algebraic formula.

3. The memory, if not addressable, must systematically traverse all of its locations. This implies a delay-line or cyclic-type memory.

4. It is highly desirable, in view of the type of memory, whose systemic characteristics are emerging in our listing, that the comparison and permuting operations be carried out at very high speeds, and specifically that (at a minimum) a pair of memory-adjacent words or other data be compared, permuted, and then finally written back into memory during the time it takes to scan a *single location.*

5. The comparing-permuting operations, in order to meet the foregoing time requirements, must be accomplished "on the fly"; i.e., the operations cannot be achieved by resetting and loading conventional registers, comparing (by either subtracting or inequivalence circuits), and then rewriting on memory.

A device of the kind sketchily specified would be capable of performing the simple select operation in at most n word times (which would depend as usual on whether the memory were serial or parallel,

* A system of the kind outlined was first suggested by P. N. Armstrong and the present writer in 1954.

and the basic information cycle, among other things); and a sort, with only a double-access memory, in at most $n^2 - n$ word times. Assuming a 1000-word serial memory and 40 bit words (operating at 1 megacycle/second), a 1000-word select would take about $\frac{1}{2}$ second. On a comparable (i.e., very slow) standard machine it would take about 8 seconds; this is assuming a 10-microsecond (either read or write), serial, immediate-access memory.

Indeed, on any comparable pair of machines there should be an increase in speed in the operations in question by a factor of 10. This is achievable by system considerations alone.

In order to establish communication with a standard machine, means would have to be provided for rapid transfer of large amounts of data, up to the capacity of the symbol manipulator, between the two. Obviously the buffering, if any, and the subsidiary memory would have to be greatly augmented for conventional file sorting and merging applications. However, here our interest has been more in word or character manipulation. There is also obviously need of appropriate additions to the standard machine order code for loading and unloading the symbol machine and for calling out operations of selection, insertion, sorting, and other nonarithmetic operations for which the system is suitable. Particularly noteworthy problems would be:

(a) means for rapidly selecting both words and associated standard machine addresses for transfer to the symbol manipulators;

(b) means for programming arbitrary (based on *ad hoc* orderings) selections, matchings, and permutations.

None of these problems appears to be as simple as that of the over-all design described here. The intention has been only to suggest an approach to a system, and not to attempt to deal with the programming and algorithmic puzzles such a system would be certain to pose. Lacking a theory of computation as such, which we do lack, this situation is not unexpected.

CHAPTER 6

A DECISION MODEL FOR
A FOURTH–LEVEL MODEL
IN THE BOULDING SENSE*

H. GOODE

Modeling systems leads to better understanding from both the practical standpoint of designing large-scale systems and the theoretical objective of making progress in unifying a system theory. I shall begin by adopting a hierarchy of system levels due to Boulding[1] which is useful in pinpointing my system level of interest. The latter is the "cell," Boulding's fourth level, an open system capable of maintaining its integrity in the face of a throughput of material, energy, and/or information. My special interest is in decision cells, and to make my ideas concrete I shall examine two practical systems, underscoring the points of decision and isolable decision cells. To narrow the problem, the decisions made in each of these cells are then classified and are found to be one of three types, of which I select one. These types are estimation, multiple alternative, and go, no-go decisions, and the third class is the one chosen for discussion. Many of the decisions are in this class, which is representative of the decision process† and at the same time is simple enough to expedite exposition of a model.

To delineate the parts of the "cell" model for the decision class chosen, I shall give a brief historical sketch of the development of the theory of go, no-go decisions, leading up to a modern statement of this type of decision in terms of three elements: a priori, productive probabilities, and values. With the parts of the decision made firm, a model is depicted which I believe adequately represents go, no-go

* This research was supported in whole or in part by the United States Air Force under Contract No. AF 49(638)-369 monitored by the AF Office of Scientific Research of the Air Research and Development Command.

† In a sense, all of these problems are the same, the mathematics being of a similar type but more complicated in the first two.

decision making at the cell level. We are then in a position to see what light the model can throw on some of the aspects of system design which have come to notice, such as the standardization of information, the centralization or decentralization of the system, etc. Some of these aspects, in the light of the model, can be sharpened to principles. Based on this discussion, conclusions can be drawn concerning the usefulness of such models and extensions can be suggested.

THE BOULDING CLASSIFICATION

In his article on general systems theory, Boulding sets forth a suggested hierarchical classification of systems as shown in Table 1.

TABLE 1. HIERARCHY OF SYSTEMS

Key Word	Characteristic	Example of System at Level
1. Framework	Static structure	Geography of earth, anatomy of cell
2. Clockwork	Predetermined motions	Steam engine, solar system
3. Thermostat	Transmission of information	Furnace homeostasis
4. Cell	Open system throughput of material and energy, system maintained in the face of throughput	Flame, river, cell
5. Plant	Division of labor among parts but not at the sensory level	Any plant
6. Animal	Self-awareness, specialized receptors, increased intake of information to form image (different from the information)	Any animal
7. Human	Self-consciousness, knows that it knows, language and symbols	Human being
8. Social organizations	"Role" and communication, history, messages, music, art	Human societies
9. Transcendental systems	Unknowables	Unknowables

It is clear that our understanding decreases with system level. As Boulding points out, most of our knowledge is at the first, second, and third levels. We are just beginning to grasp understanding at the fourth level, and my discussion is pointed toward modeling decisions at this level.

PRACTICAL SYSTEMS

Consider the air defense system. In one sense it is composed of a series of decisions which are of relatively simple types, each of which is performed by an elementary "cell"-type mechanism. Beginning at the sensory end, the system depends upon an unattended radar device which scans through a quantified set of regions on an oscilloscope and decides, on the basis of the number of energy returns above a fixed level, chosen in advance, whether a "target" is present at any particular scope region (corresponding to some particular space region). This decision is of the go, no-go type. It is passed on, if positive, to another position of the system which begins the establishment of a "track" on the detected target. This decision is of the estimation type, and it estimates numbers, course, and speed, which characterize the horizontal track. The system continues, with the analysis in Table 2 yielded by examining each step of the system.

We note first that the decisions are classifiable in a small number of classes, and second, that the go, no-go type occurs quite frequently.

A second system which may be examined on this basis is the path of a letter through an automatic post-office system. The letter arrives at the post office for a first decision concerning whether it is package or letter, then faced (if letter) into a required orientation which is one of four, then directed to local or out-of-town mail, then read for coding of address, then interpreted, etc. The system analyzed yields the following breakdown:

Culling	Go, no-go
Facing	Multiple choice
Local or outgoing	Go, no-go
Coding of address	Multiple choice
Interpretation	Multiple choice
Sort	Multiple choice

Many of the multiple choices are automatically performed by a go, no-go mechanism at each of many possible choices. Similar breakdowns are possible for many systems. Each exhibits a "cell-like"

TABLE 2.   AIR DEFENSE SYSTEM

Class of Function	Function	Class of Decision
Front end analysis	Detection	Go, no-go
	Track determination	Estimation
	Height determination	Estimation
	Split targets	Go, no-go
	Merge targets	Go, no-go
	Identification	Go, no-go
Raid decision	Speed	Estimation
	Direction	Estimation
	Strength	Estimation
	Attack	Go, no-go
Attack	With what	Multiple choice
	How many	Multiple choice
	From which base	Multiple choice
	When	Estimation
	Kill or no-kill	Go, no-go
Weapon direction	Acquisition	Go, no-go
	Track	Estimation
In missile	Seeker acquisition	Go, no-go
	Warhead detonation	Estimation

structure and in the cells are decisions of a small number of class types, an important one always being go, no-go (or its generalization, multiple choice).

GO AND NO-GO DECISIONS

We seek now to understand the elements of a go, no-go decision. The early investigators of decision theory, Laplace and Poisson, tried to make decision statements in terms of probability values with no particular worry about the logical basis of their statements. Laplace introduced a formula for a go, no-go decision

$$\frac{r+1}{n+2} \tag{1}$$

which stated that the probability of success on the next trial of an experiment was

$$p(s) = \frac{r+1}{n+2}$$

where r is the number of past successes and n the number of trials thus far. The probability of the sun rising tomorrow is therefore pretty close to 1! To apply this formula to go, no-go one noted the probability as of the last observation and bet according to his intuitive demand for odds.

Bayes connected the state of knowledge before an experiment with the knowledge from the experiment to decide between go and no-go by writing a formula for the probabilities of the two possibilities after the experiment in terms of the "probability before the experment" and the "probabilities of experimental outcome" in case each alternative might be true:

$$P_x(S) = \frac{P(S)l(x)}{P(S)l(x) + P(N)} \tag{2}$$

Thus, if our alternatives are designated hypotheses (null and special, i.e., no-go and go) and if each has a priori (before the experiment) probability $P(N)$ and $P(S)$, and if an observation x occurs from the experiment with $P_N(x)$ when N is true and $P_S(x)$ when S is true, then Bayes wrote

$$P_x(S) = \frac{P(S)P_S(x)}{P(S)P_S(x) + P(N)P_N(x)}$$

where $P_x(S)$ is the a posteriori probability that S is true if x is observed. Similarly, for $P_x(N)$ we can rewrite the formula

$$P_x(S) = \frac{l_a(H)l(x)}{l_a(H)l(x) + 1}$$

where

$$l_a(H) = \frac{P(S)}{P(N)} \quad \text{and} \quad l(x) = \frac{P_S(x)}{P_N(x)}$$

and the latter is called the likelihood ratio, already putting in evidence a quantity which turns out to be more and more important. Again decision is made according to one's fancy concerning the required probabilities of being right.

For a little while this seemed to solve the problem of going backward from experiment to hypotheses using the knowledge to date and the knowledge gathered from the experiment. But it bothered many that when $l_a(H)$ was not known people began to put unity in its place, announcing a principle of indifference, or ignorance, or what have you. Bayes' theorem fell into disuse.

Over the years, large number theory developed with the distinction between the null and special hypothesis becoming blurred (Fig. 1). A rather loose use of probability gave rise to the statement that the "population mean lies within ±3σ on either side of the sample mean" with no attention paid to either a priori knowledge or the alternatives presenting themselves or the values of decisions.

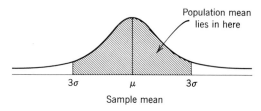

FIG. 1. Classical theory.

Fisher, dissatisfied with this state, devised the "test of significance" which, although it introduced neither prior knowledge nor alternative hypotheses, did make a precise statement on a go, no-go basis (Fig. 2). If you choose a null, Fisher said, you may adopt a policy which will fix the probability of rejecting it in error.

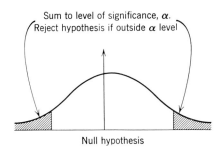

FIG. 2. Fisher theory.

Later Neyman and Pearson pointed out that one did not first accept or reject a hypothesis but almost always had another alternative in mind which would be rejected or accepted as a result of the decision (Fig. 3). They introduced the notions of type-I error (rejection of null when true) and type-II error (rejection of special when true). The likelihood ratio turned out to be the key to obtaining the smallest β (type-II error rate) for a given or fixed α (type-I error rate). This development brought the alternative hypothesis back into the picture but still left out of consideration two important desiderata: the knowledge to date and the costs of making errors.

A. Wald took into consideration the latter with statistical decision theory, which introduced a cost function to be applied to the type-I

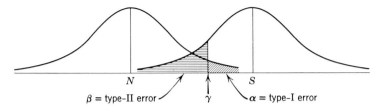

β = type-II error γ α = type-I error

Fix α; then β is determined by distributions
and distance between means

FIG. 3.   Neyman and Pearson theory.

and type-II error rates:

$$\text{Hypothesis}$$

$$
\begin{array}{c c}
 & N \qquad S \\
\text{Guess}\; \begin{array}{c} C \\ A \end{array} & \begin{array}{|c|c|} \hline V_{NC} & V_{SC} \\ \hline V_{NA} & V_{SA} \\ \hline \end{array}
\end{array}
$$

$$\text{Choice of } \gamma:$$

$$\frac{P_S(x)}{P_N(x)} = l(x) \geq \frac{P(N)}{P(S)} \frac{V_{NC} - V_{NA}}{V_{SA} - V_{SC}} = \gamma \qquad (3)$$

The theory played against nature as though she were an opponent and therefore ascribed no a priori knowledge to the experiment.

Recently, a signal detection theory has taken the last step toward bringing all elements back into the fold. By applying Bayes' theorem (eq. 2) to Wald's decision function (eq. 3) and Neyman's and Pearson's alternative hypothesis (Fig. 3), we have the following theory of the go, no-go decision: Given two hypotheses (alternatives), Null (N) and Special (S), whose a priori probabilities of occurrence are $P(N)$ and $P(S)$, a decision A implying belief in S and a decision C implying belief in N; the costs of correct statements and error being V_{NC}, V_{SA}, V_{NA}, V_{SC}; the distribution of an observed variable x being $P_N(x)$ when N is true and $P_S(x)$ when S is true; then to make a decision which maximizes the expected value, compute

$$l(x) = \frac{P_S(x)}{P_N(x)} \qquad (4)$$

If

$$l(x) \geqq \frac{P(N)}{P(S)} \frac{V_{NC} - V_{NA}}{V_{SA} - V_{SC}}$$

say that S is true. Otherwise, say N is true. The cutoff point γ for decisioning is chosen so as to *maximize the expected value* based on knowledge of costs, a priori probabilities, and productive probabilities. More detailed consideration shows that even if the expected value is not the criterion, $l(x)$ is the proper indicator, but a new criterion formula must be computed.

EXAMPLE FROM PRACTICAL SYSTEM

Consider the first "cell" of the air defense system, the unattended radar. At any region on the scope, a decision is to be made that just noise is present, or signal (plus noise). Suppose that the a priori probability of a signal is $P(S)$ (of course, a function of many things including hot or cold war conditions). When a signal is present, the returning radar energy will be collected in some indicator reading x in value. x will be distributed in a certain fashion, $P_S(x)$. When only noise is present, x will be distributed differently. If, further, the cost of saying signal when there is a signal, noise when there is a noise, false alarm, and the target miss are evaluated, then eq. 4 determines the automatic cutoff point for setting the radar. Obviously, conceptual insight rather than explanatory prediction has been achieved through this equation since many of the quantities are unknown.

AN OPEN SYSTEM OR CELL MODEL

The value of the foregoing discussion is that it leads to isolation of the important parts of an elementary decision. A system operating to make a decision may be envisaged as in Fig. 4. This diagram was originally conceived by Quastler, modified by W. P. Tanner, and again modified by the present author.

Energy (or material) is passed into the system through a transducer to provide the standardized format of the "cell." From all the irrelevant information present (which may involve millions of bits), what is wanted is the likelihood ratio, i.e., the ratio of probabilities that this phenomenon will be observed when S is in operation to that of observing it when N is in operation. However, this value cannot be computed without keeping records of these distributions for introduction to the $l(x)$ computer. Moreover, the $l(x)$ value has meaning only as it can be compared with a criterion to make a decision. The criterion depends on what we have learned to date (the a priori probabilities) and the costs of making correct statements and errors. This information comes from comparing decisions made with rewards

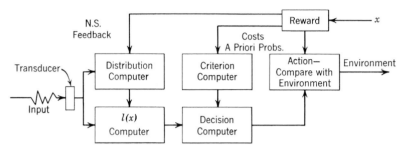

FIG. 4. A decision system.

achieved.* The reward box, its measure and reactions, comes from some external system and for this reason we are dealing with an elementary cell rather than with specialization.

APPLICATION OF THE MODEL

Let us now return to the classification system set forth in Table 1. We note that the organization of the system by boxes is a first-level "framework" system, static in structure. The various computers are second-level "clockwork" in nature, giving predetermined motions when inputs of values come from other boxes or the environment. The feedback from the reward and action boxes serves to produce a third-level "thermostatic" system (albeit complicated in nature), the whole system pulling toward a level of the criterion cutoff based on inputs from the outer world and the meaning of rewards. Finally, this system processes energy or material and information and passes on decisions, yielding an open system which maintains its identity in the face of a throughput of energy, information, and material.

It is not too great a jump to suppose that the next level of system is composed by sets of cells of this nature to specialize functions

---

*Insight into the meaning of the principle of indifference comes from asking what values one would ascribe to such a device initially when no experience has been gained. After the first random decision (yes and no equally—which says a coin is tossed to say whether $l(x) >$ criterion), $P(N) = P(S)$ and all V's equal seems the only way. $l(x) > 1$ is the criterion.

relative to the development of reward. Interaction of rewards might give a "plant"-type system.

PRINCIPLE—THE STANDARDIZATION OF INFORMATION

I should like to emphasize again that all the information from external sources necessary for any given decision is in the likelihood ratio. Now experience shows that the designer of any large system finds it desirable to standardize the form of the information flow in the system early in the single thread development. The telephone system turns the number which used to be embedded in lots of words into a digital code which then passes essential information around the system. The air defense system turns the statement about a target into a code. The post office is beginning to turn its addresses into code early in the system. But our model tells us something about how to standardize. The likelihood ratio contains all the information. Therefore, it is the number to be passed on if no decision is to be made. Moreover, to carry other stuff along is wasteful of memory and computer capacity as well as confusing. To avoid this waste, standardization must occur early in the system, in accordance with a practical system design notion.

TO DECIDE OR NOT TO DECIDE

But should a decision be made? Two kinds of deferments in decision making are recognized as frequently required in practical system design. One refers to the requirement for more information, the other to a requirement for decision at a higher level. These two points will be separately discussed under Deferred Decision Theory and Centralization and Decentralization. Here I am concerned with only the information aspect of decision making. Executing the decision destroys information.

To see that this is true, consider the air defense example. If two radars are observing and both have signals slightly below cutoff, the information will be discarded if both decide *at the radar* whether a target exists. If both had held likelihood ratios, the product of the ratios would be above cutoff values leading to a higher probability of correct decision. Therefore, except as modified by the time requirements of the environment and the memory requirements, decision should be held off.

DEFERRED DECISION THEORY

It is possible to extend the model of a decision to include three possible actions instead of two: i.e., instead of deciding that one hypothesis or the other holds, a third alternative allowing deferral of decision pending more information is allowed. This theory, under a maximum expectation criterion, makes a decision now whenever the expected value for waiting is less than that available for making a decision. The calculation of cutoff points is at present impractical, but again involves the likelihood ratio, this time leading to *two* cutoff points on the $l(x)$ axis: below (1), accept Null; above (2) accept Special; between the two hold on to the information. In the simple case where the curve of probability of a correct decision has a non-increasing slope, a simple solution is possible.

MEMORY CONSIDERATIONS

But holding onto information demands memory capacity. I believe that limitations of memory and the ability to search efficiently are the most serious limiting factors in our development of systems of great sophistication. We shall experience a revolution in automation when the memory problem has been adequately solved. Again, consider the radar example. For a scope cut into 10,000 regions we would have to remember the likelihood ratios for each region, and *transmit them*, if we deferred decision. For this reason, we do not. But we are going through a metamorphosis in memory-handling capability and 10^5–10^7 bits per cubic inch is predicted. Estimates of human capacity are 10^8–10^{11} bits per cubic inch. We begin at last to get within sighting distance. Our system model shows the extent of the memory which we must seek.

CENTRALIZATION AND DECENTRALIZATION

If we examine the various forces leading to centralization of a system, or the opposite, we see that on the side of centralization is an integrated decision using all the information available (all likelihood ratios), plus the possibility of coordination of the criterion center to yield reward at a level above the "cell" unit. In fact, if the cell only is to be optimized, we may see at once that centralization yields nothing. Further, central actions may be highly undesirable from the standpoint of the particular "cell." Thus, using *all* information and acting for the good of the larger system are the payoffs for centralizing.

On the other hand, memory requirements and computing requirements yield attenuation, high error rates, and long delay times in response, as well as congestion at the clearance center. We draw several conclusions. We must decentralize for the practical design reasons of inability to handle at the center. But changing technology demands a repeated examination of the point of decentralization. Finally, the less the coupling between cells for the survival of the system (or its reward), the less the gain from centralization.

This latter point explains the decentralization of functions in living organisms to a level sufficient to the part of the system at stake. In all probability, the cell in the body handles all of its own homeostasis at its own level, and passes on information pertinent to survival of the group. The implications for practical system design are evident. Too frequently, system engineers are biased toward centralization or decentralization with no rational basis. The model demands examination of (a) the reward system, (b) the memory and computing capacity, and (c) the attenuation, error, and delay rates.

SUBUNIT SIZE

We draw a corollary conclusion concerning the size of a subsystem. Are its decisions pertinent to itself or closely coupled to a larger piece? If the former, allow to operate as a subsystem; if the latter, do not allow autonomy. This yields a complicated structure if several functions are being carried on, but the design principle is clear.

ADAPTIVE SYSTEMS

We hear much today about adaptive, or self-adaptive systems. We may use our model to examine the notion. Adaptive systems lie somewhere between the fourth and fifth level in the Boulding classification. At the lower levels of system performance, material and energy are absorbed (feeding), the process yielding survival of the system (and, in some systems, reproduction) and subsequent disposal of waste and/or conversion of energy. On the next higher level of sophistication, the system processes information, sensing it, communicating it, making decisions (reasoning?), and effecting actions. That is the fourth level I have been describing. It may, however, carry out this process according to an accepted script with no modification of the process, or, on the other hand, the information, material, and energy entering the system may change its configuration to perform each of the lower level functions, in which case the system has "adapted" or learned. But this adaptation may be at a very low level, the result of the realization of one of several previously foreseen states of the environment, as, e.g., changing distribution values (according to a rule provided), changing criterion values (not criteria), etc., or it may adapt to a completely unforeseen environment by changing criteria and functional form. Still it has had no changes in goal or objectives. For this type of adaptation it must have its reward box* modified, which implies some change at a higher system level. We are now in the order of the fifth and sixth levels. We have thus stated our notion of adaptation in terms of the "cell" model.

CONCLUSIONS

From this discussion I conclude that we may begin to interpret our "practical" system design considerations in terms of the model, and occasionally extend the meaningful content of these considerations. Often we may correct the notion, or on occasion discard it.

Clearly, the model needs extension in two directions: first, by combination with notions from other disciplines than statistical hypothesis testing, such as information theory and game theory; and second, by beginning its extension to the upper levels in the system hierarchy— specialization of functions and awareness.

REFERENCE

1. Kenneth E. Boulding, General Systems Theory—The Skeleton of Science, *Management Science,* Apr. 1956, p. 197.

* The reward box is a stored knowledge of what is "good" and "bad" for the system.

CHAPTER 7

ON THE IMPEDANCE MATCHING PROBLEMS OF SYSTEMS THAT INCLUDE MEN AND COMPUTERS

A. OPLER

The fact that we are rushing toward a world of almost unmanageable technical complexity is becoming manifest. The rate of growth in the area of complicated systems is virtually unnerving. We can no longer talk glibly about 100 years in the future; it strains one's imagination to speak of 10 years from now.

An outstanding characteristic of the second half of the twentieth century is the tremendous increase in the rate of communication. Figure 1 is an extrapolation showing the expected number of megabits per second transmitted man to man; man to man via machine; man to machine; machine to man; machine to machine; etc.

I am not certain if the role of the computing machine in our present environment is that of the chicken or the egg. Whether the computing machine is contributing to complexity or enabling us to thread our way through our modern maze is immaterial. Computers are here to stay. Those at the forefront of technology will henceforth never be more than a digit's throw from a computing machine.

Taken at a most primitive level, a modern digital computer might be viewed as a replacement for a battery of clerks operating desk calculators. That view is just as naïve as the picture of the computing machine as a superior organism endowed with a colossal brain. What we have learned is that the finest team that can attack the problems of the 1960's includes *both men and computing machines*.

Since I will be restricting the remainder of this discussion to the relative roles and the interaction between men and devices that compute, I will simply refer to machines henceforth in the latter capacity. Although the computers to be discussed will be digital computers, much of what is said here is also applicable to analog devices.

A project director assembles a team of individual specialists to work on a task that involves many interrelated specialties. If he includes, and he usually does, computing machines as members of the team, then a host of problems arises in integrating the machines into the team.

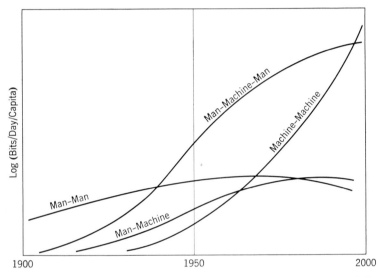

FIG. 1. Growth of communication. Redrawn from "Communication and Social Change," Richard T. Meier, *Behavioral Science*, Vol. 1, No. 1, Jan. 1956.

To understand the principal problem, man-machine communication, we must go to the machine for enlightenment since I assume that we already have a good idea of how men communicate. Fundamentally, a computing machine is an ingenious array of bistable devices. During the period involved in interpreting and executing a specific task, there is stored internally a program which, when suitably treated by computer circuitry, causes a rapid rearrangement of the states of these bistable devices. Only when the computer reads in interpretable patterns and writes out intelligible information are we aware of the effect of the internal transformations. In the past 10 years, the techniques for such reading and writing have been vastly improved. The same is true for methods for instructing the computer (programming). Although it is conceptually as difficult for a human to interpret the internal patterns of a computer as it is for a computer to interpret the normal communication modes of a human, the latter task can be performed at extremely high speeds by the machine whereas it would take hours for the human to carry out this interpretation. Thus, in the split-second world of today, and the split-microsecond world of tomorrow, it is obvious that we must throw the task of translating and bridging the gap to the machine.

Before considering a series of examples, we must distinguish between two types of communication with a machine. The first involves the statement (and, probably, frequent restatement) of the task description to the machine and the concomitant feedback from the machine to its "taskmaster," which enables the latter to have confidence that the machine "understands" and will correctly carry out its orders. A second feedback system involves the communication of specific cases to be handled under a general task description and the rapid return of the computed results for each case to the man. These two areas may be distinguished as that of programming and checkout and that of regular operation of a programmed computer.

There is an alternative to the preceding sequence of operations, namely, that of teaching the computer to learn to carry out the task by a much more complex and sensitive feedback mechanism. Although this holds great promise for the future, it is still so far from practicality that it will not be discussed further here.

To illustrate the nature of the communication problem, a number of systems of increasing complexity will be examined. Since the man-machine team does not exist in a vacuum, the interaction of the team with pertinent aspects of the physical environment will also be considered.

SYSTEM I: ONE MAN, ONE MACHINE

This system is one that has been frequently associated with the use of computers in the past. A scientist working on a purely mathematical problem requires the use of a computing machine to supplement his work. Using present methods of programming, he converts his problem to the form of a series of algebraic and logical algorithms and feeds them to the computer in this form. The machine accepts the pattern of symbols which, to the man, represents his problem and, after possibly several hundred thousand rearrangements, the machine signals that it has produced a program to use the algorithms. However, if the algorithms are either inconsistent, unintelligible to the computing machine, or written with gross violations of the system rules, one or more English language messages are displayed, pinpointing the cause for noncompletion of the translation.

In the event that the translation is successfully completed, the machine is now ready to accept from the man his data in the format most convenient for the man. The result of the computation will also be translated by the computer to the form most easily recognizable by the man.

An example of such a system is the programming of a computer to invert matrices and the subsequent use of the program on a daily basis.

In this particular example, the only rapport that needs to be established is between the man and the machine, and neither current happenings nor other aspects of the physical environment are insignificant here.

SYSTEM IA: ONE MAN, ONE COMPUTER, PHYSICAL ENVIRONMENT SIGNIFICANT

This case is a variant of the preceding one in that the man serves as a node in a double loop. After obtaining the results for any particular case, he will check this against some aspect of the physical environment for correspondence. In the event of a mismatch between the computed and observed results, he will probably instruct the machine to refine the algorithms and then to recompute the test cases and present him with the revised results. These will require further comparison with the environment and perhaps additional feedback cycles.

An example of such a system is one in which a set of partial differential equations have been formulated to represent a physical system such as a potential field within an electronic device.

SYSTEM II: ONE MAN, ONE COMPUTER, PHYSICAL ENVIRONMENT DIRECTLY CONNECTED

With three "components" connected in a system, we may have either a double loop with the computer at the node or a single loop with communication passing through all three components. An example of the former is the on-line process control computer in which the normal loop is between the process and the computer with an auxiliary loop between the computer and an operator. In general, when the system is operating with adequate feedback, the auxiliary loop is not needed. When the process variables are such that the computer cannot control them, manual intervention is required. In this latter case, the same communication problems will arise since it is necessary that the operator be informed rapidly and explicitly concerning the state of the system and that his remedial stabilizing decisions be just as quickly transmitted and fed to the system.

A more interesting case is one in which all three components are within the loop. A striking example that is becoming fairly well known is that of the safety officer's installation associated with a missile firing range. By means of suitable telemetering devices, the missile's actual position with respect to the launching area is fed to a computer which reduces the data in real time and presents to the officer a graphic position of the missile with respect to the terrain.

In the event of malfunction of the guidance system a *destruct* is sent by the officer to the missile. Here again, it is most important that the communication between man and computer be in a form that is literally instantaneous and presented with utmost clarity and specificity.

SYSTEM III: SEVERAL COMPUTERS, SEVERAL MEN, PHYSICAL ENVIRONMENT DIRECTLY CONNECTED

These systems are becoming more prominent as we begin to tackle our most complex control problems, particularly those involving the prediction and control of the position of high-speed objects (e.g., air traffic control, ballistic missile warning systems, controlling orbital vehicles). Here, in addition to problems at the man-machine and machine-environment interfaces, we also are involved with machine-to-machine communication as well as man-to-man communication with machines interspersed.

The machine-to-machine problem is not an easy one, but such communication is being established by means of suitable electronic buffering and conversion devices. This problem applies to communication between digital-digital, analog-analog, and analog-digital computers.

In the situation in which a team of men are operating one or more computers, it has been proved more productive for the machines to have multiple consoles (one per man) than it is to have a group of people clustering about a single console. This is evidence of the anomalous situation in which a single machine can communicate more easily with a group of men one by one (even though it means multiple translation of human input and output) than it can with a group together.

The impedance matching of men and machines, as you can see from these examples, is a critical factor in the successful construction of control systems in which a human is desirable.

As long as the man is present in the loop, properly designed electronic conversion devices can help. But such devices are not sufficient unless they are driven or controlled by a computer program which is doing the essential logical translation from computer language to external language.

Since it is important to utilize the best available human input channels, the most efficient computer output devices now appear to be:

1. English language statements of a situation or response. The statement may come from a printing device, an optical display, or a sound-creating device.

2. Pictures via graphical devices ranging from simple graph plotters to two- and three-dimensional cathode-ray projection schemes. The progress in this area has been exceptional in the last few years.

For input devices, the situation is not as good. Presently used devices are:

1. Push buttons for input of what are essentially binary decisions or combinations of such.

2. Input of English messages by typewriter keys.

3. Use of optical scanning devices to recognize input patterns.

4. Use of speech recognition for computer input. At present this has limited use because of poor resolving power, but it is expected that much progress will be made in the near future.

The picture I would like to leave with you, in conclusion, is that of a man in total rapport with the computing machine. He has at his desk an operative typewriter connected with the computer with two-way message transmission, a microphone and a loud-speaker for two-way voice communication, and suitable cathode-ray devices for both display and scanning of graphical information. Finally, in his rapport with the computer, it should be remembered that it is the computer that is doing the logical work to meet him 99% of the way!

CHAPTER 8

ON SOME RELATIONS BETWEEN HUMAN ENGINEERING, OPERATIONS RESEARCH, AND SYSTEMS ENGINEERING

A. CHAPANIS

Human engineering, operations research, and systems engineering are such vigorous activities today that it is difficult for most of us to recall that they are all less than a quarter of a century old. Actually, one could argue that people have been doing human engi-

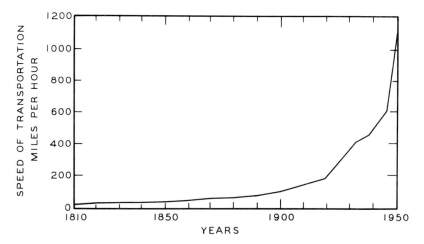

FIG. 1. Speed of human transportation, 1810 to 1950. (After Goode and Machol.[1])

neering of a sort for as long as man has been fashioning implements. One could also argue that engineers have been concerned with research on operations and with the design of systems of machines ever since the industrial revolution. And, of course, such arguments would be technically correct. But even the purist would have to agree that

these three fields have emerged as separate disciplines and have mush-
roomed into their present eminence only since the beginning of World
War II—roughly since 1940.

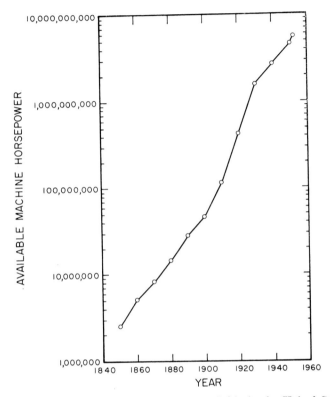

FIG. 2. Estimated total machine horsepower available in the United States for
the years 1850–1952. (Data from Dewhurst et al.[2]) Machine horsepower includes
that of automotive sources, factories, mines, railroads, machine-powered merchant
ships, farms, windmills, electric power stations, and aircraft.

Aside from their youthfulness, the three fields with which I am
concerned here have another important characteristic in common:
they are the products of a machine technology which is growing at
an explosive rate in our civilization. There are many ways of illus-
trating this fantastic development. Figure 1, for example, shows how
the speed of transportation has increased in the years from 1810 to
1950. However impressive that figure may be, it is symptomatic of
the very times I am talking about that the data shown there are
already out of date. As you know, the velocity required to put a
manned space vehicle in orbit around the earth is about 18,000 miles
per hour. As another illustration, Fig. 2 shows the total machine

horsepower available in the United States from the years 1850 to 1952. Note that the ordinate of that illustration is a logarithmic scale. If the illustration had been drawn with an arithmetic scale the curve would be indistinguishable from the base line between the years 1850 and 1900 and would rise almost vertically after 1940. One way of dramatizing this machine capacity was stated by an economist who computed that every man, woman, and child in the United States today has the equivalent of nearly 1000 slaves to do his bidding! Human engineering, operations research, and systems engineering are young disciplines which are all generally concerned with the design, construction, use, and management of this vast complex of machines which makes up our industrial civilization.

What I shall do in the rest of this chapter is to address myself to a question which many people have asked me, and for which I have not been able to find any ready-made answers in the literature, namely: "Just exactly what does human engineering have to do with operations research and systems engineering?" A satisfactory and personally satisfying answer to this question would require far more words than I have available here, but I can at least tell you some of the significant ways in which, it seems to me, human engineering contributes to operations research and systems engineering, and how human engineering in turn is influenced by the other two fields. In addition, I shall try to illustrate my presentation with concrete examples so that we do not end up with a collection of more or less aptly chosen, but contextless, statements.

SOME DEFINITIONS

A good way of beginning any scholarly discussion is to start with some definitions. This is much harder than it sounds for the three fields with which we are concerned, because they are so new and are changing so rapidly that it is difficult to see exactly how they are bounded. All sorts of things get called human engineering these days. In contrast, some of my engineering colleagues maintain that there is nothing special about systems engineering—that it is merely good engineering. Others admit the existence of a special discipline but argue that operations research and systems engineering are practically synonymous. Nevertheless, my experience has been that, by and large, people who call themselves human engineers are usually engaged in a fairly circumscribed and definable class of activities. It also seems to me that people who call themselves operations researchers (or opsearchers) *do* different things than people who call themselves systems engineers do. The following definitions reflect this experience.

Human engineering is the application of information about human behavior to the design of systems and components in order to achieve maximum effectiveness at minimum cost in the operation and maintenance of these systems.

Operations research is the application of scientific methods in attacking problems dealing with the efficient management and control of complex systems of men and machines, materials, and money in their natural environments.

Systems engineering is the application of scientific and engineering knowledge to the planning, design, evaluation, and construction of man-machine systems and system components.

Let me emphasize the critical words in each of these definitions. In human engineering, the key words are "information about human behavior." In operations research, the key words are "the efficient management and control." In systems engineering, they are "the planning, design, evaluation, and construction." By and large, the stock in trade of the human engineer is information about people and how they behave. Opsearchers, it seems to me, are mostly concerned with the management and control of systems which are already in existence. Systems engineers, on the other hand, are primarily involved with the construction of hardware—in the loose sense of that word. Although I would agree that these distinctions break down in some instances, I think they get at the essential differences.

SOME RELATIONS BETWEEN HUMAN ENGINEERING AND SYSTEMS ENGINEERING

The contributions which human engineering can make to systems engineering are several. Indeed, the human engineer is used most effectively when he is a member of the systems design team. The need for his special talents was created by the very complexity of modern machines. Many systems which were well designed from a physical or mechanical standpoint have turned out to be failures because they exceeded, or did not match, the capacities and limitations of their human operators. One can easily find examples of such mismatching in the myriads of machines which surround us in our workaday world. Gages which the industrial worker can scarcely interpret, household gadgets which mystify the housewife, highway signs that confuse the motorist—these and thousands of other similar examples are all instances of poor human engineering design.

To do his job well today the design engineer needs to have data and measurements on all kinds of human capacities, abilities, and limitations. Can people read green reflectorized signs more easily than blue ones? Are telephone numbers which make use of an exchange name and number, like STate 9-9722, easier to remember than the equivalent set of digits, i.e., 789-9722? How much aid should be provided in power-assisted steering wheels? What is the most comfortable height for ironing boards? Are push-button controls on a stove better than knobs? Should switches move to the right or to the left to turn something on? How much information can a man absorb from a radar screen? What is the most efficient language for communicating with a high-speed digital computer? What happens if a human operator is subjected to an acceleration of 12 times the force of gravity for 15 seconds? Will a man become hopelessly disorganized if he is in a zero-gravity state for several days? The need for human engineering has become acute because the answers to questions like these are vital to the effective design of modern man-machine systems. Moreover, common sense, intuition, and guesswork are no longer adequate to provide the kinds of answers the designer needs.

There are at least three kinds of contributions which the human engineer can make to the design of systems. These are in: (1) the allocation of functions to human and machine components; (2) the human engineering of systems components; and (3) the evaluation of man-machine systems.

THE ALLOCATION OF FUNCTIONS TO HUMAN AND MACHINE COMPONENTS

An important way in which the human engineer complements the systems engineer is in helping to make decisions about which functions should be assigned to human components and which should be assigned to machine components in the synthesis of an effective system. In these days when newspaper headlines daily extol the achievements of modern automatic machines, it is easy to get the impression that machines can do anything people can do. This is far from the case.

Just think, for example, about the extraordinary capacity we have for perception. For years, engineers and scientists have been trying to construct machines that will "read" printed text. Their best efforts so far have had limited success because of the difficulties of building "perception" into a machine. In the light of this experience, human ability to read material like that in Fig. 3 is no mean achievement.

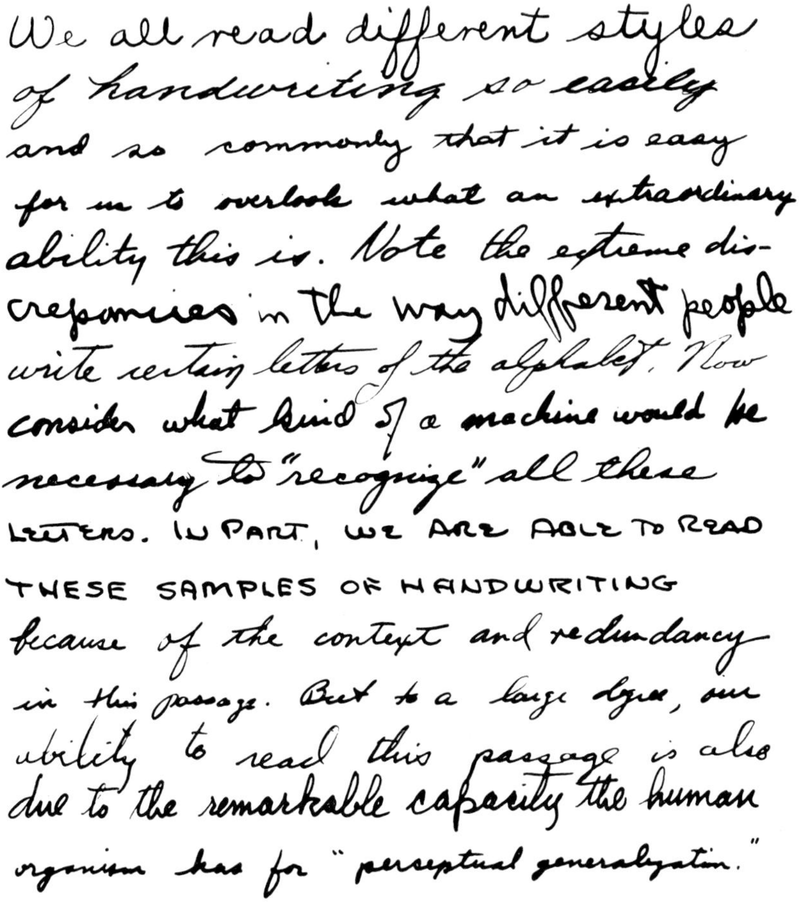

We all read different styles of handwriting so easily and so commonly that it is easy for us to overlook what an extraordinary ability this is. Note the extreme discrepancies in the way different people write certain letters of the alphabet. Now consider what kind of a machine would be necessary to "recognize" all these LETTERS. IN PART, WE ARE ABLE TO READ THESE SAMPLES OF HANDWRITING because of the context and redundancy in this passage. But to a large degree, our ability to read this passage is also due to the remarkable capacity the human organism has for "perceptual generalization."

FIG. 3.   Humans greatly surpass machines in perceptual capacity.

To my mind one of the best illustrations of the advantages of a living organism can be found in the fact that adjacent to one of America's most outstanding electronic laboratories is a farm on which seeing-eye dogs are trained. Despite years of research and development on radar, the plain fact of the matter is that electronic guidance devices for the blind cannot even begin to replace the perceptual capacities of a dog!

An Air-to-Ground Missile System

Since I have recently had occasion to discuss elsewhere the comparative advantages of men and machines as systems components and the assignment of functions to men and machines,[3] I shall not devote any time to the more theoretical aspects of the problem here. Instead, I want to illustrate the kinds of allocation decisions a systems engineer must make in the design of a real system. The illustration I have selected[4] is interesting because it traces the evolution of a

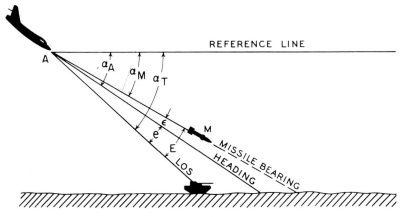

FIG. 4. A simplified two-dimensional representation of some factors involved in air-to-ground rocketry. (After Bibbero.[4])

designer's thinking as he considers alternative man-machine combinations. The article from which my illustration is drawn was not concerned with human problems. Nonetheless, it is particularly appropriate to my discussion because one can observe in it how the author was continually forced to evaluate what people can and cannot do.

The illustration selected is an air-to-ground guided missile system.* The geometry of the problem is shown in simplified form in Figs. 4 and 5. Point A is the instantaneous position of the aircraft or its position at the moment a rocket is launched. The line which makes an angle a_T with the reference line is the line of sight (LOS) from the plane to the target. The angle between the heading of the pilot's

---

* Despite the spectacular plans and achievements of ICBM, IRBM, and space-flight programs, the guidance of ballistic missiles and the navigation of space vehicles present much less challenge (aside from hardware and reliability problem) than does the design of a system for knocking out ground targets from the air.

reticle as he sees it in his sight and the reference line is a_A. Finally, a_M is the angle between the bearing of the missile and the reference line. In the situation illustrated in Fig. 4 the missile will have a

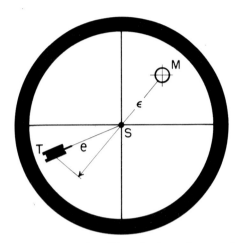

FIG. 5. The situation illustrated in Fig. 4 is shown here as the pilot might see it in the reticle of his sight. (After Bibbero.[4])

total error E, consisting of a sighting error e plus an error ϵ due to other sources: wind, motion of the target, trajectory of the missile, and random error (or dispersion).

Reducing Errors by Reducing Flight Time

One way to reduce the total error would be to reduce the time of flight to zero, or as nearly zero as possible, and to release the rocket at that instant of time when e is zero. In part this can be done by using high-velocity rockets: a short time of flight reduces errors due to wind and target motion, leaving only the sighting and dispersion errors. If, in addition, the range is reduced, the error due to normal dispersion is reduced and the system can be diagramed as a simple closed-loop system, as in Fig. 6. Under these circumstances the missile becomes, for all practical purposes, an extension of the aircraft. The pilot needs only to adjust the controls of the aircraft until the reticle aligns with the target, and then release the rocket.

What are some of the implications of this design for the operator of the aircraft? Obviously, such a system will perform best if the flight time is zero, i.e., if the pilot flies his rocket directly into the target. If we rule out this expensive possibility, however, then in any real situation the rocket will have a finite velocity and distance to travel and so will be subject to errors produced by dispersion, gravity, wind velocity, and target motion.

Assuming, however, that we were to design such a simplified system, what functions would the pilot have to perform to minimize the error of the system? First and foremost, he must recognize the target. Second, he must track that unstable platform we call an airplane so

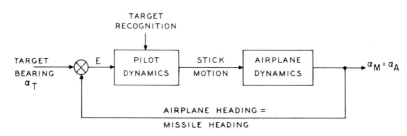

FIG. 6. A schematic representation of an air-to-ground missile system in which range and flight time are reduced to a minimum. (After Bibbero.[4])

that the target is centered in his reticle. Since this tracking function cannot be performed with perfect accuracy, he must perceive when the target appears centered in his reticle and, at that precise moment, release the missile. Even if the pilot were able to perform these functions with near perfect accuracy, however, computations show that in any real situation, using realistic missile velocities and ranges, missiles would miss their targets a sizable proportion of times because of the uncontrolled errors arising from dispersion, gravity, wind, and target motion.

Introducing Mental Computations into the System

A refinement in this system could be made if it were possible to educate the pilot to compute mentally a lead angle, or bias, to allow for the integrated effects that wind, gravity, and target movement have on the path of the rocket, as shown in Fig. 7. The value of this bias plus any sighting error are now combined during the time the rocket is in flight and are subtracted from the real values of the external disturbances. This design brings us face to face with an extremely important question: How well can a pilot be trained to do such mental computations? Although this is a question we might try to answer on the basis of common sense, or intuition, the designer is on far safer grounds if he has some dependable data about human performance in this kind of task.

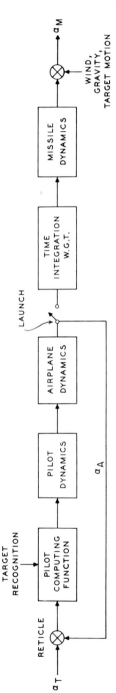

FIG. 7. If the pilot were required to compute a lead angle to compensate for wind, gravity, and target motion, the missile system could be diagramed in this way. (After Bibbero.[4])

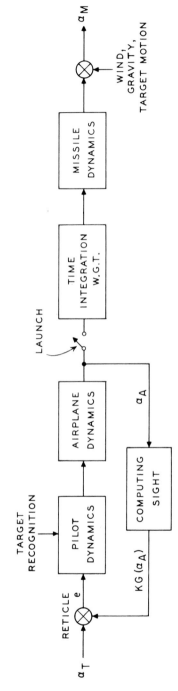

FIG. 8. This is the same missile system as illustrated in Fig. 7 except that the computing function has been assigned to a machine. (After Bibbero.[4])

Automating the Computing Function

Let us consider another possible refinement in the system. Suppose we were to automate the computing function and leave the pilot with only the tasks of recognition and tracking, as shown in Fig. 8. In this type of system, the computing element, being a dynamic element in a feedback loop, introduces some errors of its own. Now the designer has this question to answer: Will the error introduced by a computing sight simplify the pilot's task enough to compensate for the errors which the sight itself introduces into the system? Here again is an important question about the relative performance of two different man-machine combinations.

Having the Pilot Steer the Missile Remotely

A design that differs quite markedly from the foregoing one would close the loop around the rocket dynamics, as illustrated in Fig. 9, thus making it possible to compensate for all errors occurring after the missile is launched. One way of doing this would be to allow the pilot to control the missile remotely throughout the full length of its flight path to the target, inserting corrections into the flight path as needed from observing the total error angle E. What would our pilot have to do in this system? First, he must still fly his aircraft. Second, he must also steer the missile. Although it might appear that we have decoupled the two vehicles (the aircraft and missile), in actual fact we have not because the LOS is measured from the airplane. Variations in the flight path of the aircraft mean variations in the LOS, and, since the pilot now has to fly two vehicles instead of one, we might expect deviations in the flight path of the aircraft to be greater than in any of the systems mentioned earlier.

To some extent, of course, variations in the LOS can be regarded simply as errors to be compensated for in controlling the missile. If the variations become too great, however, it will be impossible to compensate for them. Now some critical questions are these: How well can a pilot fly his own aircraft and maneuver a missile at the same time? Would there be any advantage in placing the aircraft under automatic control during the critical period when the pilot is steering the missile? As a general rule autopilots cannot perform complex tracking tasks as well as a human controller. But it might just be possible to capitalize on a trade-off in this situation: even though an autopilot might not be as precise as a pilot who has nothing else to do, there might be a net gain in the performance of this system simply because the autopilot would free the pilot of one of his two tracking tasks.

There is still another question to be answered before we leave this system: How well will the pilot be able to see the missile as its

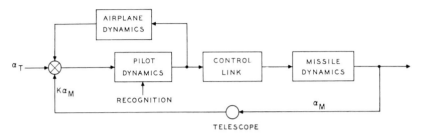

FIG. 9. If the pilot were required to steer the missile into the target, the system could be diagramed this way. (After Bibbero.[4])

distance increases? A telescope will improve the situation within limits, but the determination of the magnification and other optical specifications for the best telescope in this situation is a complex design problem in itself.

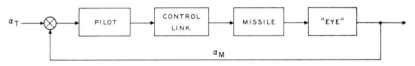

FIG. 10. Putting an electronic "eye" or other type of sensing device in the missile eliminates the error due to motion of the aircraft. (After Bibbero.[4])

Using a Sensing Device in the Missile

One way of eliminating the visual problem mentioned here is to have the pilot view the target through a television, infrared, or radar "eye" in the missile, the picture being relayed to the airplane, as shown in Fig. 10. Any error due to motion of the airplane would now be eliminated, because the reticle would be essentially at the same place as the missile. At the present time a system such as this is impractical because of the cost and weight of the missile-borne "eye" and relay equipment.

A variation of this scheme would be to use some sort of seeker in the missile of Fig. 11. This would eliminate the pilot completely because the sensing device in the missile would transmit error-correcting information to its own steering mechanism. However attractive this system might seem at first glance, it would be of limited tactical usefulness. There is no sensing device at the present time which can compete with the pilot's intelligence and perceptual capacities for the great majority of significant targets.

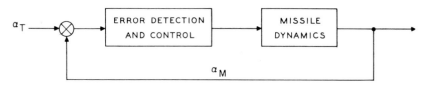

FIG. 11. Putting a target seeker in the missile would eliminate the pilot and aircraft action completely in the final stages of flight. (After Bibbero.[4])

Summary

Although these illustrations do not exhaust the full gamut of possible systems which Bibbero considers in his article, they are, I believe, sufficient for our purposes. Several important generalizations are well illustrated in this sequence of designs. Let us look at them one by one:

1. *The assignment of functions to men or machines.* Repeatedly throughout these examples we saw how the designer was forced to consider what functions should be assigned to men and what to machines. Should the task of computing a lead angle be assigned to a human, or to a machine (Fig. 7 versus Fig. 8)? Should the task of steering the aircraft be assigned to a human pilot or to an automatic pilot (Fig. 9)? Should a human eye or a machine sensing device be given the job of recognizing and perceiving targets (Fig. 9 versus Fig. 11)?

In the article from which I took these examples, questions of this type were implicit in the discussion but were never stated explicitly. Although this is usually what happens in most systems design problems, it does not eliminate the problem. We must not assume, simply because a systems designer has not actually formulated questions of this type in the early stages of his design work, that they do not exist. The human is never eliminated completely from any system. He is always there—if in no other role, then at least as a parent, monitor, and maintenance man. But even these solutions mean that the designer has made a series of decisions about what functions should be assigned to men and what to machines. His decisions may not have been faced squarely, they may even have been wrong, but they were made nonetheless. It is my contention that the importance of this kind of consideration is too often over-looked in systems engineering.

2. *The role of research in the assignment of functions.* The second important generalization I want to draw from the preceding discussion is that empirical testing and research is the only way we can answer some of these assignment problems. Sometimes, to be sure, the answer is readily available. If you want a sensing device to recog-nize targets of opportunity, then you cannot replace the human eye at the present time. No particular research is needed to arrive at this decision. If you want a sensing device to respond to infrared radiation emitted from a target, then some sort of mechanical trans-ducer is the only answer. Again, we need no special research to answer this question. But when you ask: How well can a pilot fly his aircraft and at the same time steer a missile into a target? or, How well can a pilot be trained to compute a lead angle to com-pensate for wind, gravity, and target motion? you are asking questions for which there are no ready-made answers. The only way I know to answer questions of this type quantitatively is to subject them to careful experimental test. We simply do not have enough informa-tion about human capabilities to answer them on an a priori basis.

3. *Continuous re-evaluation of assignment decisions.* The third generalization I want to draw from this discussion is that assignment decisions are not static and fixed, but relative. Assignment decisions are always made at some point in time, and relative to a particular state of development of engineering science. Not so very many years ago a question about the allocation of computing functions to a human or to a machine would have been meaningless. Computers for performing this kind of function have only recently become pos-sible. Similarly, although it is essentially meaningless now to ask whether a machine sensing device should be used to recognize targets, this question may not be meaningless 20 years from now. The state of electronic art is changing so rapidly that we may be sure that some things which are impossible today will be possible tomorrow.

Designing a system is something like writing a book. Unless you draw a line in time and work against that deadline, you will never complete either job. This continual re-evaluation means, to para-phrase a common adage, that a human engineer's work is never done.

Is it possible that in our automatic world of tomorrow the human engineer will be worked out of a job? I think not. Oddly enough, rapid advances in automation have, in general, increased rather than decreased the need for human engineering. When machines were simple and uncomplicated, common sense and crude testing were sufficient to answer most problems of man-machine system design. The very existence of automatic machines has created a whole host of human operations which were unheard of, and indeed unthinkable, a few decades ago. I foresee that the increasing complexity of machine systems will continue to raise more and more pressing and novel problems of man-machine integration. Indeed, I do not see how it can be otherwise.

THE HUMAN ENGINEERING OF SYSTEMS COMPONENTS

After the major decisions have been made about the allocation of functions to human and machine elements in a system, there is usually a lot of human engineering work to be done on the machine components themselves. By this I mean all of the detailed design decisions which have to be made about dials, gages, symbols, letters, numbers, cranks, knobs, lights, colors, buzzers, microphones, seats, foot rests, pedals, etc., which are put on machines and used by human operators. This is the area in which human engineers have been most active and in which they have formulated a very large number of recommendations. Indeed, so much research* has been done on this aspect of systems design that it would be impossible to give an adequate summary of it in only a few pages. The reader who is interested in a more comprehensive review of this literature should consult one of the two relevant textbooks in the area.[8, 9] I shall refer to only a couple of the many hundreds of human engineering findings which can be applied to the design of systems components.

The Selection of Visual Indicators

Three basic types of symbolic indicators are commonly used for conveying information from a machine to an operator, or vice versa. These are: the moving pointer with a fixed scale, the moving scale with a fixed pointer, and the direct reading counter, all shown in Fig. 12. The most important human engineering consideration which should govern the choice of one or another of these three indicators is the use to which the instrument is to be put. The results of a large

---

* The bibliography by McCollom and Chapanis[5] contains over 5000 titles; each of the two prepared by Tufts University[6, 7] over 2000 titles.

number of experiments on such indicators are summarized in Fig. 12. Along the left-hand side of the figure are various usages of these indicators considered from the standpoint of the operator who must do something with the information. The signs inside the boxes are recommendations. Three pluses indicate a satisfactory usage; a single plus indicates an acceptable, but not completely satisfactory, usage; a minus sign indicates a usage which should be avoided.

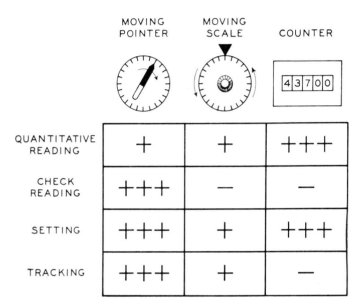

FIG. 12. Recommended uses for three basic types of symbolic indicators.

Indicators are often used to provide precise quantitative information about a machine or instrument setting. In general, the counter is the best indicator for this purpose. Research studies show that operators can get exact numerical values fastest and with fewest errors when the counter is used for displaying quantitative data.

The second major use of visual indicators is for check reading. Much more often than many people suppose, the operator of a piece of equipment is not concerned with precise quantitative readings but only with a rough check on the functioning of his equipment. The pilot, for example, usually does not care whether the manifold pressure is 47.2 or 48.9 inches. He merely wants to know if the pressure is all right or not all right. The typical driver of an automobile is not concerned about whether the temperature of his engine is 149, 150, or 160 degrees, or, indeed whether the gage reads in degrees Fahrenheit or centigrade. He glances at the temperature gage occasionally to see if the engine is in the normal range of operating temperatures and becomes concerned only if it is too hot.

Whenever an operator is interested merely in discovering whether a machine is functioning within or outside of a normal range, he is obtaining a check reading. For this purpose the moving pointer instrument is excellent. The location of the pointer is easily detected and it provides a useful cue in making check readings: the operator soon learns that when the pointer is oriented in a particular direction the machine is functioning normally. In fact, after only a little familiarization with such an indicator the operator usually does not read the numbers or the scale at all. In addition to these advantages, changes in settings are easily detected so that an operator can readily see if the quantity being measured is increasing or decreasing. The moving scale and counter, on the other hand, are poor for check-reading purposes. Neither of these instruments permits an operator to judge the direction and magnitude of a deviation without first reading numbers or a scale.

The third major use to which visual indicators are often put is to set information into a machine. For this purpose both the moving pointer and counter are excellent, although sometimes the designer should use one rather than the other. With the moving pointer instrument it is possible to design simple and direct relations between the motion of the pointer and control. In addition, the position of the pointer helps the operator to monitor the changes which he makes with his control. The counter allows the operator to monitor numerical settings with great precision. However, the relationships between the motion of a control and the movement of the counter dials are always somewhat ambiguous. An additional disadvantage of the counter is that it is ordinarily not readable during rapid movements. The disadvantages of the moving scale will be amplified later.

The fourth major use to which indicators are put is tracking. This is the kind of task the pilot engages in when he attempts to keep his aircraft headed in a particular compass direction. The steersman on a ship often has a similar kind of task. The display for a tracking system might be, for example, a compass or a speedometer. For tracking purposes the moving pointer instrument is clearly the best. The position of the pointer is readily monitored and controlled. In addition, this instrument provides for the most simple and direct relationships between the movements of the pointer and the control which activates it. The moving scale indicator is only fair for tracking. There is no pointer position to aid in monitoring and there is generally an ambiguous relationship between the movements of the scale and the control. The counter is poor for tracking purposes because changes on the counter are difficult to monitor. The relationships between the movements of the counter and the control which activate it are ambiguous and the counter is not generally readable during rapid changes.

FIG. 13. On the left is the model 746 counting dial and on the right the model 1301 microdial. (Courtesy Borg Equipment Division of the George W. Borg Corporation.)

The Moving Scale Indicator versus Counter

An application of the research findings summarized in Fig. 12 is illustrated in Fig. 13. The control on the left is a moving scale indicator commonly found on many types of panels and consoles. In the center of the scale is a knurled knob which can be turned by hand. The scale shown above the knob moves in the same direction as the knob. Actually, there are two scales: one division on the inner one equals one complete revolution of the outer one. The moving scale indicator has some interesting psychological characteristics. It is impossible to design a conventional indicator of this type without violating one of three important design principles:[10]

1. A clockwise rotation of the knob should increase the value of the thing being controlled. For example, if this control were used to regulate the rate of flow of a liquid, a clockwise rotation of the knob should increase the rate of flow.

2. The knob and the scale should move in the same direction.

3. The numerals on the scale should increase in a clockwise direction around the scale in order to reduce reading errors.

You will notice in Fig. 13 that this moving scale indicator violates the third principle. If you will try to read the setting on that one, perhaps you will appreciate why operators make errors in reading such indicators.

On the right of Fig. 13 is another indicator making use of a direct-reading counter. In this case the operator rotates the knurled flange around the outside of the control. Clockwise rotation of the flange increases numbers in the windows, counterclockwise rotation decreases the values. Both of these control devices are available commercially from the same company. You should not be surprised to learn that experimental studies of these two types of controls have confirmed that the one on the right leads to far fewer setting and checking errors.[11] Incidentally, did you discover that both indicators in Fig. 13 are set to the same value?

The Design of Scales

A considerable amount of research effort has gone into the study of scales and the way in which they should be designed. Figure 14 shows in tabular form the recommendations which came out of these studies.

The left-hand column of this figure shows the graduation interval scale. This is the value of the smallest division on the scale. Notice that there are only three values recommended—the 1, 2, and 5, or decimal multiples of these digits. No other values are acceptable because research shows that people cannot readily interpret or use scales which are graduated in any other way. The numbered interval values are the values between the major graduation marks to which numerals are attached. Here again the only recommended numerals are the 1, 2, and 5, or decimal multiples of them. Fortunately, research shows that one can multiply or divide the basic numerical values on scales by factors of 10 or 100 without appreciably affecting the speed or accuracy with which scales can be read. By this I mean that a scale which is numbered 0, 1, 2, 3, . . . , is just about as easy to read as one which is numbered 0, 10, 20, 30 . . .

At the extreme right of Fig. 14 are shown recommendations about the graduation marks to be used on the scales. There are three kinds of graduation marks: major, minor, and intermediate marks. Some scales make use of all three types of markings; some use only the major and minor marks; and some use the major and intermediate marks. With the samples shown in the figure it should be possible to redesign any scale to conform to these recommendations.

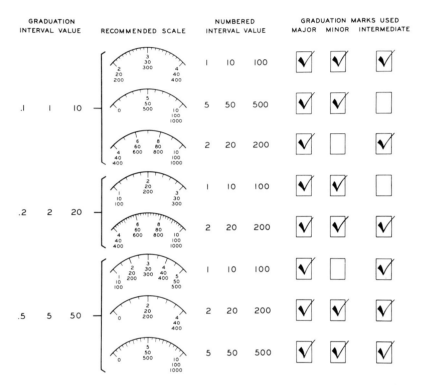

FIG. 14. Recommendations concerning the design of scales. (Adapted from Baker and Grether.[12])

An Illustration of These Principles

It is important to point out that the problems I have been talking about are not abstract laboratory problems. Illustrations of poor dial design are easy to find and Fig. 15 is only one of many which could be used for this purpose. It is a "before-and-after" illustration. The dial on the left shows a type of scale which used to be made by a manufacturer of a wide variety of meters and recording instruments. The scale on the right is one which was redesigned on the basis of good human engineering practice. The comparison between the two is so striking that it hardly requires any discussion. In addition to being more legible, the scale on the right has a much more satisfactory numbering system.

FIG. 15. On the left is a pneumatic indicator dial as originally manufactured; on the right the same dial after redesign. (After Fleming.[13])

Summary

As I said at the beginning of this section, it would be impossible for me even to begin to summarize adequately the major human engineering design practices which can be applied to the design of systems components. The few illustrations I have discussed merely serve to suggest some of the kinds of advice the human engineering specialist can give.

THE EVALUATION OF MAN-MACHINE SYSTEMS

The third area in which the human engineer becomes involved in systems engineering is in the evaluation of systems. Most current definitions of systems engineering emphasize the importance of evaluating the entire system before it is actually put into production. As we have already seen in my discussion of air-to-ground missile systems, the human operator plays a vital part in any of several different ways in which the system might be designed. Thus, any reasonable attempt to evaluate the performance of the system must include an evaluation of the performance of the human operator working with the equipment provided him. Tests have to be made of the interrelationships between the operator and the equipment to find out how well the combination will work.

Systems engineers who have actually run tests on complicated man-machine combinations usually come to appreciate quickly that such tests are much more complicated than doing ordinary engineering evaluations. People differ, and tests run on one operator may not be at all typical of the performance of the average operator. People learn during the course of an experiment; often they become bored or fatigued; they are sensitive to the kinds of instructions which precede the experiment and to words of praise or reproof given during it; they interact with the experimenter in strange and sometimes unexpected ways—they may try to outguess the experimenter, or, on occasion, may deliberately sabotage the outcome of the tests. These and still other factors must be anticipated and controlled if the results of man-machine experiments are to be trusted.

Psychologists, of course, have been face to face with these problems for years and, in the course of their work, have evolved techniques for handling many of them. For this reason it perhaps is not surprising to find that human engineers are frequently consulted for their advice on problems of technique and methodology. A book I prepared recently[14] is an attempt to pull together some of this information in a single source.

SOME RELATIONS BETWEEN HUMAN ENGINEERING AND OPERATIONS RESEARCH

Many operations research problems, it seems to me, involve little systems engineering or human engineering. The reason for this is that the operations research man very often goes into an organization which is already functioning, studies it carefully, and then attempts to change the organization or operation of the system so as to make it more efficient, make it more economical, or to suit some other objective. In most problems of this type he is not concerned with the *design* of machines, but rather with procedural or policy matters. Studies undertaken to provide a basis for making decisions about an optimum inventory policy in an established industry are clearly of this nature. Those leading to allocation, routing, and replacement policies are also in this same category.

MAINTENANCE POLICIES FOR THE POLARIS FIRE CONTROL SYSTEM

There are cases, however, in which the work of the operations research man becomes intimately connected with that of the systems engineer and human engineer. This occurs when the opsearcher is asked to analyze and make predictions about the most efficient utilization or operation of a system which has not yet been constructed. In problems of this type the recommendations resulting from an operations research analysis may interact in a vital way with decisions which the systems engineer and human engineer reach. A good example of this kind of problem is Mosbaek's study of the economic analysis of various maintenance alternatives for the Polaris fire control system.[15] Even though the Polaris system had not yet been constructed and put into operation, it was important for the systems designer to know what would probably be the most efficient way of maintaining the system after it had been put into operation. In fact, this information is needed early in the development of the system because decisions about maintenance policy determine how the system should be designed for maintenance purposes, what kinds of test equipment and auxiliary equipment should be provided, what sorts of repair facilities will be required, and the number of spares that should be stocked at the various operational units.

The Polaris missile is a two-stage, inertial-guidance, solid-fuel missile designed to be fired from a submarine below the surface of the water. The specific purpose of the study was to investigate the most economical maintenance policy for digital boards of the current generation system for this missile. In particular, it was concerned with the question of whether it is cheaper to repair or discard a defective board, and, if it is cheaper to repair the board, whether repairing it on board the submarine, on the submarine tender, or at the factory is most economical.

Influences of Operations Research Decisions on Systems Engineering and Human Engineering

Even without going into the intricacies of this report we can see some interrelations between this type of analysis and both systems engineering and human engineering. The answer to the question of whether it is more economical to repair or discard a subassembly influences the way in which the systems engineer should design the system. If the module is to be a repairable unit then it must be designed according to good human engineering principles; it should be easily accessible to the maintenance man, test points should be provided within the assembly, parts and components should be properly coded and labeled, simple maintenance instructions and manuals must be written, etc. If the subassembly or module is to be designed as a nonrepairable unit, on the other hand, many of these human engineering considerations can be disregarded.

The Operations Research Analysis of the Polaris System

The digital boards upon which the study was based number 25 types and there are almost 1000 of them in the fire control system. The different boards contain transistors, diodes, resistors, capacitors, and other parts, totaling on the average about 84 parts per board. The analysis assumed an over-all system consisting of six submarines and a submarine tender and an expected operating life of five years. The determination of the various costs involved in this analysis is a highly technical problem which is irrelevant to our discussion. Table 1, however, shows some of the parameter values used in arriving at the decision model in this study.

One of the immediate and most interesting outcomes of this analysis was to show the importance of various types of costs for alternative maintenance policies. If the modules are designed as throwaway units, then the major item of expense is that of stocking spares, as indicated in Fig. 16. If the boards are to be repaired on board the

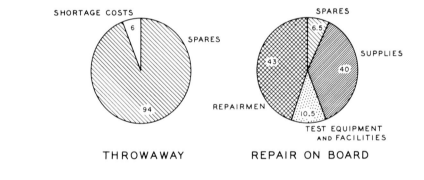

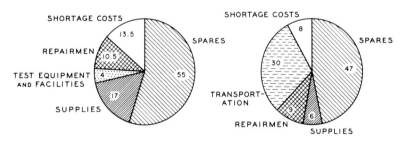

FIG. 16. Relative values of various items of cost in four alternative maintenance policies for the Polaris fire control system. (After Mosbaek.[15])

TABLE 1. PARAMETER VALUES USED IN AN OPERATIONS
RESEARCH STUDY OF MAINTENANCE POLICIES FOR THE
POLARIS SYSTEM

Item	Cost

Part A

Weighted average price per board	$241
Six comprehensive testers (if purchased as a lot)	$206,000
Six testers for repairing short-circuited transistors only	$41,200
One comprehensive tester (repair on tender policy)	$42,500
Cost of repairman per year	$12,000
Effective interest rate	$33\frac{1}{3}\%$
Price reduction for increased order size	$q^{-0.320}$
Life of system (3 cruises/yr; 1000 operating hours/cruise)	5 years
Number of hours worked per day per repairman	0.7(8) = 5.6 hr
Space for repair facilities on submarine	150 ft^3
Living space per man	120 ft^3
Cost of space per cruise	$30/ft^3
Volume of storage space per digital board	120 in.^{3} (0.069 ft^3)
Expected failure rate per board	0.05/1000 hr/transistor
Salvage value of discarded board	15%
Change in reliability with repeated repair	$R(X) + 1)^{-0.152}$
Expected time to repair failed board on submarine	1 hr
Expected time to repair short-circuited transistor	45 min
Cost of system being down owing to part shortage	$6000/hr
Cost of piece parts to repair failed board on submarine	15% cost of board
Cost of piece parts to repair failed board on tender	9% cost of board
Cost of repairmen per failed board on tender	one-third that on submarine
Cost of repairmen per failed board at factory	one-sixth that on submarine
Cost of transporting failed items to and from factory	10% each way

Part B

Number of spares in initial outlay	
Repair on board	86
Repair on tender	1508
Throwaway	1131
Expected number of boards used per year with discard	2238/submarine
Expected shortage hours per submarine per year	
Repair on board	0.23
Repair on tender	3.30
Throwaway	3.30

submarine, however, the cost of providing repairmen is the largest single item, with the cost of providing test equipment and facilities becoming a fairly substantial item. If the decision is made to repair the boards at the factory, then transportation of the boards to and from the factory becomes an appreciable item.

Figure 16 merely shows how the costs of various maintenance policies are apportioned among the various categories. Figure 17, on the other hand, shows the expected *total* costs for the four mainte-

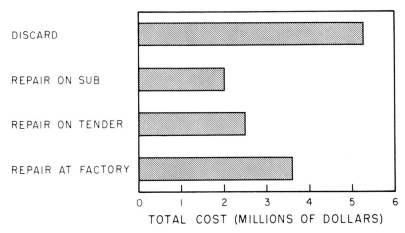

FIG. 17. The expected total costs of four maintenance policies for the Polaris fire control system. (After Mosbaek.[15])

nance policies. There it is evident that the cheapest policy is to repair defective assemblies on the submarine. A policy of discarding defective assemblies would be almost 2½ times as expensive as the most economical maintenance policy.

In addition to being more economical, the policy of repairing defective assemblies on the submarine has some additional advantages which are difficult to assess but real nonetheless:

1. This policy provides maximum protection against unforeseen emergencies because it requires each submarine to carry skilled technicians and maintenance men.

2. It provides performance information and failure data of great value to the designer and systems engineer. Failure data obtained during the operation and repair of the system can be tabulated and fed back to the manufacturer and so provide a basis for the redesign of the system for better operation.

3. It allows modifications and changes in the system to be carried

out efficiently in the field. As new design changes are made during the operation of the system they can be efficiently carried out if skilled technicians are already aboard the submarine.

4. It takes full advantage of the high technical skill levels which are expected to be aboard the early Polaris submarines.

Varying the Maintenance Policy during the Life of the System

The cost of alternative maintenance plans depends very strongly upon the numerical values of the system characteristic entered into the decision model. If these characteristics are expected to vary markedly over the operational life of the system, the maintenance

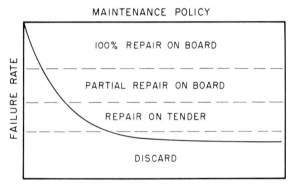

FIG. 18. A schematic way of showing how the maintenance policy might vary during the operational life of a system. (After Mosbaek.[15])

policy might also have to vary. Figure 18 shows, for illustrative purposes only, a possible relationship between optimum maintenance policy and failure rate within the system. When the system is first put into operation we might expect a high initial failure rate. Under these circumstances, the most economical maintenance policy would be that of repairing all defective subassemblies on board the submarine. As the system matures and the failure rate drops, however, it might be more economical to repair some of the modules on the submarine and the remainder on the tender. For example, it might be more efficient to repair only short-circuited transistors and diodes on the submarine, leaving all other work for repair on the tender. When the failure rate drops still further, repairing defective subassemblies on the tender would be the most economical policy. With high system reliability a policy of discard would become the most economical one.

Although the change in maintenance policy illustrated in Fig. 18 has the virtues of flexibility and economy, we must not overlook the implications of such a policy for the systems engineer and the human engineer. If the system is designed with the intent of changing the maintenance policy throughout the operational life of the system, then the system designer must design the subassemblies and modules as repairable parts. In addition, the design of all subassemblies and modules must be human-engineered for easy and effective maintenance even though at later stages in the operational life of the system the subassemblies and modules may be discarded.

In concluding this discussion, it is perhaps important to mention that human engineers have been active in the preparation of design principles for effective maintenance. Many of these can be found in a comprehensive report by Folley and Altman.[16]

THE VALIDATION OF ASSUMPTIONS
INVOLVING HUMAN VARIABLES

As we have already seen, one important step in the typical operations research approach to a problem involves the construction of a mathematical model to represent the system under study.[17] The purpose of the model is to express the effectiveness of the system as a function of a set of critical variables. Oftentimes these critical variables involve human behavior, and the relationships between the variables are inferences based on "logic" or common sense. This is an important source of error to which all models of man are, I think, particularly prone. It is easy to be misled about the way variables are connected in human behavior, even when logic and common sense seem to be on your side.

Because psychologists work so intimately with that tangled skein of relationships which constitutes human behavior, they are not much inclined to trust their common sense, intuitions, or logical powers of analysis when it comes to matters of this kind. Most good human engineers, I find, are always a little uneasy when they have to make decisions unsupported by empirical findings. To such people one good experiment is worth 100 guesses because they know how often guesses turn out to be wrong. It is, unfortunately, an easy matter to find examples of equipment which is poorly designed precisely because design decisions were based on such shifting grounds.

The human engineer's faith in sound experimentation and distrust of common sense is both a handicap and an advantage. In the everyday business of designing machine systems, the practical man cannot wait for experiments. He must make his decisions now—today. As a result, the two kinds of engineers—human and systems—do not often understand each other. The one is reluctant to play his hunches and argues constantly for empirical evidence; the other is impatient at the long-haired scientific attitude which demands validation and argues that an "informed guess" is better than none. In the long run, however, the validity of any model must face the stern test of empirical validation. In this respect the human engineer's scepticism can contribute to the work of the operations analyst.

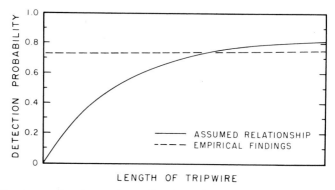

FIG. 19. Assumed and experimentally determined relationships between detection probability and length of a tripwire. (After Peters.[18])

An Operations Research Model for a Land-Mine System

Peters[18] has a good illustration of precisely the kind of thing I have been trying to say. His problem was to determine the effectiveness of a tripwired land-mine system under certain operational conditions. In typical operations research fashion an analytic model was constructed to predict the effectiveness of the system as a function of several variables. One important variable was the probability that the tripwire would be seen. It seemed logical to assume that an enemy soldier would be able to see a long tripwire placed across his path much better than a short one. As the length of the tripwire was increased indefinitely, however, the probability of detection should level off at some reasonably high value. Figure 19 shows the relationship which was assumed to hold between the length of tripwire and detection probability. The solution derived from the model was that the length of the tripwire should not exceed a certain value. Since Peters was properly sceptical about this type of reasoning, he ran a carefully controlled experiment to check the assumptions on which this critical relationship was based. A simulated mine field was constructed in a slightly wooded area of heterogeneous background. Tripwires were carefully laid out to simulate what might be expected under combat conditions. Each subject was instructed to search for and to try to find a series of concealed tripwires while following a marked path through the mine field. Five hundred and sixty trials were made with 35 subjects and 16 tripwires of 4 different lengths.

The results of these tests showed that the original formulation based upon logic and common sense was erroneous. The probability of detection did not vary with the length of the tripwire! On the contrary, detection probability was a constant over the critical range of lengths tested (see Fig. 19). Revision of the model to take account of these empirical findings led to an entirely different solution, namely, that the over-all effectiveness of the system could be enhanced by increasing the length of the tripwire substantially.

SOME IMPLICATIONS OF THE SYSTEMS POINT OF VIEW FOR HUMAN ENGINEERING

Both systems engineers and operations analysts have what is sometimes referred to as the "systems point of view." In general, this means that they are both strongly oriented toward the final criteria of system performance. Every design decision the systems engineer makes is, or should be, evaluated in terms of its contribution to the over-all performance of the system. Similarly, operations analysts try to express the effectiveness of system performance in terms of some common measure—often cost in dollars—and to assess the contribution of systems variables in terms of that common measure.[17] Human engineering data, on the other hand, are often expressed in terms of more immediate criteria. Two very common criteria are the time required to operate a device and errors made in operating it. One reason for this state of affairs is that most human engineering data come from basic research studies done in university laboratories. Almost by necessity, such investigations have to be made in abstraction—without reference to any particular system. More immediate criteria are convenient and easy to apply in such research. Nonetheless, it raises some very important problems about the generality of human engineering data when they are applied to real-world problems. It is this general problem I want to discuss now.

THE GENERALITY OF MANY HUMAN ENGINEERING DATA

An important and interesting characteristic of many human engineering data is that they have great generality: they are good by almost any criterion you pick. This is quite unlike the situation in systems engineering or operations research where, it seems to me, variables are more often opposed or pitted against each other. Increasing the precision of an electronic guidance device very often means increasing its complexity and cost and decreasing its reliability. An important question for the systems designer is that of choosing the correct balance among these conflicting criteria. Similarly, in operations research waiting-line problems increasing the number of service units means shorter queues, shorter waiting times, and fewer losses in revenue from customers. But these have to be balanced against the increased costs of providing more service units and the costs of having service units idle.

Human engineering data have fewer of these conflicting criteria. It is easy to find instances in which the better "human-engineered" of two devices can be used more quickly, with fewer errors, by less skilled operators, with shorter training times, and yet cost no more or even less to build. This is such an important generalization that I want to illustrate it with two examples.

The Design of Scales

Earlier, I spoke about some human engineering recommendations dealing with the design of scales in Fig. 14, and showed the application of these design principles in a particular instance in Fig. 15. This is an illustration of precisely the kind of thing I mean. The redesigned dial is better by almost any criterion you want to pick: it can be read faster, with fewer errors, by less trained personnel, and it costs no more to manufacture. That illustration is only one of many. As a matter of fact, the experience of the manufacturer is very instructive in this regard. The company redesigned a number of their dials on the basis of human engineering principles, and discovered some unexpected bonuses. They had been plagued by one of their instruments being returned by the purchasers so often to the factory for "recalibration." After the scale was redesigned these "recalibration" problems vanished because they were not recalibration problems at all, but rather scale-reading problems. As reported by Fleming:[13] "We are just amazed at the consequence of simply changing scale markings."

The Redesign of a Control

This matter is sufficiently important that it might be well to illustrate it with one more example, this time from an ordinary household device—a portable electric heater. The heater consists essentially of a set of electric coils and a fan which moves air past the coils into

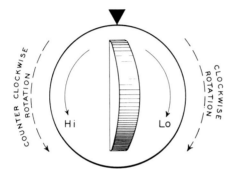

FIG. 20. A type of control knob used on a household electric room heater.

the room. On the top of one such heater is a control for adjusting the amount of heat, shown in Fig. 20. It is a circular knob with a raised flange so that it can be grasped by the fingers. On the knob are two arrows pointing in opposite directions. One arrow terminates in the word "Hi," the other in the word "Lo." On the casing of the heater is a fixed index mark.

The operation of this device seems simple enough. To increase the amount of heat one grasps the knob and rotates it past the index mark. But one moment—which way do you rotate the knob? There are two possible interpretations to this question. On the one hand, perhaps you should rotate the knob counterclockwise to increase the amount of heat, i.e., rotate it in the direction of the arrow which points toward "Hi." The other interpretation is that you must rotate the knob clockwise, i.e., bring the word "Hi" up closer to the index mark. Clearly these two interpretations differ radically and, in a random sample of people, one finds divided opinions about the proper method of operating this kind of control.

In this particular device (a household heater) such ambiguity has no serious consequences. At most, the user may experience some annoyance and temporary discomfort, but no great loss, if he happens to make an error. However, I have seen control devices of precisely this kind* used on instruments and systems where the consequences of an error could be extremely serious. To take one example, I was once consulted about a jet training device manufactured by an electronics firm for the Navy. A prototype model of this jet trainer was tested on a number of Navy pilots with results which the designer found perplexing. About half of the pilots operated the controls in

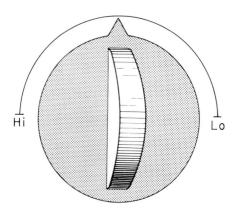

FIG. 21. The control in Fig. 20 is here redesigned to eliminate ambiguity.

the manner in which the manufacturer had intended. Unfortunately, however, the remainder of the pilots consistently made movements in the wrong direction. I am sure you will agree that errors of this kind in a jet trainer, or aircraft, could be disastrous.

The remedy for this kind of problem turns out to be rather simple. One merely needs to reverse the locations of the index mark and scale, as shown in Fig. 21. Psychologists have a special name for this kind of problem—they call it a "figure-ground" problem—and the net effect of the change is to convert the device from a moving scale indicator to a moving pointer indicator. The redesigned indicator now contains no ambiguity. It can even be used by untrained operators without difficulty.

For our purposes, the important point to note is that it costs no more to produce one kind of a design than the other. The basic structure of the control, the rheostat, and electrical connections inside the device are completely unchanged. The only difference between the two lies in the markings. Here then is another instance in which

* They are known as moving scale indicators (see Fig. 12).

a substantial human engineering improvement can be effected at no increase in cost.

ON COSTS AND OTHER SYSTEMS CRITERIA

Although it is reassuring to the human engineer to know that many of his recommendations are extremely general, there are, unfortunately, many instances in which he, like the systems engineer and operations analyst, has to decide between conflicting alternatives. In such cases it *is* important for human engineering principles to be evaluated in terms of systems criteria; this is an area in which human engineers have much to learn and much more work to do.

The Operations Research Evaluation of Human Engineering Principles

In one of the illustrations I used earlier there is a clear-cut conflict between human engineering desirability and cost. Figure 13 showed a control with a direct-reading, counter-type dial, and a control with a moving scale dial. The former is better than the latter in terms of reading speed, accuracy, and readability by relatively untrained personnel. Unfortunately, unlike the scales in Fig. 15, the counter-type control costs very much more than the moving scale indicator. Now we are faced with a direct conflict: Is the cost of errors sufficiently great so that it would be worthwhile using the more accurate, but more expensive, device?

This conflict can be illustrated even better with another example. Figure 22 shows dial faces from two types of kilowatt-hour meters in common use throughout the country. During World War II when there was a shortage of meter readers some gas and electric companies asked householders to read their own meters. In general, they did this for only one month—the returns were absolutely chaotic! Now in some areas, when a meter reader cannot get in to read a meter, the householder receives a card with the dial faces printed on the card. He is instructed to look at his meter and draw in on the card exactly where the needles are pointing. The card is then returned to the company for interpretation. These dials are difficult to read because they violate two important human engineering principles: (1) dials are read most easily if the numerals increase clockwise around a scale; and (2) in multiple-dial displays, the direction of increase should be consistent.

Figure 23 shows, on the other hand, a kilowatt-hour meter which is

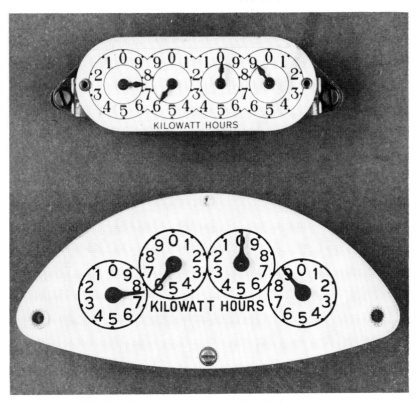

FIG. 22. Dial faces from two kilowatt-hour meters.

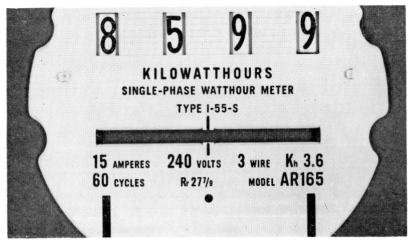

FIG. 23. Dial face for a kilowatt-hour meter which is much easier to read than those in Fig. 22. (Courtesy General Electric Company.)

clearly easier to read because it makes use of the principles summarized in Fig. 12. But does this mean that companies with old-style kilowatt-hour meters (Fig. 22) should immediately change all of their meters to the more easily read kind (Fig. 23)? Not necessarily. However difficult it may be to read the dials in Fig. 22, they do have one virtue: engineering simplicity. The dial face in Fig. 22 costs only about $0.50 to manufacture in quantity; the one in Fig. 23 about $10.50.

This is a case where I think the human engineer needs to make use of operations research techniques in evaluating the desirability of making a human engineering improvement. Cost might very well be a proper criterion to use in making such an evaluation, since one goal of the company is, after all, to make money. Some of the factors which should be entered into the operations research equations are:

1. The cost of making an incorrect meter reading.
2. The number of errors that will be made with each type of dial.
3. The cost of each type of dial.
4. The cost of maintaining each type of dial (since the counter-type dial might well require more frequent adjustment or repair).
5. The useful life of each type of dial.

The Need for Realistic Comparative Data

At this point we are brought face to face with an extremely serious shortcoming of most human engineering data: since they were not obtained under realistic conditions, they cannot be directly entered into cost equations. Consider, for example, the recommendations given in Fig. 12 and applied in Figs. 13 and 23. There have been a number of experiments comparing dials with counters, and all those I know about have been done under carefully controlled laboratory conditions. This has both advantages and disadvantages. Laboratory experimentation has associated with it a number of powerful and attractive features: variables can be isolated and studied without contamination; the entire situation is arranged in advance so that observations can be made with precision; the conditions of experimentation are carefully specified so that the experiment can be repeated and duplicated.

There are, however, some disadvantages of laboratory experimentation and one of these is that when a phenomenon is brought into the laboratory for study under carefully controlled conditions the situation is no longer realistic. In a certain sense, the data which come out of laboratory experimentation are, at one and the same time, both more precise and less precise than data obtained from field experimentation. Laboratory data are more precise for discovering whether a particular independent variable does, or does not, have a genuine effect on some dependent variable. They are, however, less precise if one wants to extrapolate to what one should expect to find in the way of exact numerical differences in real life.

Let me explain what I mean. In doing a laboratory experiment to compare the readability of a dial versus a counter, the investigator would almost certainly control a whole host of variables. For example, the tests would be made under standardized conditions of illumination, irrelevant distractions would be minimized, the visual displays would always be located in the same place, carefully selected and trained subjects would be used, carefully selected (and comparable) numerical readings would be set into the two indicators, and the order and sequence of tests would be arranged to counterbalance for the effects of training, boredom, and fatigue. The reason these extraneous variables are so controlled is to eliminate any contamination they might introduce into the experimental findings. This is what gives the method of experiment its power. The outcome of a well-designed experiment allows one to say confidently that a particular difference is or is not significant.

In exchange for this power and certainty we have sacrificed a very great deal of realism. Kilowatt-hour meters are *not* read under carefully controlled conditions of illumination, they are *not* read in the absence of irrelevant distractions, they are *not* always located in the same place, they are *not* necessarily read by carefully selected and trained operators, and they are almost certainly read under diverse conditions of boredom and fatigue. All of these differences mean that it is extremely difficult to extrapolate from laboratory data to real data. If the results of laboratory tests show the following percentages of error for the two devices

Counter: 2%
Dial: 9%*

it would be extremely dangerous to assume that these are the percentages of error we would obtain under realistic conditions. We can have confidence that there is a genuine difference between the two instruments, but the exact size of the difference we would obtain in actual use is subject to very large errors of estimate. Yet, for any

---

* These are, in fact, the percentages of errors obtained in one experiment on this very problem.[19]

operations research analysis of the costs involved in changing from one to the other, it is precisely this kind of realistic data we need.

To sum up, then, most human engineering data have been obtained under carefully controlled laboratory conditions. Human engineers face a real challenge in obtaining data under more realistic conditions so that the precise effect of human engineering principles can be assessed in terms of their cost and contribution to real system performance. This is a very large order.

ON FINDING SYSTEMS-RELEVANT CRITERIA

I have already commented on the fact that most human engineering data have been obtained with immediate performance criteria which can be easily abstracted and measured in the laboratory. Very often these are time and errors. In certain types of human engineering studies (e.g., those on radar and speech intelligibility) psychophysical threshold* criteria are used. These laboratory criteria are extremely useful in discovering important relationships under carefully controlled and specifiable conditions, but they are often extremely difficult to translate into terms which are relevant for and meaningful to the systems engineer.

Let me illustrate very briefly. A good many years ago we did a substantial number of experiments at Johns Hopkins on factors affecting the detectability of targets on radarscopes. One of these factors is the electrical bias put on the grid of the cathode-ray tube. The effect of this variable was evaluated in terms of a psychophysical criterion—visibility measured by the number of decibels a reference signal could be attenuated and still be seen. The results of one such experiment are illustrated in Fig. 24. The greater the attenuation needed to reach the threshold the more easily the signal can be perceived. Although these data are very interesting and dependable, it is difficult to say what they mean in terms of systems performance. The systems designer is not interested in the decibel attenuation of a signal. He wants to know how the performance of the system will be affected if the grid bias is not maintained at its optimum value. He needs, in short, to be able to translate *decibels of attenuation* into some measure of radar performance, e.g., maximum distance at which the radar will pick up targets.

Thornton[21] has made such a translation for us and his curve is

* Generally speaking, such criteria are measures of the weakest signal, or smallest change in a signal, which can be detected by the human observer.

shown in Fig. 25.* Now we can see that if the grid bias is allowed
to deviate by only 4 volts from its optimum value, there will be a

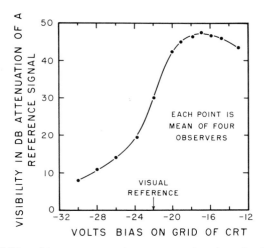

FIG. 24. Visibility of targets on a radarscope as a function of grid bias. (After
Williams et al.[20])

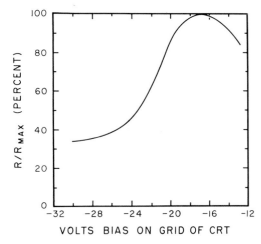

FIG. 25. The data in Fig. 24 have been converted here to show the effect
which variations in grid bias have on the maximum range of a radar. (After
Thornton.[21])

20% reduction in range of the radar. If the grid bias is increased
by 6 volts, the range of the radar will be cut almost exactly in half.
These are very impressive and meaningful figures.

* Although the curve in Fig. 25 resembles that of Fig. 24, a careful comparison
of the two will show that they are not linear functions of one another.

Some other successful translations of this type have been achieved in the Laboratory of Aviation Psychology at Ohio State University. Investigators there have been engaged in a series of experiments on the human engineering aspects of air traffic control.[22, 23] In this connection they have been able to express the dependent variables of their experiments in such systems-relevant measures as the amount of fuel that would be consumed by aircraft, the length of time aircraft would be under ground control, and the separations that would be maintained between aircraft in flight (an indication of potential collision hazards). Quite a different kind of illustration comes from a fine experiment by Baldwin and Nielsen,[24] who expressed the outcome of a psychophysical experiment on colored television pictures in terms of the bandwidths that would be required to yield varying degrees of sharpness in the picture.

The Effects of Anoxia on Human Performance

Let me conclude with just one other example of the difficulties of translating between ordinary human engineering data and systems criteria. By now everyone is familiar with the condition of anoxia —oxygen lack at high altitudes. We know that commercial and military aircraft which fly above about 12,000 feet have to be pressurized, or carry supplemental oxygen, if the passengers and crew are to be comfortable or, indeed, survive. Most everyone knows some of the symptoms of anoxia. When unacclimatized but otherwise healthy males are transported to altitudes between 15,000 and 18,000 feet without oxygen, one can demonstrate a variety of effects: vision and hearing are dimmed, there is an increase in muscular tremor, reaction time is increased, depth perception is impaired, the normal powers of reasoning and judgment are affected, etc. What is not so commonly known, however, is that these effects occur at different altitudes. For example, darkening of vision due to anoxia has been demonstrated at altitudes as low as 6000 feet, but impairment of hearing due to anoxia is not ordinarily detectable below about 16,000 feet. Moreover, the onset of effects due to anoxia is gradual. They are certainly worse at 14,000 than at 12,000 feet, but the fact of the matter is that we cannot specify exactly when effects first become demonstrable.

Pressurizing an aircraft, or providing supplemental oxygen, is done at a price, and the price is cost and weight. More pressurization, or more oxygen, means more equipment, more weight, and so less pay load. Many interminable arguments between systems engineers and human engineers have occurred, and have remained essentially unsolved, because the two groups simply could not converse in these same terms. The systems engineer can provide the human engineer with exact figures about the weight and cost penalty of providing pressurization to keep the interior of an aircraft at altitudes equivalent to 10,000, 12,000, or 14,000 feet. He can tell us how much the pay load of the aircraft will be reduced if he has to maintain the pressure at an altitude equivalent to 12,000 feet rather than 14,000 feet. And at about this point, the systems engineer is likely to turn to the human engineer with the question, "How much difference will it make to the mission if the operator is kept at 14,000 instead of 12,000 feet?" The human engineer, unfortunately, is at a loss. He can tell the systems engineer that this 2000-foot difference in altitude will produce a 5% change in the oxygen saturation of arterial blood, that the operator will need about 24% more light to see, that the operator will be able to recall about 8% fewer words spoken to him in random order, and that the operator's handwriting will become a little unsteadier. But in all the laboratory data that have been collected on anoxia there is nothing the human engineer can give the systems engineer to help him compute the costs—the human costs— of providing pressurization for 14,000 feet rather than 12,000 feet. To do this we would need to know such things as (1) the increase in probability of mission failure as anoxia increases; (2) the increase in probability of air or ground collision as anoxia increases; and (3) the increase in probability of damaging the aircraft on landing as anoxia increases. These data are the kind that could provide some meaningful estimates of the cost of *not* providing enough oxygen. Unfortunately, they do not exist.

Summary

In summary, one of the challenges which the systems engineer has given the human engineer is that of discovering ways in which the outcomes of laboratory experiments can be expressed in terms which are relevant to the performance of systems. Although we can point to some significant and important work in this direction, we still have a very great deal more to do.

REFERENCES

1. Harry H. Goode and Robert E. Machol, *System Engineering*, McGraw-Hill Book Co., New York, 1957.
2. J. F. Dewhurst and associates, *America's Needs and Resources*, The Twentieth Century Fund, New York, 1955.
3. Alphonse Chapanis, "Human Engineering," Chap. 19, pp. 534–582, in Charles D. Flagle, William H. Huggins, and Robert H. Roy, *Operations Research and Systems Engineering*, The Johns Hopkins Press, Baltimore, 1960.

4. Robert J. Bibbero, How Systems Engineering Affects Missile Design, *Automatic Control*, vol. 8, no. 6, June 1958, pp. 7–12.

5. Ivan N. McCollom and Alphonse Chapanis, *A Human Engineering Bibliography*, San Diego State College Foundation, San Diego, 1956.

6. Institute for Applied Experimental Psychology, Tufts University, Human Engineering Bibliography, 1955–1956, *Report No. ACR-24*, Office of Naval Research (Department of the Navy, Washington); *Report No. PB 131507*, Office of Technical Services, Department of Commerce; *Report No. AD-149950*, Armed Services Technical Information Agency; Oct. 1957.

7. Institute for Applied Experimental Psychology, Tufts University, Human Engineering Bibliography, 1956–1957, *Report No. ACR-32*, Office of Naval Research (Department of the Navy, Washington); *Report No. PB 131507S*, Office of Technical Services, Department of Commerce; *Report No. AD-206931*, Armed Services Technical Information Agency; Oct. 1958.

8. Alphonse Chapanis, Wendell R. Garner and Clifford T. Morgan, *Applied Experimental Psychology: Human Factors in Engineering Design*, John Wiley & Sons, New York, 1949.

9. Ernest J. McCormick, *Human Engineering*, McGraw-Hill Book Co., New York, 1957.

10. James V. Bradley, Desirable Control-Display Relationships for Moving-Scale Instruments, *WADC Technical Report 54-423*, Wright Air Development Center, Air Research and Development Command, United States Air Force, Wright-Patterson Air Force Base, Ohio, Sept. 1954.

11. Roger J. Weldon and George M. Peterson, Effect of Design on Accuracy and Speed of Operating Dials, *Journal of Applied Psychology*, vol 41, no. 3, June 1957, pp. 153–157.

12. Charles A. Baker and Walter F. Grether, Visual Presentation of Information, *WADC Technical Report 54-160*, Wright Air Development Center, Air Research and Development Command, United States Air Force, Wright-Patterson Air Force Base, Ohio, Aug. 1954.

13. John G. Fleming, Improve Power-Plant Instrumentation by Applying Human-Engineering Data, *Power*, vol. 98, no. 1, Jan. 1954, pp. 86–89 *et passim*.

14. Alphonse Chapanis, *Research Techniques in Human Engineering*, The Johns Hopkins Press, Baltimore, 1959.

15. Ernest J. Mosbaek, Economic Analysis of Repair versus Discard Alternatives: Polaris Fire Control System Components, *Report No. RM 59TMP-40*, Technical Military Planning Operation, General Electric Company (Santa Barbara, Calif.), Aug. 20, 1959.

16. John D. Folley, Jr., and James W. Altman, Guide to Design of Electronic Equipment for Maintainability, *WADC Technical Report 56-218*, Wright Air Development Center, Air Research and Development Command, United States Air Force, Wright-Patterson Air Force Base, Ohio, Apr. 1956.

17. Russell L. Ackoff, The Development of Operations Research as a Science, *Operations Research*, vol. 4, no 3, June 1956, pp. 265–295.

18. George A. Peters, Errors of Estimate in Operations Analysis, *Operations Research*, vol. 5, no. 6, Dec. 1957, pp. 848–851.

19. Alphonse Chapanis, Speed of Reading Target Information from a Direct-Reading, Counter-Type Indicator versus Conventional Radar Bearing and Range Dials. *Report No. 166-I-3*, Systems Research Field Laboratory, The Johns Hopkins University, Baltimore, Nov. 1, 1946.

20. Stanley B. Williams and Ellwood King, The Effect of CRT Bias on Visibility of Targets on a Remote PPI. *Report No. 166-I-6,* Psychological Laboratory, The Johns Hopkins University, Baltimore, Dec. 10, 1946.
21. G. B. Thornton, Radar Range Performance as a Function of CRT Operating Conditions, *Report No. 163-3, Project No. D77-94-20-22 (H.R. No. 109),* Defence Research Medical Laboratories, Toronto, 1957.
22. J. S. Kidd, Maynard W. Shelly, Gabriel Jeantheau, and Paul M. Fitts, The Effect of Enroute Flow Control on Terminal System Performance: A Study in Human Engineering Aspects of Radar Air Traffic Control, *WADC Technical Report 57-663 (ASTIA Document No. AD 142096),* Wright Air Development Center, Air Research and Development Command, United States Air Force, Wright-Patterson Air Force Base, Ohio, Apr. 1958.
23. John Versace, The Effect of Emergencies and Communications Availability with Differing Entry Rates: A Study in Human Engineering Aspects of Radar Air Traffic Control, *WADC Technical Report 56-70 (ASTIA Document No. 118320),* Wright Air Development Center, Air Research and Development Command, United States Air Force, Wright-Patterson Air Force Base, Ohio, Dec. 1956.
24. M. W. Baldwin, Jr., and G. Nielsen, Jr., Subjective Sharpness of Simulated Color Television Pictures, *Journal of the Optical Society of America,* vol. 46, no. 9, Sept. 1956, pp. 681–685.

CHAPTER 9

IN SEARCH OF QUANTIFIABLE PARAMETERS OF GROUP PERFORMANCE

A. RAPOPORT

INTRODUCTION: THE ROLES OF "MODERN" AND "CLASSICAL" MATHEMATICS IN THE THEORY OF ORGANIZATION

Attempts to extend rigorous theoretical methods to the study of organized systems are beset with the well-known difficulties of creating appropriate mathematics. It is often maintained that classical mathematical analysis, created specifically to deal with continuous functional relations among a few magnitudes represented by real numbers, is not appropriate to deal with the complex set of relations which describe an organized system. The "modern" branches of mathematics, such as topology, set theory, and matrix algebra, are sometimes cited as being more suited as foundations of mathematical theories of organization. Let us see in what sense this may be so.

The application of some of these "modern" branches of mathematics to behavioral science has at times remained no more than a pious hope. Years ago Kurt Lewin[1] wrote about topological psychology, but, as far as I know, to this day no theorem of topology has been related to a psychological observation or even to a psychological hypothesis. On the other hand, Rashevsky[2] and his associates have been developing at least a new conceptualization of biological theory primarily based on topological or quasi-topological methods. Also, Harary and Norman[3] have pointed out the potential usefulness of graph theory to sociology and to social psychology. There is no doubt that the language of graph theory is well suited to the construction of abstract models of sociograms, communication networks, organizational charts, etc. Also, the theorems of graph theory (and their isomorphic counterparts in matrix theory) are useful for deducing the structural properties of such complexes. One can, for example, construct useful algorithms for detecting all the "cliques" of a social structure.[4] One can also determine critical nodes in communication nets, the degree of "balance" in a sociogram represented as a directed-sign graph,[5] etc.

All these mathematical techniques are useful if the underlying sociological and social-psychological concepts (cliques, degree of balance, etc.) are valid. The latter are indeed valid if theoretical assertions involving them have important observable correlates in behavioral science. The following are examples of such assertions, some or all of which may be false, but all of which are in principle verifiable.

1. The directed-sign graph representing the sociogram of a middle-sized intimate group (fraternity house, small firm, submarine crew) tends toward greater balance (in the sense of Heider-Cartwright-Harary) with time.

2. For a given volume of information flow and information-handling facilities, there exists an optimal net of channels with respect to certain criteria of performance.[6] The criteria and an operational definition of information flow in the given context are presumed given.

3. The ratio of the number of roles involved in intraorganizational activity to those involved in extraorganizational relations is a function of the size of the organization of a given kind, measured in a prescribed way.[7]

All these assertions have a familiar ring. They are of the type that dominate classical physical science—generalizations of the "if so . . . , then so" type of assertion made precise by quantifying the predicates. The language used for making and deducing such assertions is, be it noted, that of classical mathematics—calculus. What, then, is the role of "modern" discrete, relational, nonmetric mathematics in developing a science of organization? If in the last analysis rigorous theoretization of social phenomena is to be still in the form of mathematical functions of the classical type, and if the "bent stick" is still the picture of every rigorously described relation or time process, what is there new in all the "new" methods, hailed as more appropriate for theories of organization, namely matrices, set-theoretical and topological formulations, the convex bodies of game theory, and all the other departures from the type of thinking symbolized by $y = f(x)$?

I will now explain how I understand (and agree with) the statement that "modern" methods are better suited to deal with situations where "classical" methods fail and will go on to show how nevertheless the classical methods of quantitative correlation must still enter into the analysis at a certain stage.

The weakness of "classical" methods when applied to behavioral science, particularly to the study of organized systems, is not so much that these methods necessitate the isolation of a very few variables (mostly only a pair at a time). I do not think one can ever get away from such isolation if one is to do *any* sort of analysis (the protests of the "holists" notwithstanding). The weakness of classical methods is that these methods never cope with the problem of *determining* the important variables. The classical method does its work when the variables are *given*. Occasionally, an important parameter makes itself known as some mathematically determined invariant. For example, the energy and entropy changes in a system reveal themselves as "state variables" in the thermodynamic sense by being represented as certain line integrals independent of the path of integration. Here a mathematical invariance points to a physical "reality." Once this principle is recognized, one naturally hunts for other invariants, and a number have proved their conceptual usefulness, e.g., the Helmholtz work function, the enthalpy, etc. But by and large, theoretical physics could develop magnificently even when no new invariants were being discovered. Witness what has been done from 1650 to 1800 with mechanical conservation laws alone!

The drawback in the development of social physics is that fundamental variables and invariants do not lie around to be picked up and do not fall out of formal mathematical manipulations. In behavioral science, we have no Hamiltonians, no Lagrangians, no Christoffel-Riemann tensors, not to speak of the universal constants like Planck's, velocity of light *in vacuo*, etc. To the extent that social physicists have had to improvise, i.e., take any variables which may suggest themselves for setting up classical models and invent coefficients christened by units to satisfy the mathematical grammar of the models, to that extent their efforts may have been superficial.

In short, the classical models were and remain powerful tools for deducing relations among given variables, but they teach us little about picking or discovering variables to be related. Moreover, the very power of the method has seduced, I believe, a number of thinkers into picking or inventing variables in a hurry, in order to get on with applying the mathematical machinery.

The importance of the "new" methods in my opinion lies in the very area where the old methods have little or nothing to contribute. For example, if a network of relations in a social group can be schematized by a linear graph and if the mathematical properties of the graph are indeed abstractions of important social properties of the group, then the theory of linear graphs (not contained in classical mathematics) has suggested important variables to be singled out for attention. Here "new" mathematics has indeed done a service to social science. But if the social psychology of groups is to go beyond the purely descriptive phase, if more is to be done than classify groups by types, species, genera, what not, then these deep-seated variables uncovered by the new mathematics have to be related to something else— perhaps to the size of groups of the stresses to which the group is subjected or perhaps merely to the age of the group. Once this is established, we have again a simple quantitative relation, pictured by a curve, made precise by a function of a real variable. Again classical mathematics, which deals primarily with properties of curves, comes into its own.

As another example, consider the theory of games. There is hardly a formula in the whole theory. The theory predicts nothing. Many of its most important assertions are in the existential and not in the quantitative mode. The bulk of game theory is "anatomical." It describes, classifies, and deduces properties of certain systems of assumptions called games. It is more like the synthetic geometry of Euclid than the dynamic analytical mathematics of 1650–1850. I suspect this synthetic quality is what gives game theory its austere classical beauty.

Now game theory has been hailed as a major breakthrough in social science. In what sense can it be so considered? Can any theorems of game theory be translated into assertions of social science? I doubt it. The value of game theory is conceptual, not predictive. It offers no usable models of behavior aside from norma- tive ones, which are of no practical significance except in the simplest cases, because no game beyond the trivially simple ones can be com- pletely analyzed by a human mind, and game theory always assumes such analysis to have been carried out. But game theory does provide *concepts* with which to work. These concepts are the products of game theory. But they can be taken as the raw material of a behavioral theory to be developed in real contexts. I shall give an example later.

In summary, the main contribution of "modern" mathematical ideas, particularly those which have arisen around the *descriptions* of organized systems, has been, I think, in providing a new repertoire of concepts, which cannot have arisen in the context of "$y = f(x)$"

mathematics. Once the job of finding or inventing such new variables has been done, ordinary mathematical analysis can again take over and study the quantitative relations among these variables in the usual way.

PARAMETERS OF PERFORMANCE
IN SMALL GROUPS

We turn to our specific topic. What shall we study in the behavior of small task-oriented groups? Obviously we shall want generalizable concepts, such as will pertain to many different groups. In fact, we shall want to make assertions about these concepts considered as variables or parameters in functional relations. Our task therefore will contain the following steps:

1. Find or invent significant generalizable group variables.

2. Find empirically or deduce from a model the relations among such variables or between them and external conditions.

3. The mathematical description of these relations will contain constants, which, of course, will be constant only in a given situation. Such "constants," which vary from situation to situation, are called parameters. Interpret the parameters.

4. Find empirically or deduce from a model the relations among these parameters or between them and external conditions.

5. The mathematical description of these relations will again contain parameters. Proceed as before.

All the steps except the first are standard operating procedures of what is conventionally described as "scientific method." For example, if the phenomenon investigated were bodies falling down inclined planes, the first equation would establish the proportionality between the distance fallen and the square of the time elapsed. The "constant" of proportionality, however, would be not a universal constant but a parameter whose behavior would be investigated next. This parameter would then be found proportional to the sine of the angle of the plane's inclination—another equation with another constant of proportionality. The latter, being, as we now know, the acceleration of gravity, would again be a parameter, this time showing a complicated variation along the surface of the earth and in surrounding space.

We know that this method can be pushed "all the way," i.e., to the universal constant of gravitation, which in the framework of Newtonian theory is not further reducible. However, the general theory of relativity carries the process a step further, showing the constant of gravitation to be a consequence of fundamental properties of space-time, which is the "rock bottom" of *this* theoretical framework.

So far, I have not discussed the very first step in this scheme: the singling out of the variables. This, of course, is the difficult step—one whose success depends on unspecifiable ingenuity and probably on a great deal of luck. If that step fails, so will all the succeeding ones. Then all we can do is start over.

I shall pick two sets of concepts, both deriving from recent developments, one from information theory, the other from game theory. My choice of variables will be guided by these concepts. The supposed relations among the variables, once specifically hypothesized, will constitute a mathematical model. The constants of the model will be the parameters. The research strategy will be directed at constructing another mathematical model, in which the variables will be the parameters of the old model and the constants will be the new parameters. In the next section this program is carried out to the point where the parameters of the first model have been isolated and an empirical relation between them and imposed experimental conditions has been observed. Thus the groundwork is laid for the second model. In a following section, only an empirical investigation is described which, I hope, will lead to the formulation of the first model. Thus both investigations are in the early stages, although the first is somewhat more advanced than the second.

GROUP LEARNING TASK

The first set of concepts derived from information theory relates to the theory of organization in the following way. Suppose it is possible to quantify the amount of information to be absorbed by a three-person group in the process of learning a certain task. Suppose, moreover, that the task is so designed that in learning it the information to be absorbed can be apportioned among the members of the group but also must be properly collated in the performance. Suppose, further, that there are different ways of apportioning the information to be stored. At one extreme, every member of the trio will have learned the whole task. The job of integrating the information becomes unnecessary, since any individual can in this case perform the task independently of the others. The task can be performed without inner communication. At the other extreme, there is no overlap among the memory loads. Each member carries a minimum memory load, and thus there is the greatest dependence on inner communication to coordinate the performance. The intermediate cases, including the extremes, will be described by a single parameter—the overlap in the amounts learned, or, assuming equipartition of information absorbed, the parameter will be taken as $R = 3h - H^*$. Here h is the information absorbed by each individual and H^* is the total information in the task. Evidently R is a sort of redundancy measure. We shall designate $3h$ by H.

It remains to design a situation in which H and H^*, hence R, can be calculated from experimental data and where the possibility of apportioning the subtasks is not *immediately* obvious, otherwise the characteristics of organization will have too little variance under different conditions to serve as an interesting parameter.

In the task we have designed, the memory loads can be apportioned in a variety of ways, each leading to a different value of R if adopted from the beginning.

The other parameter, k, will be described in connection with the mathematical model itself.

The Task

The three members of the group sit in a triangular arrangement, each facing a pair of lights, as shown in Fig. 1. Below the lights is a lever which can be moved right or left toward either light. When released, the lever returns to the central position. The task is to extinguish the lights in any prescribed order. Relays are so arranged that the lights can be extinguished only in pairs as shown, whenever both subjects adjoining the pair move their levers toward each other. It follows that the three pairs of lights will be extinguished in one of six possible orders $(3! = 6)$. The assignment of a digit, called a "target number," to each of these six orders constitutes a problem. There are $6! = 720$ possible problems. The entire learning task is completed when the group has learned a prescribed number of problems, i.e., has learned to extinguish the lights in the correct order corresponding to every target number in all problems.

Since the knowledge of one problem provides no information regarding another, in which the assignment of the six target numbers to the six orders of extinguishing the lights is different, it follows that the information gained in the learning of successive problems is additive. Therefore, if we compute the amount of information in each problem, we can compute the amount in the entire task. Since the six target numbers can be assigned to the six orders in 720 ways, it follows that the amount of information per problem is $\log_2 720 = 9.5$ bits. Hence the task of learning each problem has 9.5 bits.[6]

If h is the average amount of information stored by each individual, the total amount stored by the group will be $H = 3h$. Then $R = H - (9.5)n$, where n is the number of problems. To calculate H, we make

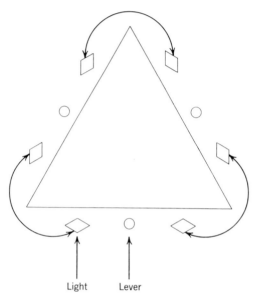

Light   Lever

FIG. 1. Schematic representation of the group learning experiment. Each connected pair of lights is extinguished when a pair of players move their levers toward those lights.

use of a theory developed elsewhere.[8] It has been shown that in many cases the cumulative error curve in a rote learning process is well described by the following equation

$$w = \frac{H}{k} - \frac{M}{k} \log_e [(e^{H/M} - 1)e^{-kt/M} + 1] \tag{1}$$

where w = cumulated number of errors at t stimulus presentations

t = number of stimulus presentations

M = number of different stimuli to which correct responses out of a certain repertoire are to be selected

H = total information stored in learning the task, measured in "nits" (natural bits), i.e., 1 nit = $\log_e 2$ bits

k = a constant (free parameter)

Equation 1 is derived from the following two assumptions:

1. The rate of gain of information (information stored) per error is constant: $dh/dw - k$. Hence k, the second group parameter to be examined, is to be interpreted as the rate of information storage per error by the group.*

2. The information gained is equally distributed over the different stimuli.

If all the repertoires of possible responses associated with each of the M stimuli are disjoint and equal, eq. 1 becomes identical with one derived by H. D. Landahl[9] from another set of assumptions involving a model of instrumental conditioning. Equation 1 is more general since it does not require, as Landahl's does, that the M repertoires of stimuli be disjoint and equal. Indeed, in our task all the M repertoires (the various orders in which the lever motions are to be performed) are identical.

Note now that the limit of w as $t \to \infty$ is $W = H/k$. Since W is the total number of errors made when the task has been learned completely, it is directly observable and moreover not very sensitive to fluctuations resulting from occasional accidental errors which persist even when the learning has been completed. We therefore read off the value of H/k directly from the data. To get H and k separately, we attempt to fit the theoretical curve given by eq. 1 to our observed cumulative error curve.

Elsewhere[8] it was proved that if $H/k = W$ is kept constant, then the predicted value of w increases monotonically with H (and k) as H (and therefore k) increases. Our theory, therefore, says that the observed values of w cannot fall below the theoretical curve given by eq. 1, calculated for $H = H^* = \log_e 2 (9.5) n$, since H^* is the *minimal* uncertainty inherent in the task itself. In general, the information gained in the learning process will exceed this minimal value, since redundant information will be inadvertently absorbed. We therefore take R, the excess of information stored by the group over the information inherent in the task, as one of the group parameters.

Distribution of Memory Loads

Let us now analyze our problem somewhat more closely from the point of view of the individual group member. A schematic representation of a target number is shown in Fig. 2.

* Actually this number is a little less, because the probabilities of guessing the assignment of target numbers in each successive problem are governed by "sampling without replacement." However, for a small number of problems, this makes little difference.

The entries in the grid represent the successive movements of the lever to the left or to the right. The production of the target number represented requires that first A and B move toward each other, then A and C, finally B and C. A glance at Fig. 2 will immediately make clear that all of the target numbers represented by the 3×3 grid will have two entries of opposite direction in each column.

Consider now what each individual has to learn to produce some target number. *All he has to know is whether to move to the right or to the left on his first move.* The remainder of the process is

	1	2	3
A	L	R	
B	R		L
C		L	R

FIG. 2. Time sequence of left and right moves which extinguishes the three pairs of lights in one of the six possible orders.

determined thereafter, for he must keep the lever in the position to which it was first moved until the light on that side goes out. Thereupon he moves the lever to the other side and keeps it there until the other light goes out (i.e., until his partner on that light joins him). The blank boxes in the grid indicate the moves when the position of the lever is immaterial.

From the symmetry of the situation it follows that in each problem there will be three target numbers for which a given player must move first to the right and three for which he must move to the left. If each problem is viewed in this way, all that has to be learned by each individual is which three target numbers require a left move. The rest follows by deduction, hence involves no uncertainty and so no information to be stored.

Let us calculate the amount of information per problem which must be stored if this is the system adopted. Three things can be selected from six in $\binom{6}{3} = 20$ different ways. Hence the amount of information to be gained by each group member is $\log_2 20 = 4.3$ bits per problem. The group will therefore have gained $3 \times 4.3 = 12.9$ bits of which $12.9 - 9.5 = 3.4$ bits are redundant, i.e., $R = 8 \times 3.4 = 27.2$ bits.

Now let us look at another system of apportioning memory loads. Note that, in the target number pictured in Fig. 2, A and only A moves the lever on the first two moves. The situation is similar with every target number. Each member has two target numbers on which he works the lever on the first two moves. He is the "kingpin" for those two numbers. Suppose the memory load is divided on that basis. Each member remembers the two target numbers in each problem where he is the "kingpin." In addition, however, he must remember the direction in which he goes on one of them (the direction on which he must go on the other is thereby determined). Two things can be selected from six in $\binom{6}{2} = 15$ different ways. Hence the amount of information to be gained by each group member will be $(\log_2 15) + 1 = 4.91$ bits. (The extra bit represents the choice of direction for one of the two target numbers.) In this case, the total redundancy will be $8(3 \times 4.91 - 9.5) = 41.84$ bits.

We note further that each member by his own moves reveals the particular permutation of the six target numbers which constitutes the problem. Therefore, to the outside observer each single player communicates by his moves the entire information contained in a problem. If he stores only a part of the total information, where does the rest of the information come from? Obviously it is *communicated* to the member by the other members either verbally or through the apparatus. For example, if the first method described of apportioning memory loads is used, each member must know that one of his lights is extinguished before he moves the lever toward the other. If he watches the lights, he gets this information via the apparatus (i.e., the fact that his partner has moved is conveyed to him through the light). But the lights are not actually necessary for the performance. In another series of experiments described elsewhere,[10] the subjects did not see the lights at all and signaled to each other to coordinate their motions.

If the second method of apportioning information loads is used, the "kingpin" must indicate who his partner is on his first move, since the others do not learn their motions for the target numbers on which they are not "kingpins." Whatever the method, the information not stored by each member must be communicated to him by other members who have stored it. This is why we say that the less the overlap in information loads, the greater the dependence on inner communication.

Results

The data we are about to discuss are taken from experiments on three-person groups learning to produce the coordinated motions in response to the target numbers as command signals. Each group learned eight problems under the following schedule. Each target number was called out three times in succession regardless of whether the correct sequence was produced for that target number or not. After each response, the subjects were told whether the sequence they produced was correct or not. Thus learning could proceed only by elimination of incorrect sequences.

The responses to the three consecutive commands of the same target number were labeled a, b, and c, respectively. For the purposes of the present analysis only the a responses are relevant. (The number of times the same target number is called in succession determines essentially the amount of feedback the group receives in the learning process, hence is directly related to the parameter k.) After the six target numbers of the first problem have been called out, problem no. 2 is presented regardless of the progress made on problem no. 1. So the eight problems are run through. Then problem no. 1 is presented once more and so on around. A cycle of eight problems takes about 45 minutes to run through; hence about eight cycles are completed in an experimental run of six hours. If the group makes any progress at all, they are usually able to learn the eight problems in six hours. Under conditions of fatigue (to be discussed below) often hardly any progress is made, and so the slope of the cumulative error curve remains approximately constant.

When learning is successful, the cumulative error curve reaches an asymptote and the parameters k and R can be approximately determined. In the experiment from which our data were taken, we were interested in the possible effects of sleep deprivation on these parameters. Accordingly, our experimental groups were kept without sleep for 32 hours. In this period they performed various tasks so scheduled that some groups performed the learning task during the first, second, third, and fourth eight-hour period respectively. In what follows, we will compare the average cumulative error curves of three groups performing in the first eight-hour period and of two groups performing in the fourth. In plotting our theoretical curves, we shall use two values of H, namely, 52.7 nits (= 76 bits) and 74.5 nits (= 108 bits). As we have shown in our theoretical discussion, the first value obtains if there is no overlap in the memory loads; the second value obtains if an overlap results from the "kingpin"

TABLE 1. COMPARISON OF THEORETICAL AND OBSERVED
CUMULATED ERROR CURVES AVERAGED OVER THREE
GROUPS PERFORMING FROM 4 TO 12 P.M. IN THE FIRST
EIGHT HOURS OF A 32-HOUR SLEEP DEPRIVATION PERIOD

Cycle	Theory: $H = 52.7$ $k = 0.57$	Observed Cumulated Errors	Theory: $H = 74.5$ $k = 0.81$
1	29	31	34
2	51	56	59
3	66	74	75
4	77	80	84
5	83	83	88
6	87	87	90
7	90	91	91
8	91	92	92

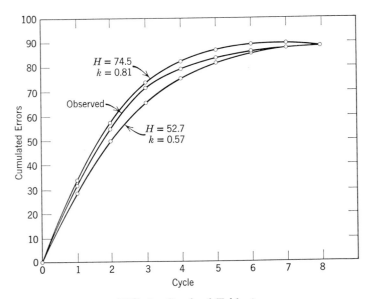

FIG. 3. Graph of Table 1.

method of apportioning the memory loads. Thus we do not treat H
as a free parameter but calculate it theoretically.

The parameter k remains a free parameter and is calculated from
$kW = H$, where W is the observed total number of errors. The
results are shown in Tables 1 and 2 and in Figs. 3 and 4.

As is apparent, the experimental values of W are bracketed between

TABLE 2. COMPARISON OF THEORETICAL AND OBSERVED
CUMULATED ERROR CURVES AVERAGED OVER TWO GROUPS
PERFORMING FROM 4 TO 12 P.M. IN THE LAST EIGHT HOURS
OF A 32-HOUR SLEEP DEPRIVATION PERIOD

Cycle	Theory: $H = 52.7$ $k = 0.4$	Observed Cumulated Errors	Theory: $H = 74.5$ $k = 0.635$
1	33	33	35
2	56	58	66
3	77	83	88
4	92	101	105
5	104	116	116
6	113	126	123
7	119	131	127
8	124	133	130

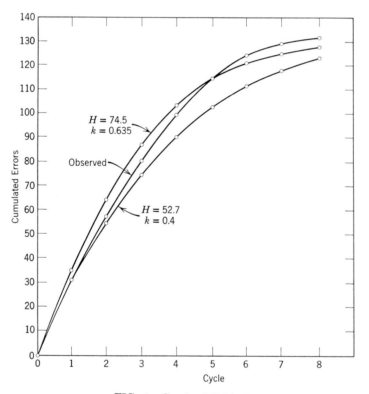

FIG. 4. Graph of Table 2.

the two theoretical curves in both cases. Comparing the performance under the two conditions, we see that k (the rate of information storage) becomes smaller after 24–32 hours of sleep deprivation by a factor of about 0.7. The "efficiency" of apportionment remains approximately the same unless one chooses to interpret the data as indicating that the overlap gradually increases in the sleepless condition (the experimental points switch from the lower curve to the upper), possibly as a consequence of less efficient intragroup communication.

Needless to say, these preliminary results are shown only to illustrate the method, not to establish any definitive conclusions.

CHOICE OF COOPERATIVE AND COMPETITIVE ACTS

Groups and organizations may be classified by the extent to which their internal structure or relations to the outside world predispose the members of the group to cooperate with each other. Conceivably the situation may be such that only cooperative acts are advantageous to every group member. An idealized team playing against an opponent finds itself in such a situation, if we assume that no jealousies or rivalries exist among the individual team members. The rewards for correctly chosen and correctly coordinated acts accrue to the team as a whole. If these rewards are shared equally (or in constant ratios) among the members, it follows that the interests of all the members are identical and also identical to the interest of the whole group. Such groups have been called "teams."[11]

A weaker form of cooperation obtains if the interests of the members do not necessarily coincide with the interests of the group as a whole, it being understood, however, that the interest of the group is still clearly identifiable and taken into account by the group members. For example, if in scoring a basketball game the team is rewarded for victory, but the reward is divided among the members in proportion to the baskets scored by each, there may be a conflict of interest between the individual member and the group. For conceivably the individuals may compete for an opportunity to shoot for the basket, and such competition may adversely affect the total score made by the group. Such groups have been called "foundations."*

* Presumably the members of a foundation identify with the aims of that organization, but may nevertheless have their own aims not coincident with those of the foundation.

In some groups, there may be no identifiable group interest. Suppose, for example, the basketball players were paid only in proportion to the baskets they scored individually with no extra bonus for winning the game. Here there is no group interest as such ("glory" is not counted here). However, it may still serve the players well to cooperate in the game so as to increase the chances for individual scoring. Similarly, if labor and management cooperate solely in view of their separate interests without regard to the possible interests of the industry as a whole or of the nation, we have a situation of this kind. Groups in such situations have been called "coalitions."

Finally, there are situations where cooperation among the individual members may be pointless. Such groups in which every individual necessarily acts only in his own interest have been called players of a "game."

The mathematical theory of games, in which similar situations are treated, uses somewhat similar classifications of N-person games. A team is an N-person game in which the grand coalition of all players has formed. A game where every man plays strictly for himself is either a game with no coalition allowed or a game in which coalitions are to no one's advantage (so-called inessential games). Foundations and coalitions of Marschak's classification which have just been described[12] correspond to the "essential" games of game theory. These, in turn, can be differentiated according to whether the payoff utilities are or are not transferable, conservative, etc.

Interesting situations arise in the theory of nonzero sum games in which coalitions would be clearly advantageous but where facilities for forming coalitions (negotiation, bargaining, etc.) do not exist. Such a situation underlies the experiments to be described next.

The Three-Person Prisoner's Dilemma Games

A type of nonzero two-person game, known in the literature as the Prisoner's Dilemma, is illustrated in the following payoff matrix:

$$
\begin{array}{c}
 \\
a_1 \\
a_2
\end{array}
\begin{array}{cc}
b_1 & b_2 \\
\left[\begin{array}{cc}
5,\,5 & -10,\,10 \\
10,\,-10 & 5,\,-5
\end{array}\right]
\end{array}
$$

In the pair of strategy choices (a_1, b_1) each player helps the other to win a positive payoff, and the sum of the payoffs is maximum. If we label this pair of choices the cooperative choice, we see that each player is tempted to defect from this choice since if he defects (alone) his payoff is increased. This prospect is somewhat illusory, because if both players defect both are punished (hence the dilemma). This two-person game can therefore be characterized as follows: "One defector is rewarded; two are punished."

Three-person games of this sort can be of several kinds. For example, using similar characterizations:

Type 1. One defector is rewarded; two are rewarded.
Type 2. One defector is rewarded; two are punished.
Type 3. One defector is punished; two are rewarded.

In all cases at least one case of defection must be rewarded, and all three defectors must, of course, be punished, to preserve the chief feature of the "dilemma."

There is, however, another interesting class of games in which unanimous "defection," like unanimous cooperation, is rewarded. Clearly, we do not speak of defection in this case. Instead, we have a situation in which any unanimous choice is rewarded; the problem for the group is to decide (in the absence of communication) *which* choice to agree upon. The treatment of this problem is discussed by T. C. Schelling.[13]

In our experiment, we have included one example of such a game, namely game IV to be described below. We add, therefore:

Type 4. One defector is punished; two defectors are punished; three defectors are rewarded.

The variety of games can be further increased by the distinction between games in which the non-cooperative solution is or is not a Nash point, i.e., whether in departing (alone) from the non-cooperative choice a player stands to lose. Games where this is the case are labeled by N. The payoff matrix of the eight games included in our experiment and their designations by type are shown in Table 3.

The Experiment

The subjects were partitioned from each other and forbidden to communicate during the run. In a preliminary orientation session, they were told how their collective choices to press one or the other of two buttons (right or left) affected all three payoffs in each of the eight games. Each had the entire payoff chart in front of him, which he could study for a half hour during the orientation session and the "dry runs."

In the experimental run, the number of the game to be played appeared on a display board visible to all. The subjects were given six seconds to make their choice. When all three buttons were pushed, the payoffs to all the players appeared on the display board and their

TABLE 3. TYPES OF GAMES AND THEIR PAYOFF MATRICES

If players A, B, and C each choose the right or the left button as shown in the first column, the respective payoffs will be as shown in the remaining columns

A B C	Game I Type 1N			Game II Type 2			Game III Type 3N			Game IV Noncompetitive			Game V Type 1			Game VI Type 2			Game VII Type 3N			Game VIII Type 2		
	A	B	C	A	B	C	A	B	C	A	B	C	A	B	C	A	B	C	A	B	C	A	B	C
R R R	-1	-1	-1	1	1	1	-1	-1	-1	1	1	1	1	1	1	-2	-2	-2	1	1	1	-2	-2	3
R R L	2	2	-2	-2	-2	6	2	2	-2	0	0	-1	-1	-1	3	-1	-1	1	1	1	-1	1	1	1
R L R	2	-2	2	-2	6	-2	2	-2	2	0	-1	0	-1	3	-1	-1	1	-1	1	-1	1	1	-2	-2
R L L	3	-2	-2	1	-2	-2	-2	1	1	-1	0	0	-1	2	2	6	-1	-1	-3	3	3	-2	3	-2
L L L	1	1	1	-1	-1	-1	1	1	1	1	1	1	-2	-2	-2	1	1	1	-2	-2	-2	-2	-2	1
L L R	-2	-2	3	-2	-2	1	1	1	-2	0	0	-1	2	2	-1	-1	-1	6	3	3	-3	-1	-1	-1
L R L	-2	3	-2	-2	1	-2	1	-2	1	0	-1	0	2	-1	2	-1	6	-1	3	-3	3	3	-2	-2
L R R	-2	2	2	6	-2	-2	-2	2	2	-1	0	0	3	-1	-1	1	-1	-1	-1	1	1	-2	1	-2

winnings or losses were added to the respective cumulative scores, also visible to all three. The scores were convertible to money at a mill per point.

In each experiment, each of the eight games was played 150 times, 1200 plays in all (about six hours). The games were presented in "shuffled" order, according to a random number schedule, somewhat modified to equalize the total frequencies of each of the eight games.

In one run (group 18), communication was disallowed throughout the entire run. In each of the other 17 runs, communication was allowed during the break, which occurred usually after about 400 responses. Although no mention was made of possible "negotiations," the groups came to a coalition agreement in almost all of the runs where communication was allowed. Thereafter cooperative choices were made almost exclusively except for occasional "chiseling" moves, which, as a rule, were taken as playful deviations, so that the coalition did not break up contrary to possible expectation. Some variants in agreements were noted. For example, in games II and VI, where the *total* payoff could be increased if one of the players defected, sometimes an agreement was made for each player to defect in turn in those games. Sometimes certain games were specifically set aside as not subject to the agreement (to keep some of the competitive zest). At other times coalitions were to be in force only until the members were "ahead" in winnings, after which competitive playing could start again.

In group 18 where no communication was allowed, the grand coalition became operative in only two games, namely games III and IV. This result will be discussed later.

Results

We shall first examine a very rough measure, namely, the per cent of individual cooperative choices in each of the seven competitive games, i.e., barring game IV. Table 4 shows the results. The average is 40% of cooperative responses throughout the session. Since 50% would be expected from entirely random responses, we must see whether the scatter is not due simply to random fluctuations.*

Taking three other groups at random, we examine the corresponding rank orders from least to most cooperation. The results are shown in Table 5. The rank order is seen to be approximately preserved. In fact, only game VII is in an anomalous position in group 18. The ranks of the other games show very small variance.

* No rigorous statistical analysis is undertaken here. I shall merely estimate the possible significance of the results by inspection and comparison.

TABLE 4.   THE RANKS OF THE GAMES
IN GROUP 18

Game	Per Cent Individual Cooperative Choices
I	15
VII	28
V	32
VI	44
II	45
VIII	50
III	75

TABLE 5.   THE RANKS OF THE GAMES (THE
LEAST COOPERATIVE GAME RANKS 1) IN FOUR
EXPERIMENTAL GROUPS

		Group			
		2	3	5	18
	1	V	I	I	I
	2	I	V	V	VII
	3	VI	VI	VI	V
Rank	4	II	II	II	VI
	5	VIII	VII	VIII	II
	6	III	III	VII	VIII
	7	VII	VIII	III	III

The average ranks and standard deviations of rank (for comparison) are shown in Table 6. From the small variances in rank, except

TABLE 6.   AVERAGE RANKS AND STANDARD
DEVIATIONS

Game	Average Rank	Standard Deviation
I	1.25	0.43
V	2.00	0.71
VI	3.25	0.43
II	4.25	0.43
VII	5.00	1.80
VIII	6.50	0.50
III	6.50	0.50

in game VII, we can tentatively conclude that the induced disposition for cooperative response is different in the different games. This disposition can be attributed to several criteria. Here I shall mention only two.

Criterion 1 (expected payoffs). If each player views each game as a choice between two simple gambles, each with four equiprobable outcomes (associated with the four possibilities of what the other two players may do), then each of the two choices has associated with it an expected payoff. If now the player compares the advantage of defection in terms of the excess of the expected payoff for defection over that of cooperation, we have the results shown in Table 7. The agreement with experimental results shown in Table 7 is quite good, although the positions of games VI and VII are interchanged.

TABLE 7.   RESULTS OF RANK-ORDERING
FOR CRITERION 1

Game	Advantage of Defection over Cooperation in Expected Payoff
I	11
V	9
II, VII	3
VI	0.5
III, VIII	0

Criterion 2 (advantage over the others). In defecting from the cooperative choice, the player does not know whether other players will also defect. Suppose he computes the advantage (the difference of payoffs) over the *nondefecting* player(s) averaged over the two possibilities, namely that either no other player defects or that one other player defects. (If both other players defect, there is no advantage, since in that case all three payoffs are equal.) The results of rank-ordering the games according to this criterion are shown in Table 8. Comparing this rank order with the experimentally observed average rank order of Table 6, we see that the agreement is practically perfect.

Clearly, many other criteria can be tried and compared. Moreover, the comparisons need not be between rank orders. At some point in the development of the theory, a "metric" should be introduced so that the actual frequencies of cooperative choices are theoretically related to certain numerical criteria characterizing the games. Once such numerical relations are established, we shall have the parameters

TABLE 8.   RESULTS OF RANK-ORDERING
FOR CRITERION 2

Game	Average Advantage over Nondefecting Players
I	4.5
V	3.5
II, VI	2.5
VII	2.0
VIII	1.0
III	0.5

of our model and shall be ready for the next step, i.e., the design of experiments where these parameters will themselves enter as dependent variables related to experimental conditions.

It is also evident that the foregoing examples serve to illustrate a natural extension of decision experiments (in risky choice situations) to genuine game situations in the attempt to chart consistent bases for decisions. In ordinary decision theory these bases are predominantly utilities of the scores and subjective probabilities. In game situations the projected *comparisons* of scores and the projected decisions of the opponent(s) may also play an important part. So far, however, we have been able to explain the results (confined to the rank order of games on the non-cooperative-comparative scale) in terms of simple expectations of absolute and relative advantage respectively. It is not expected that these simple criteria will continue to serve as well when more precise predictions are required.

We turn to the time course of frequency of cooperative choices in our six-hour run. Figure 5 shows the grand average of the frequency (per cent) of individual cooperative choices as a function of time, where the run is divided into six periods of 200 responses each.

As is apparent, the incidence of cooperative choices starts at slightly less than chance expectation and then *steadily declines*. Toward the end, however, cooperation picks up enough to recover the lost ground.

One might suspect that the latter effect may be due simply to the introduction of random responses toward the end of the run. But the high incidence of *unanimously* cooperative responses in the last period (21% compared with an expected 12.5%, indeed with an expected 9% on the basis of individual incidence of 45%) is evidence against this conclusion. Moreover, the break-up of the curve shown in Fig. 5 into seven separate curves for the seven competitive games provides additional evidence against randomization of responses. These curves are shown in Figs. 6, 7, and 8. We see that the games remain highly differentiated in the last period with regard to the frequency of cooperative responses. Indeed, the rank order of the games is the same in the last period as it is for the entire run. Randomization of responses would have tended to obliterate this differentiation.

The time course pattern in games I, II, V, VI, and VIII is about the same as for the grand average. One exception is game III, in

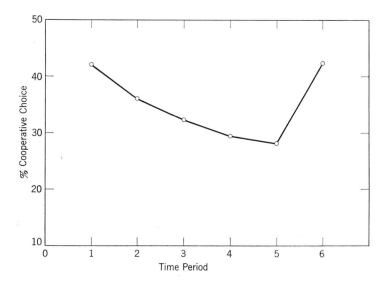

FIG. 5. Time course of frequency of cooperative choices averaged over the three individuals and over the seven competitive games.

which almost total cooperation is achieved in the fourth period and in the last. The dip in the fifth period remains unexplained, but will be discussed later. Another exception is game VII, which fails to "recover" at the end. Thus the source of the abnormally low standing of this game on the cooperative scale is found but still not explained.

We now look at the three individuals separately. Their cooperation curves are shown together in Fig. 9. Except for the slight humps in A's and B's curves the picture is the same as in the combined curve, namely a steady decline in the first four or five periods, followed by a "recovery."

Further examination of the individual curves, plotted separately for the seven games (not shown here), reveals nothing of further interest, except that the dip suffered in game III occurs in *all three individuals* and cannot therefore be attributed to the persistent failure

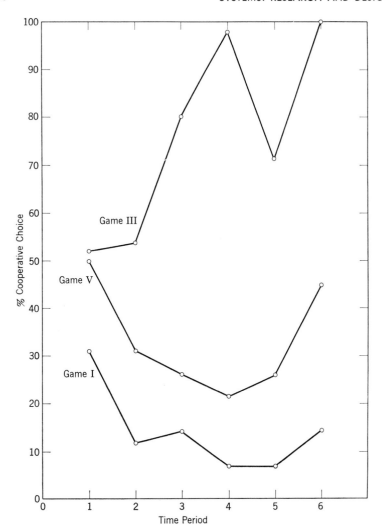

FIG. 6.   Time course of frequency of cooperative choices in games I, III, and V.

of *one* individual to abide by the tacit agreement to cooperate, which seems to have been reached in this game.

Finally, we turn to the noncompetitive game IV. Here there is no advantage in defection. The problem is to come to a tacit unanimous agreement in the absence of communication as to which button to push, right or left. The plot of the percentage of unanimous agreement on the *right* button (which was the one finally fixated) is given in Fig. 10.

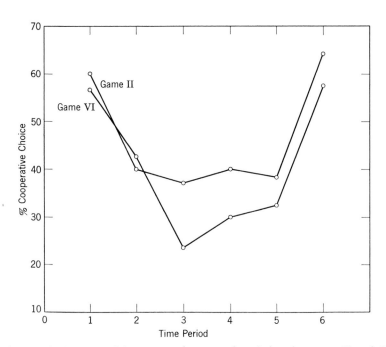

FIG. 7. Time course of frequency of cooperative choices in games II and VI.

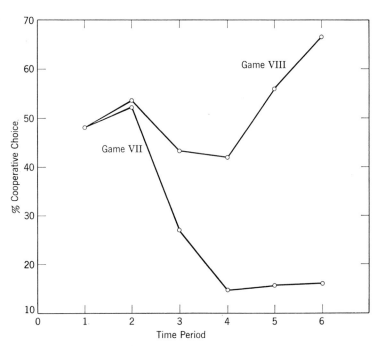

FIG. 8. Time course of frequency of cooperative choices in games VII and VIII.

The dip in period 3 is due entirely to A's persistence in pushing the left button, which, as is evident, was finally "overcome." In other groups it was noted that convergence of all three players on either the left or the right button always occurred, mostly quite early. This is to say, where no temptation of competitive advantage disturbs the tacit process of agreement, it does inevitably occur.

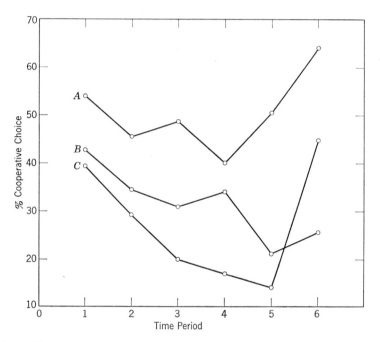

FIG. 9. Time course of frequency of cooperative choices of players A, B, and C.

These still rather rough observations lead us to the following conclusions on the behavior of three-person groups in prolonged runs of nonzero games in randomized order.

1. There may be an initial "reservoir of good will" reflected in a fairly high initial incidence of cooperative choices. This finding, however, must await further confirmation. The nearly 50% initial incidence of cooperation may well reflect the initial unfamiliarity with the structures of the several games.

2. At first the incidence of cooperative choices declines.

3. Later the incidence of cooperative choices rises, sometimes quite sharply.

4. The games are differentiated according to certain criteria of *apparent* advantage of non-cooperation over cooperation.

5. Where no competitive advantage exists, tacit agreement on a particular (a priori arbitrary) cooperative choice is reached.

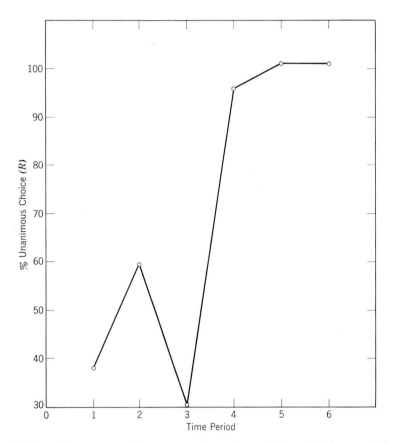

FIG. 10. Time course of frequency of unanimous choices (R) in game IV.

These results are in partial agreement and at partial variance with results obtained from experiments with two-person nonzero sum games of similar types.[14] The general findings are such that tacit cooperation occurs more frequently in the three-person game of prolonged run. The fact that cooperation picks up only at the end suggests that previous experiments may not have been carried out far enough for the players to learn (by bitter experience) to cooperate.

PROJECTED EXTENSIONS

We have examined a scheme for studying group learning and another scheme for studying distributions of cooperative and competitive acts in a small group. We have seen that the disposition to act cooperatively is a function both of the situation as viewed by the group members (e.g., the game played) and of time. Typically, in most of the games studied and in all individuals, the disposition to act cooperatively at first declines and later increases. It is natural to suppose that these over-all trends are the results of the group's experience, i.e., are a learning phenomenon. We have, in fact, a classical learning situation: a choice of two acts, each of which is either punished or rewarded in each instance.

Note, however, two important special features of the situation.

1. The probability that one or the other choice is rewarded (or punished) does not remain constant.

2. Each response can be viewed by a group member as both a *choice,* which is *subject* to reward or punishment and an *act* which is *itself* an act of rewarding or punishing others. Thus, in a sense, rewards and punishments are not being meted out to the group from the outside, but by the group members themselves. In particular, it becomes quite apparent to the members that the group as a whole (and all its members) could be riding high all the time if only "the group wanted to."

What will be the characteristics of learning under these conditions? We have in experiments, such as those described, an opportunity of combining the study of group learning with group cooperation, in particular an opportunity to study how a group learns to cooperate, if it does.

In evaluating the data, we must adopt some method of grouping the choices and the outcomes. We have been talking about cooperative and competitive choices of the group members and have assumed that positive payoffs are viewed as rewards and negative ones as punishments. Although the latter assumption is reasonable, the former is anything but compelling. Suppose the classification of "cooperative" or "competitive" choice does not enter the subject's mind at all; for example, suppose he views the two buttons simply as "right" and "left." Then any learning that he exhibits must be viewed as learning to associate "right" and "left" with probabilistically scheduled rewards and punishments. There is nothing in the data that prevents one from assuming such an interpretation by a group member. Our purpose, however, is to make a virtue out of a difficulty. We can make *both* assumptions in turn, namely that the subject views the buttons as "right" and "left" and that he views them as a choice of cooperation or defection. Examining the reward and punishment schedules impinging on that subject with respect to his *right* and *left* choices and then the reward and punishment schedules associated with his cooperative and defecting choices, we can see which interpretation exhibits "learning" more clearly.

To take an example, divide all the cooperative choices of a given member into two classes, those that have resulted in a positive payoff and those that have resulted in a negative payoff. Compare the frequency of cooperative choice following a cooperative choice which has been rewarded with the frequency of a cooperative choice following a cooperative choice that has been punished. The difference, if any, measures the relative "strengths" of the two induced conclusions, "It pays to cooperate" and "It does not pay to cooperate." If a steady state is approached, it can well be the result of a Markov process. If we name four states, (a) cooperation rewarded, (b) cooperation punished, (c) defection rewarded, and (d) defection punished, we can obtain from the data the transition probabilities between the states which are, to be sure, not constant, but functions of time.

The analysis could proceed by comparing the stochastic processes resulting from different definitions of "state." In the example just cited, we have taken four particular states. But we can just as easily take other sets, e.g., "right button rewarded," "right button punished," etc.; or, broken down by games, "cooperative choice in game I rewarded"; or taking pairs of successive states as single states, etc. Nor do we need to adhere to our individualistic definition of reward and punishment. It is conceivable that the individual evaluates the entire outcome as punishing or rewarding or differentiates degrees of punishment or reward.

Proceeding in this way, we can get a set of transition probabilities either over an entire run or in successive time periods among any of a set of states we wish to examine. Comparing the resulting stochastic processes, we can judge what the group members learn individually or collectively. In this way, I hope eventually to combine the two aspects of group behavior, which I have singled out for intensive study, namely group learning and cooperation.

REFERENCES

1. K. Lewin, *Principles of Topological Psychology*, McGraw-Hill Book Co., New York, 1946.
2. N. Rashevsky, Topology and Life: In Search of General Mathematical Principles in Biology and Sociology, *Bulletin of Mathematical Biophysics*, vol. 16, 1954, pp. 317–348.
3. F. Harary and R. Z. Norman, *Graph Theory as a Mathematical Model in Social Science*, Institute of Social Research, Ann Arbor, 1953.
4. R. D. Luce, Connectively and Generalized Cliques in Sociometric Group Structures, *Psychometrika*, vol. 15, 1950, pp. 169–190.
5. D. Cartwright and F. Harary, Structural Balance: A Generalization of Heider's Theory, *Psychological Reviews*, vol. 63, 1956, pp. 277–293.
6. A. Bavelas, A Mathematical Model for Group Structures, *Applied Anthropology*, vol. 7, 1948, pp. 16–30.
7. M. Haire, Biological Models and Empirical Histories of the Growth of Organizations, Chap. 10 in *Modern Organization Theory*, edited by Mason Haire, John Wiley & Sons, New York, 1959.
8. A. Rapoport, A Derivation of a Rote Learning Curve from the Total Uncertainty of a Task, *Bulletin of Mathematical Biophysics*, vol. 22, 1960, pp. 85–97.
9. H. D. Landahl, Studies in the Mathematical Biophysics of Discrimination and Conditioning II: Special case: Errors, Trials, and Number of Possible Responses, *Bulletin of Mathematical Biophysics*, vol. 3, 1941, pp. 71–77.
10. A. Rapoport, A Research Study for the Development of Measurements of Group Stress Tolerance, *Report No. 7*, Part II, Mental Health Research Institute, Ann Arbor, 1960.
11. J. Marschak, Elements for a Theory of Teams, *Management Science*, vol. 1, 1955, pp. 127–137.
12. J. Marschak, "Towards an Economic Theory of Organization and Information," Chap. XIV in *Decision Processes*, edited by R. M. Thrall, C. H. Coombs, and R. L. Davis, John Wiley & Sons, New York, 1954.
13. T. C. Schelling, Bargaining, Communication, and Limited War, *Conflict Resolution*, vol. 1, 1957, pp. 19–36.
14. A. Scodel, J. S. Minas, P. Ratoosh, and M. Lipetz, Some Descriptive Aspects of Two-Person Non-Zero-Sum Games, *Conflict Resolution*, vol. 3, 1959, pp. 114–119.

CHAPTER 10

EVOLUTIONARY DESIGN OF COMPLEX SYSTEMS

J. M. SALZER

AS SYSTEMS GROW

In the broad sense, large systems have existed for a very long time. Extensive industrial operations have always posed difficult problems in organization, information flow, and control. The control of air traffic has—for some time—required a nation-wide, coordinated system of navigation and scheduling. The command and deployment of military forces has been a most complex operation in logistics and planning for many a war.

Recently, important changes have occurred which put a new light on our whole approach to the requirements, designs, and solutions to systems problems. These changes are primarily technological, but they influence systems concepts in several different ways.

For one, technological advances have increased the tempo of our life to such an extent that problems of entirely new orders of magnitude have been created. In business, rapid changes in market conditions over broad geographic areas must be evaluated posthaste to achieve appropriate production and business planning. In aviation, both the number and the speed of aircraft continue to increase to formidable proportions. The modern weapons of mass destruction and the frightening speed of their delivery require that both over-all and detailed military decisions be reached in far shorter time than was tolerable in the last war.

Although our technology can be blamed for many of our problems, it is also technology that comes to our rescue in providing us with more advanced tools to deal with the situation. For example, we have devised improved ways of linking remote segments of a complex system, evaluating and correlating the various facets of its operation, and providing the human operator of the systems with better data earlier and in improved form. The impetus for adding these capa-

197

bilities is our dissatisfaction with systems where such methods are not utilized but could be of advantage. These refinements, however, increase system complexity and the dynamic interrelationships of various parts of the system. The result is the proverbial vicious circle.

Technology also provides new analytical and theoretical techniques which have an effect on the solution of systems problems, i.e., similar to the "vicious circle" effect of technology on implementation techniques. Our analytical capability rests on improved methods in game theory, linear programming, transportation analysis, information theory, etc. Automatic aids and computers make these tools even more powerful to further increase our appetite and capacity for new problems.

The net effect of these technological advances and influences are numerous and not yet fully understood. Only two cardinal factors will be recognized here, as they have the most to do with the topic at hand. They are: (1) the degree of interrelationship between elements of a system, and (2) the degree and pacing of changes which a system must accommodate.

AS SYSTEMS RELATE

The word "system" itself has long been controversial. It is used in many contexts; it is defined and redefined; and although it is avoided by some, it has never been replaced. For the sake of this portion of the discussion, however, let us replace the word "system" by "subsystem." Such a substitution does not solve the problem, but it serves to stress that any system is part of a bigger one which in turn is part of a bigger one, etc. As a matter of discipline we should probably think of every system as a subsystem, and during the design of a subsystem we should force ourselves to think of its relationship to some bigger subsystem of which it is a part. In this larger framework our design formulations will progress in a manner more fully satisfying the interrelationships not only within the subsystem being designed but also between it and the other related subsystems.

The problem of interrelationship is very often referred to as the interface problem. Since boundaries of systems and subsystems are seldom sharply defined, the separations are not easily made and should be the subject of continuous re-examination. The boundaries between subsystems can be defined on the basis of various considerations, such as functions, equipment, and organization, but the boundaries satisfying one aspect in an optimum fashion may not do so for the others. For example, message collection and weather reporting are separate functions in a military command system, but it may be practical for them to use the same communication links and data-processing center so that the equipment boundaries are not identical. Similarly, it may not be practical to break down the organizational structure of the command post along exactly the same functional lines. Interface problems are compounded by the strong interaction of human and machine components of intellectronic systems and therefore require compromises for their solution. Interfaces also change as the organization changes, as the functions are redefined, and as the equipment implementation progresses.

AS SYSTEMS EVOLVE

The "subsystem" viewpoint I have discussed aids the system designer in understanding and even anticipating some of the changes that seem to beset system specifications. The reasons for these changes are often detectable in the bigger picture. But there are many other changes to cope with. For one, the development of a complex system can take several years even when the equipments used are largely off the shelf. During this time, changes can occur in requirements, in better understanding of the over-all problem, in new developments of equipment, in the organizational setup, in the philosophy and implementation of related subsystems, and in the attitude and co-operation of the customer. And so the system evolves!

When this evolution is gradual, we can meet the problems as they arise and, without too much regard to possible future changes, arrive at satisfactory system operation at all times. It is particularly easy to adapt a manual or semimanual system, since the time spent and the costs incurred are due mainly to the familiarization and training of personnel. It is also true in such cases that often the procedure or system which is being modified has relatively little effect on the operation of other parts of the organization. For example, a manual production control system can be revamped in great detail without requiring the revamping of the inventory control system used in the same organization.

As changes become more rapid and profound, planning and estimating become important system functions. Fortunately, the changes are predictable to some extent. For example, we can anticipate to a certain degree the military threat in 1970 by estimating the general nature and quantities of weapons the enemy might possess. Industry may not know in detail the type of computers it might be able to use five years from now, but it can have a good feel for the nature and cost of data-processing capabilities that might be available and required at that time. The design of the present system must progress in full view of these plans, which may be constantly modified as time progresses.

The degree of automation now being incorporated into systems and planned for future systems makes the interrelationships between parts of a system and between itself and other systems quite critical. It is becoming more difficult to make changes in one part of the system without re-examining the operation of the rest of the system or of other systems and to institute changes in them as well.

The problems of changes are further compounded by the fact that the whole industry and military is going through a massive educational process in the manner of using modern automatic means in systems operations, especially information-handling devices. Thus, the introduction of automation for a particular purpose often establishes the basis for an organization to educate itself in the general potential and utility of modern intellectronic techniques. As a result, new applications are created or found within the organization so that the total system application grows, diversifies, and leads to additional and new requirements. The self-sustaining character of this cycle is apparent and further illustrates why systems are in a constant evolutionary state.

AS THE DESIGN EVOLVES

Even when we assume that the final systems specifications are completely firm and not subject to change, the implementation of a complex and far-flung system could proceed in various different ways.[1]

In the *giant-step* approach of Fig. 1, the complete system is designed from the specifications, and a detailed implementation design is obtained. The associated procedures and programs are also worked out, and the total system is then installed. The drawbacks of this approach are apparent: instantaneous and large capital investments; simultaneous integration of the system into existing operations; and the potential disruption of existing operation owing to problems in training, refinement of procedures, and possible bugs in equipment.

If we choose to consider a city a system, Brasilia (the new capital of Brazil) is an example of this approach.

At the other extreme is the *piecemeal* approach of Fig. 2. In this case, specific portions or parts of the system are independently

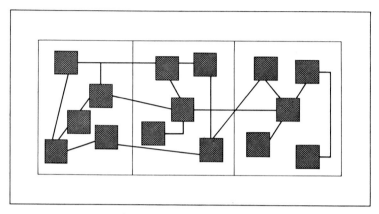

FIG. 1. Giant-step system design.

designed, mechanized, and put into operation one at a time. The system which would eventually result might turn out to be a hodge-podge of individual designs, and the likelihood that the parts could

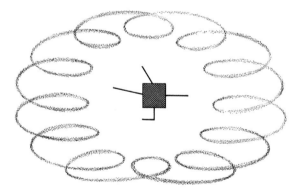

FIG. 2. Piecemeal system design.

be efficiently integrated into the whole would be small. Considerable redesign and patching are likely to be needed in order to achieve an integrated, smoothly functioning system. One finds many cities which show the results of piecemeal planning.

Intermediate between these two extremes of system approach is the *time-phased* approach in Fig. 3. In this case, the total system is designed as in the giant-step approach, but the implementation of equipment, procedures, and programs progresses step by step. As a result, investment is gradual, new installations cause minimum disruptions, the total system effectiveness is continually improved, the training of personnel can be properly timed, and the new procedures are introduced in stages.

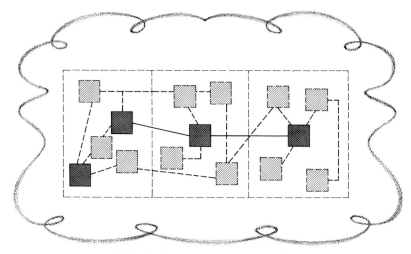

FIG. 3. Time-phased system design.

Now, when the system requirements undergo changes during the development phase, another dimension is added to the problem of system design. The *evolutionary* system design approach is essentially similar to the time-phased approach just described, but it allows for the changing needs and specifications of the total system. As portions of the system designs are implemented on a carefully timed basis, certain commitments in the system design occur, but the rest of the system design can continue to adapt itself to changes in requirements, technological capability, and new equipment available. The phasing of the implementation becomes even more critical than if no changes are contemplated. The portions of the systems to be designed and equipped at any one stage must be critically examined to insure the least physical and functional disruption, the least commitment of an undesirable type, and the smooth integration of the parts into the total system.

For the purpose of discussing evolutionary design methods, let us use the word "system" to denote that entity which is being designed and the word "subsystem" to denote portions of this entity. We do this without compromising our previous discussion on subsystems and without neglecting the fact that the system itself is part of a bigger framework.

The design of a system in an evolutionary environment would proceed in steps of the following sort:

1. *Define the problem.* In cooperation with the user, study the requirements of the problem and arrive at some tentative set of specifications.

2. *Visualize the bigger framework.* Examine, again with the cooperation of the user, the broader picture within which this system has to operate. This study will throw additional light on the system requirements, and it will give an indication as to the degree of certainty of the various specifications.

3. *Define the subsystems.* Break down the system into its parts in such a manner that the designs of the subsystems can proceed in parallel.

4. *Analyze the subsystems.* This is a preliminary analysis to determine the nature of each problem area. This analysis would result in decisions as to which subsystem needs changing or automating and which might be put aside for later review.

5. *Study the interrelationships.* Re-examine the division of the system into its subsystems and optimize in regard to best separation into parts.

6. *Decide the implementation sequence.* Based on the criticality of certain subsystem requirements and on the definiteness of subsystem specifications, time phasing of the design and implementation process can be laid out. This is in effect the scheduling of subsystems in the framework of the over-all system schedule.

7. *Design the subsystems.* The detailed design of the various subsystems can now proceed more or less in parallel and based on the schedule defined. The usual methods of analysis, simulation, testing, and training would be employed as appropriate.

8. *Re-examine the system requirements.* In parallel with activities 3 through 7, and in view of the results of the specifications, continue to study the over-all system requirements. This continuous re-examination of the system jigsaw puzzle should serve to insure an integrated design. In this process the objectives of the system are continually re-examined and the bigger framework in which the system fits is studied. Changes in requirements, philosophies, pro-

cedures, etc., are investigated to define their effects on the system and subsystem designs.

9. *Feed back the design results.* As the design of the various subsystems progresses, some of the practical and detailed considerations should be allowed to react on the system specifications.

10. *Continue the design cycle.* By the time the design cycle is once completed, many changes have occurred in specifications, philosophy, environment, etc. The various steps of the design procedure are therefore repeated, the problems and their solutions are re-defined, and the new subsystem designs are created. It is even appropriate to re-examine the schedule and the phasing of the various subsystem implementations. This cycling procedure continues until commitments must occur. The redesign of the subsystem can continue even after implementation, since many of the devices used are general-purpose ones and can be reprogrammed, readapted, reconnected, or supplemented.

This procedure is a "living design" and even after a complete implementation of a system, one should maintain a design effort of however moderate size to continue re-examining the requirements, the needs, and the new techniques available to meet them. System procedures, computer programs, supplementary pieces of equipment, and additional tasks can all be used to modify the system and subsystem performance. Indeed, in today's complex environment a system design is never complete and must be conceived of as a maintaining effort, just as spare parts provisioning, maintenance, system operation, and utilities are.

AS THE IMPLEMENTATION EVOLVES

I have discussed how the changing environment, new requirements, and advances in equipment capabilities can continually change the role of a system. At the same time commitment of a certain equipment configuration imposes some restrictions and generally results in a freezing of the specifications. Yet the evolutionary state of a system cannot be disregarded, and it is necessary to consider what flexibility can be left in the system even after the implementation has begun or is complete. There are several ways of keeping up with the changing conditions:

1. *Replacement.* Naturally equipment can be replaced with newer, better, and more capable equipment, but the cost of such replacement

might be a serious consideration. Even if equipment is rented, as digital computers might be, their replacement involves an extensive redesign of the programs, and the expense of this effort must be considered a replacement cost. Nevertheless, over several years in which a system operates, such replacements can be justified in many cases.

2. *Modification.* Modification of the equipment to achieve increased capability or to perform additional functions is possible in many cases. Typical might be the change in terminal equipment connecting to the same communication channels or the retrofitting of certain functions in data-processing devices.

3. *Supplementation.* It is often possible to add capacity or new functions to an installation by mere addition of new devices without changes in the already existing set of equipment. Parallel outlets in a communication network or additional tape units in a data-processing installation are examples.

4. *Equipment versatility.* General-purpose equipment available in many cases permits reprogramming or reconnection within the device to change its functions. A stored-program general-purpose computer is a typical example of this kind of versatility. Again, replacement or modifications of the program involve certain costs which must be justified in terms of needs. Typical in an evolutionary system is the maintaining effort for programming which serves to continually improve efficiency. A new advance in computer design is the stored-logic computer in which not only the programs can be changed but also the type of instructions the computer accepts. These instructions are changed by simple inputs from a tape and can adapt the same computer to achieve best efficiency in the particular application.

5. *Interconnection versatility.* The telephone system is an outstanding example of providing a versatile manner of interconnecting a large number of different units. This type of versatility is becoming more and more desirable for other devices to achieve ease of reconnections and intercommunications on a real-time basis. Carried over into data-processing systems this approach is called the polymorphic concept, denoting a configuration of many shapes, as in Figs. 4 and 5. Under control of the various computers and other modules in the system, complete flexibility of intercommunication between the various information devices is possible at high speed. This versatility is particularly useful when the system requirements call for a large number of different problem solutions arising in different combinations during varying operational conditions.

In the links between man and machine it is particularly difficult to provide the flexibility and versatility needed. If modern electronic

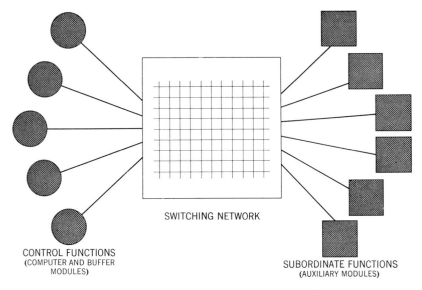

SWITCHING NETWORK

CONTROL FUNCTIONS
(COMPUTER AND BUFFER
MODULES)   SUBORDINATE FUNCTIONS
                                                (AUXILIARY MODULES)

FIG. 4. Organization of polymorphic data-processing system.

FIG. 5. RW-400 polymorphic data-processing system installation.

systems are to be truly the extension of man's intellectual capability, these input-output problems must be solved. The operator must be able to make requests in his own language and obtain information from a system in a manner which is easy for him to interpret. An

FIG. 6. Display and analysis console.

example of a console and display design which can be used in a great variety of different situations is shown in Fig. 6. For each problem a different overlay on the bank of push buttons, as in Fig. 7, permits the statements of human requests in terms of the operator's language, and the operator merely has to push the right button to make a request. The versatility of displays becomes merely a programming problem once the appropriate display mechanisms are provided.

6. *Formats and standards.* One of the most important system design considerations is the formats and standards which are used in the system. In many cases these have a more restrictive influence on the use of the system than the various pieces of equipment installed. The definition of formats and the determination of standards are, indeed, tantamount to system design itself and must be so construed as to leave sufficient flexibility in their use. The mechanisms which handle

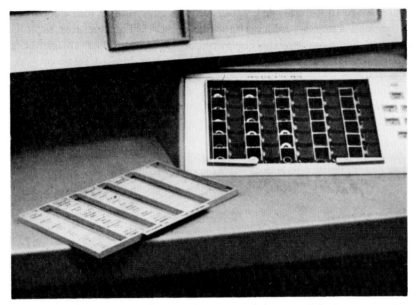

FIG. 7. Process key overlay removed from push buttons.

formats automatically and the programs which are designed around
some standard message structure are difficult and costly to change,
and the conversion of a system to a different format or standards is
often uneconomical. To provide flexibility in these basic considerations is a truly important system design task.

AS EXAMPLES DEMONSTRATE

Many examples of evolutionary system design can be cited, and
several were noted in my discussion to illustrate some of the points.
Other cases could demonstrate the inadequacies of systems designed
on the basis of short-range, rather than evolutionary, considerations.
It seems best to concentrate here on a single and actual example
which contains most of the elements of the long-range and circumspect
approach advocated. The following discussion is based on ref. 1 and
on my first-hand knowledge of this project. The material is un-
classified and is presented here with the permission of the contracting
agency.*

* This project is a systems effort and includes no provision of hardware by the
contractor. The equipment shown in Figs. 5, 6, and 7 was developed in connection with other contracts,

The project at hand concerns itself with the integration of automatic data-processing techniques into the operation of the Field Army. At the request of USCONARC (U. S. Continental Army Command) toward the end of 1956, OCSIGO (Office of the Chief Signal Officer) organized a technical analysis group to examine this problem. A USCONARC committee (representing the user and customer) specified

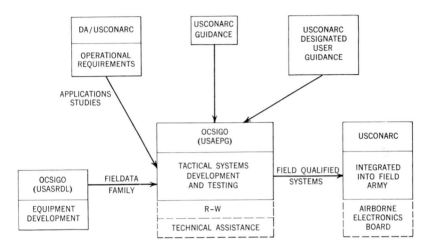

FIG. 8. ADP system project program organization.

100 separate applications. The Signal Corps technical group examined these applications and issued a voluminous report recommending a feasible program.

The program undertaken is a two-pronged effort of equipment and system development. The FIELDATA program represents the equipment development effort which began at a relatively early stage compared to the system effort. Although the equipment commitments pose certain limitations on the system design, the parallel development effort permits realistic and timely system testing using some of the actual operational hardware. Moreover, the FIELDATA family includes a variety of general-purpose computers, which can be readily fitted to the various applications.

The functional organization of the system effort is illustrated in Fig. 8. USAEPG (U. S. Army Electronic Proving Grounds) located at Fort Huachuca, Arizona, has the responsibility of developing and testing the tactical system. To carry out this task USAEPG formed an ADP (Automatic Data Processing) department and engaged an industrial contractor (Ramo-Wooldridge, a division of Thompson Ramo Wooldridge Inc.) to provide technical assistance.

Inputs to the system activity are shown in Fig. 8. Equipments developed by the Signal Corps Research and Development Laboratory include the FIELDATA computers as well as other devices. Application studies were based on the operational requirements and on the recommendations of the technical group report. USCONARC selected about 37 areas for detailed study. In addition, the Department of the Army undertook the study of another 28 areas. Throughout the whole program guidance is obtained from USCONARC and the various user groups in the Army. The outputs of the system program are the equipments, procedures, and programs fully qualified for field operational use. Their integration into the Field Army operation is the responsibility of USCONARC.

Figure 9 shows within the dashed lines the major steps making up this particular system development effort. The application studies already noted are reviewed. Some are held for later investigation; others are analyzed in detail. Part of the analysis is the preliminary programming of the data-procesing tasks. At this point some are eliminated as being unsuitable for automatic data processing, but other applications are further studied by simulation on a computer test facility. Based on the studies and simulations several applications are combined into a subsystem. This results in the definition of subsystems.

Once defined, the implementation of these subsystems is scheduled and approval is obtained to proceed on each subsystem. Finally the design of the specific subsystems is undertaken. This includes detailed analyses, extensive simulations, and elaborate tests. The design is followed by thorough operational field tests before it is turned over for integration into the Field Army.

Note the long rectangular box at the upper right of Fig. 9 referring to parallel system studies. This is the effort that brings the effect of the bigger picture to the system project. The Army structure and concept undergo continual changes. We have all heard of the PENTOMIC (pentagonal atomic) army which was refined into PENTANA (pentagonal atomic nonatomic army), then MOMAR (modern mobile army), then revised MOMAR. There is no intention here to define these Army evolutions, but each implies new organizations, new weapons, and new missions, which have their effect on the data-processing tasks. Similarly, the data-processing and communication capabilities developed can have their influence on the Army organization and philosophy.

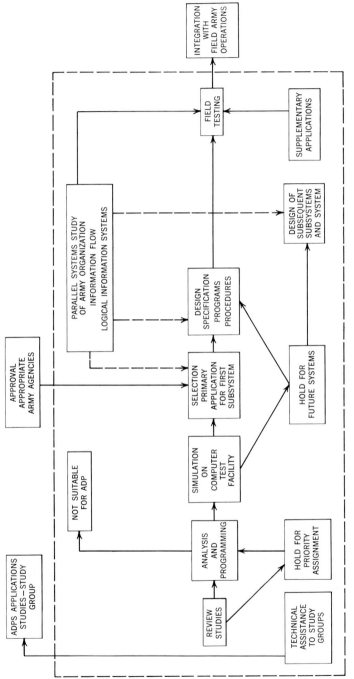

FIG. 9. Systems engineering approach to the ADP problem.

The first four subsystems that were identified in this program are: (1) Fire Support; (2) Personnel and Supply; (3) Intelligence; (4) Logistics. There is no intention to give even an abbreviated description of these subsystems or the developments. Rather, I would like to point out those factors in the programs which exemplify evolutionary design.

Subsystem 1 concerns itself with the Field Artillery operations and command problems and includes such tasks as fire direction, target assignment, surveying of positions, weather reporting, and tactical ammunition status; this has proceeded in close collaboration with the Army Artillery and Missile School at Fort Sill, Oklahoma, representing the user requirements. Work on this subsystem design started in the middle of 1959. The first stage of this subsystem will be field-tested in 1961, and this so-called Subsystem 1a will include a number of the functions of Subsystem 1. It will serve as an early demonstration of the tactical and operational feasibility of the systems approach and will be so conceived that it can be augmented into the full Subsystem 1 without obsoleting or replacing the equipment chosen or the programs worked out. This schedule illustrates the long evolutionary period to which such systems are subject.

The manner in which new equipment and new techniques are introduced into the existing system is illustrated in Fig. 10. The portion of the diagram above the dotted line shows those functions, equipments, and communication links which are part of the Field Artillery operations prior to the introduction of automatic data-processing techniques. The lower portion of the diagram shows the introduction of new data-processing equipment including a BASICPAC computer, two COMPAC computers, message entry devices (M.E.D.), battery display units (B.D.U.), electrical tactical maps (E.T.M.), etc.

It requires no emphasis that the integration of this equipment into the Field Artillery operation must be done in carefully prepared and thoroughly planned steps. An example of gradual phasing of new methods into the existing system is the utilization of present voice communication equipment to transmit digital information from one computer to another or from special input devices to the computer. By separating out a 200-cycle-per-second band in the middle of the audio-frequency range, both voice communication and digital communication can proceed simultaneously over the same audio channel. Appropriate filtering equipment will be added at the terminals to permit this mode of operation as well as the utilization of the full voice channel for digital transmission. In the future, special digital wide-band communication links may be introduced.

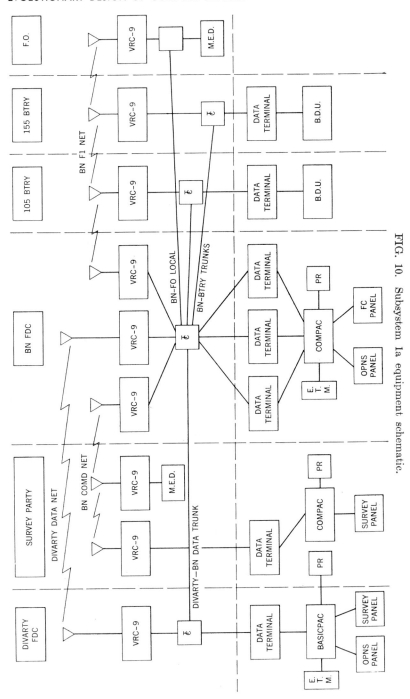

FIG. 10. Subsystem 1a equipment schematic.

TABLE 1. SUBSYSTEM 1 ADP TASKS

Administration	
Personnel	
Reports	
Intelligence	
Target acquisition	Map distribution and inventory
Artillery intelligence	Survey
Combat intelligence	Intelligence warnings
Intelligence reports	
Operations	
Fire control	Tactical ammunition control
Fire planning	Training management
Fire support coordination	Operational warning
Operational reports other than ammunition	Meteorology
Supply	
Logistics	
Reports	
Communications	

The functions of Subsystem 1 are enumerated in Table 1, and illustrate the manner in which the interfaces with other subsystems clearly arise. The Intelligence Subsystem will certainly be an input to the Field Artillery Operation and Command Subsystem, as it should affect, for example, the target assignment procedure. Similarly, information from the Logistics Subsystem would clearly affect plans and operations of the tactical Field Artillery. Table 1 clearly indicates the inherent magnitude of the interface problems.

AS SUMMARIES GO

The sketchy illustration of the evolutionary system design serves to pinpoint some of the aspects of the general discussion contained in this chapter. Problems of system design are too varied and too specific to be dealt with in general terms or to permit the application of any one scientific technique for dealing with them. The purpose of my discussion was to emphasize a certain facet of system design which is becoming more and more important as our technology develops. Some of the comments, conclusions, and descriptions are common sense—those "off-course" things most of the readers have or would have done—but the evolutionary nature of complex systems and the viewpoint required for their scientific solution require emphasis and must be cultivated with special intent.

REFERENCE

1. Plan for Automatic Data Processing Systems Development 1959–1964, U. S. Army Electronic Proving Ground, Fort Huachuca, Ariz., Dec. 1959, USAEPG-SIG 902-18.

CHAPTER 11

RELIABILITY AS A PARAMETER IN THE SYSTEMS CONCEPT

S. W. HERWALD

The stated objectives of this symposium are to clarify the philosophy of systems engineering and to emphasize the interdisciplinary approach to the formulation of complex systems. In line with these objectives, my talk will describe several important systems concepts in the field of reliability engineering, one of the many disciplines which must be brought to bear on the problem of formulating optimum systems.

My purpose is to show (1) that reliability must be treated as a major parameter of system design and (2) that new mechanization techniques may drastically change many present-day reliability concepts. Reliability will first be examined to show the reasons for considering it as a crucial system parameter. This will lead into a description of the techniques presently available for treating reliability analytically as a system parameter. Then the future will be considered—a future which, in all probability, will be characterized by radically new design and mechanization concepts. The significant gains in reliability which these new techniques may bring about, as well as the problems that are likely to arise, will be examined. Finally, a concluding optimistic note will show that future developments may significantly ease many present reliability problems related to both system performance and the prediction of that performance.

For many years electronic reliability has been one of the most talked about and written about problems in the military business. However—and this is the unfortunate aspect of the situation—the operational reliability of modern electronic equipment has not increased at nearly the rate of increased interest in the subject. There

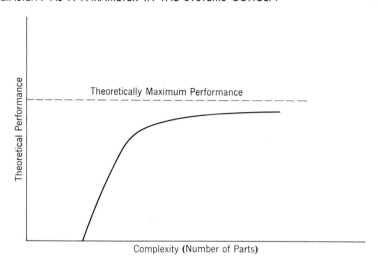

FIG. 1. System performance versus complexity.

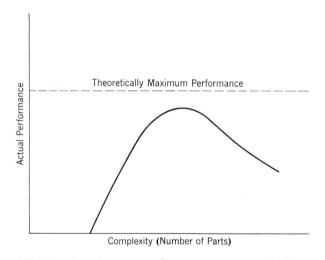

FIG. 2. Actual system performance versus complexity.

are good reasons why this has happened. Figure 1 shows theoretical system performance as a function of complexity. Until there is some complexity, there is no system at all. Added complexity means a gain in performance until a certain point on the curve is reached, and then increased complexity produces little gain in performance.

Figure 2 shows the performance actually obtained from the system as its complexity increases. As would be expected, increased complexity causes a decrease in obtained performance as a result of the severe degradation brought about by reliability problems. In the relentless march toward higher and higher performance levels, it has been necessary to add more and more complexity. In actuality, however, nothing has really been accomplished, for regardless of how potentially good a system is, it is obvious that it must operate long enough to realize this potential. Although increased complexity has put us on the threshold of high performance, it has at the same time prevented us from obtaining the final goal we are really seeking, i.e., an operationally useful system.

Now, how can the techniques and concepts of systems engineering lead us out of the quagmire? First, and most important, we must accept the existence of the curve shown in Fig. 2; i.e., we must appreciate that high *potential* performance is a false god to worship. Second, we must accept the truth that reliability is in fact a system performance parameter in its own right—at least as important as, for example, range or speed of the weapon. Too frequently in the past, the system was designed for high performance and then reliability was considered. As should be obvious, this is a hopeless and marginal way of doing things. The techniques of systems engineering provide the tools for designing reliability into the product at the point in that product's life where it is most meaningful to do this, which is at the time of the initial product or system conception and formulation.

It is, of course, true that many things affect the operational reliability of a piece of equipment. Among these are the quality of the parts used in the equipment, how well it is maintained, the physical environment in which it must operate, and the manufacturing and inspection processes employed. However, it is generally agreed that the basic equipment design concept places the upper limit on the reliability that the equipment will ever be able to attain. All that can ever be done by using the best materials known, by building and inspecting the equipment properly, and by maintaining and protecting the equipment in the best possible way is to ensure that we do no worse than the predestined reliability the design concept has established. It is because of this accepted fact that the techniques of systems engineering can be so valuable in helping to alleviate the reliability problem by forcing a consideration of reliability in the system concept stage as a first-class system parameter, subject to optimization and trade-off studies in the same manner that we trade off weight against range, for example.

RELIABILITY AS A SYSTEM PARAMETER

Let us briefly take a look at the mechanics of treating reliability as a system parameter. For purposes of discussion, consider the problem of designing a missile fire control system for an interceptor aircraft. Figure 3 shows how the system effectiveness, independent of reliability now, varies with the radar detection range. Through the use of known kinematic relationships and analytical formulations it is possible to generate just such a curve, once the speeds and

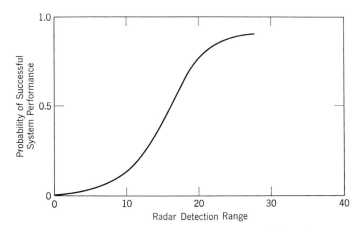

FIG. 3. System effectiveness versus range of detection.

maneuvering characteristics of the interceptor and its target are known, along with the flight characteristics of the missile, the missile warhead lethality, etc. This curve bears out what is intuitively known, namely that the earlier the target is seen, the more time there is to get into an optimum firing position, and thus the probability of destroying the target is higher.

However, increased radar detection range is not obtained free as indicated in Fig. 4. An increased range requires more complicated transmitters, more sensitive and thus more complex receivers, and larger antenna drives—all of which tend to degrade the reliability that can be reasonably expected. From Figs. 3 and 4 it is clear that the problem is difficult and requires a compromise solution. Detection range and reliability must be traded off to arrive at the maximum system effectiveness, all other things being equal. It therefore becomes clear that increased system effectiveness cannot be obtained by merely adding theoretical detection range. Perhaps a more judicious choice of missile configuration or a change in attack tactics can help—but the avenue of increased detection range is closed.

Experience with steam-driven electric power generation problems furnishes another example of the attention that must be paid to trade-off between performance and reliability in fields other than military electronics. Increasing steam temperatures makes possible the construction of generators of higher and higher thermal efficiency.

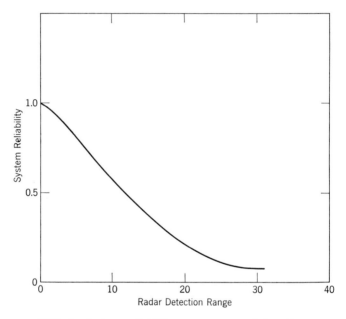

FIG. 4. System reliability versus range of detection.

This results in power delivery at decreased fuel cost. Experience has shown, however, that high thermal efficiency tends to bring about lower reliability than was characteristic of some earlier equipments with lower efficiencies. Furthermore, the newer generators tend to have much larger capacities than those which were installed a few years ago. The combination of increased size and decreased reliability tends to make it necessary for a utility company to install more reserve capacity than would have been necessary formerly, thus partially canceling the increased performance of the newer machines. The use of sound systems engineering in the choice of an optimum generator design for a given utility allows us to obtain the best compromise between performance and reliability.

Thus, it is seen that the concept of systems engineering can help ease the reliability problem. Specifically, the concept that a potential system can be described mathematically, within the framework of a system model, and then analyzed for sensitive parameters and ranges of potential performance, all long before a soldering iron touches a component, is invaluable in modern-day systems work. Of course, the idea of mathematically representing a mechanical or electrical system is not really very new. However, the body of techniques developed to treat extremely complex systems, constructed of many interacting subsystems, has been developed only recently. It is the application of just such techniques which offers us the ability to understand reliability as a system parameter in relation to the other more conventional performance parameters.

Now, it must be obvious that in order to perform such trade-offs it is necessary to be able to predict what the reliability of any given system will be long before it is in fact built and operated. For many relatively simple electrical and mechanical devices this is not an overwhelming problem. For example, the load under which a steel beam will crack can be predicted with relative accuracy. The distribution of light bulb life can be predicted as a function of the number of times it is turned on and off. However, the task of predicting the probability that a complex of many thousands of separate pieces will operate satisfactorily for a specified length of time within the specified environment is indeed a difficult one.

There are many reasons why this is so, for the most part all traceable to the lack of understanding of the behavior of electronic devices. For example, the failure distribution of a class of vacuum tubes in a given environment can be determined, but in most cases there is no understanding of what brings this distribution about, nor exactly how it can be altered. Furthermore, the moment the environment is changed, the life distribution changes, again in a relatively unknown manner. Why is it that a batch of tubes, as identical as we can make them and as thoroughly tested and matched as we know how, will have lives varying from 0 to 50,000 hours, in the same application and in the same environment? A further factor which is known to influence system reliability but which cannot be defined or measured is the interaction which undoubtedly exists between the individual pieces in the systems. In many unfathomable ways, the changes which occur in one component most certainly affect its neighbors. However, since it is not known how they will be affected, it is impossible to predict what is going to happen. Finally, there are the Herculean problems involved in predicting how up to 100,000 of these electronic devices will operate together, so that even if all the life-and-death characteristics of all present-day electronic devices were known it would be extremely difficult to handle these data in a sound analytical manner.

RELIABILITY PREDICTION

Now for a brief look at what is done today to predict reliability as a function of system complexity. This might be called a state-of-the-art report on reliability prediction. Electronic equipment has been found to exhibit characteristic failure behavior with time. As can be seen in Fig. 5, the failure behavior can be divided into three

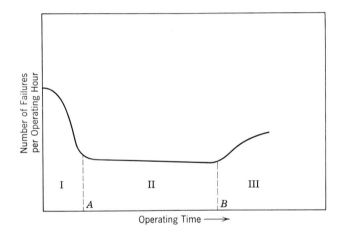

FIG. 5. Failure behavior.

stages. Each stage can be represented by a distinct mathematical model, as well as by a specific time period in the operating life of the equipment. Stage I is characterized by initial failures owing to defective component parts finding their way into the equipment, rough handling during shipment and installation, and perhaps initial debugging of the equipment. This is analogous to the infant mortality phenomenon in humans. Obviously, the time between 0 and A is short relative to the entire life of the equipment.

In stage II (bounded by A and B), most failures occur randomly in time and at a relatively constant rate. These random failures are a result of accidental, unexpected, and unusually severe conditions arising during the operating period, as well as randomly occurring failures of parts. During this period, the probability of the accidental failure of a given equipment in any time interval is entirely independent of the time the equipment has already operated. For the most part, reliability is measured during this period and, as will be shown later, the prediction of future reliability is based upon the existence of a long period of the equipment's life in which the number of failures per operating hour is constant.

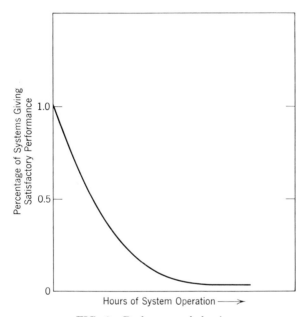

FIG. 6.   Performance behavior.

The final hump in the curve beyond B represents increased wear-out failures which occur because of a large number of component parts gradually reaching a more or less failed state as a result of deterioration of the physical structure of the parts.

If a large sample of identical electronic equipments were to be operated in stage II until all the equipments failed, a curve similar to Fig. 6 would be generated. Since this curve has the form of an exponential decay process, it can be represented mathematically by a simple equation:

$$R = e^{-rt} \qquad (1)$$

where R = reliability

r = system hourly failure rate

t = time, during which satisfactory performance is desired

Equation 1 has been found to be a reasonable enough representation of the performance exhibited by complex electronic equipment so that it has come to be known as the exponential reliability law. This law is the basis for almost all reliability analysis performed today.

Let us briefly examine how the reliability of a system may be predicted. Working within the framework of the life model just described, the "product-rule" prediction technique is the one most widely used in reliability work today. Basically, the product rule states that the probability of an electronic system operating satisfactorily is equal to the product of the operating probabilities of all the components comprising the system. This probability rule holds only when the performance of every component is assumed to be entirely independent of the performance of every other component. This condition is rarely encountered in real life since few electrical components operate independently of their associated components. However, the product rule does give a good first approximation of the potential reliability of the equipment and becomes even more useful when the relative reliabilities of two or more systems are being evaluated. Furthermore, the product rule also assumes that the failure of any single component will result in a complete system failure, i.e., it assumes that the entire system is one giant series circuit. Since this is also not completely true, the product rule tends to give a pessimistic estimate of reliability.

Equations 2, 3, and 4 show some of the important basic relationships in reliability prediction:

$$R_{\text{system}} = R_1 \cdot R_2 \cdot R_3 \cdots R_n \tag{2}$$

$$R_{\text{system}} = e^{-r_1 t} \cdot e^{-r_2 t} \cdot e^{-r_3 t} \cdots e^{-r_n t} \tag{3}$$

$$r_{\text{system}} = r_1 + r_2 + r_3 \cdots r_n \tag{4}$$

Equation 2 is merely the statement of the product rule, i.e., system reliability is equal to the product of all the component reliabilities. This is equivalent to eq. 3, in which each of the components is assumed to exhibit exponential life characteristics. Finally, eq. 4 follows from eq. 3 and expresses total system failure rate as the sum of the individual component failure rates.

As we shall now see, eq. 4 is the one we use in the mechanics of the reliability prediction process. The actual process of predicting the reliability of electronic equipment with as many as 10,000 or more individual components would be impractical if it were necessary to add up 10,000 individual failure rates. The procedure generally used is to group all similar components into a series of 10 or 12 classes, such as capacitors, resistors, and tubes. Each class has an associated failure rate per hour, based on past history for that component class. For example, vacuum tubes in air-borne equipment have shown a failure rate of 200×10^{-6} per hour. Multiplying the failure rate for any given component class by the number of components in that class will give the failure contribution of the class. Performing this for all the classes and then summing the failure contributions will give the over-all system predicted failure rate. Finally, if the calculated system failure rate is substituted in the over-all reliability equation $(R = e^{-rt})$, a predicted reliability curve is generated.

The mathematical model for predicting reliability that was just described is one which is obviously tied to the complexity or number of components in the equipment. Thus, it is relatively simple to arrive at the probability of successful equipment operation as a function of complexity, providing, of course, one knows how the complexity specifically changes with increased performance. Unfortunately, this is not always known with sufficient accuracy.

To summarize, it has been shown how reliability can be treated as a system parameter in optimization and trade-off studies in order to arrive at the optimum design configuration. Further, it has been demonstrated how the reliability predictions that are required for system trade-offs can be made. With this background, the future will now be considered.

MOLECULAR ELECTRONICS

From the previous discussion it is probably clear that the present-day reliability problem stems, in large part, from the complex nature of the equipment involved. Specifically, it accrues from the extremely large number of individual component parts required in modern equipment, as well as the correspondingly large number of soldered and mechanical connections. From a consideration of the product-rule concept of reliability it is seen that systems composed of roughly 10,000 parts plus soldered connections require that each part have astronomically high reliability if the over-all system reliability is to be satisfactory. Although there has been an improvement in the reliabilities of typical electronic parts, such as resistors and capacitors, and vacuum tubes have been replaced with the more dependable transistors, the battle appears hopeless. As soon as component reliability is increased, performance requirements add new components, thus canceling the advantages gained from increased component reliability. One can legitimately wonder where this vicious circle stops and how the reliability problem will ever be solved. Obviously, the equipment must be made simpler. Nobody argues with the concept of simplicity being the mother of reliability; however, the problem has always been how to attain this simplicity. Since it is characteristic of present-day military equipment that higher and higher performance is required, it is clear that simplicity cannot be attained merely by eliminating system functions. Instead, a basically new concept of electronic equipment design must be developed which is inherently and fundamentally simpler than existing methods. Such a concept will allow the sophistication of military electronic equipment to be maintained without suffering the attendant reliability problems. Molecular electronics, often called "molectronics," probably comes as close as any present concept to meeting the requirement for a fundamentally new and simpler electronic mechanization technique.

The molectronics concept had its origin in the search for a fundamental solution to the complexity problem, as well as for a means to decrease size, weight, and power requirements for electronic equipment. This concept discards the circuit schematic and component approach and utilizes instead a method based on the structure of matter. The objective is to synthesize a monolithic block of material with its domains so arranged that a desired electronic function is achieved. This function is expressed in terms of the control or transformation of energy; both the inputs and outputs could be electromagnetic radiation, heat, mechanical displacement, electric voltage, etc. Since most of the work is concerned with the control of electric signals, the field of semiconductors, and particularly the action of p-n junctions, is of primary interest. Technology in this field has reached a stage where the molectronics approach is feasible and where planned research can lead to the design of materials exhibiting predetermined properties.

An example of the complete elimination of the circuit schematic as a basis for mechanization is a light telemetry system which generates a frequency depending upon the amount of light striking it. Using tubes in a conventional circuit as in Fig. 7, the subsystem has a volume of 4 cubic inches, weighs approximately 26 grams, requires 5 watts input power, and consists of 16 components and 18 soldered joints. In transistorized form as in Fig. 8, the subsystem has a volume of 1 cubic inch, weighs 7 grams, and requires 0.75 watt input power. There is no appreciable gain in reliability, however, since the circuit still has 14 components and 15 soldered joints. In contrast, reliability is significantly improved and the size and weight are

Circuit

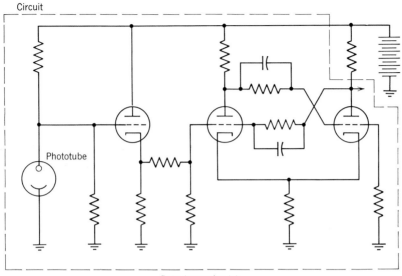

Data (approximate):

1. Volume 4 cu in.   4. Components 16
2. Weight 26 grams   5. Solder joints 18
3. Input power 5 watts

FIG. 7.   Yesterday's philosophy of circuits (light telemetering subsystem).

Circuit

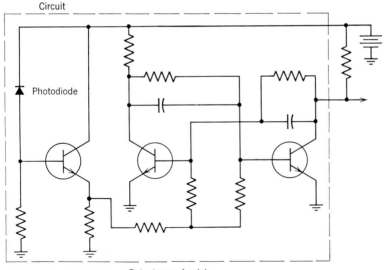

Data (approximate):

1. Volume 1 cu in.   4. Components 14
2. Weight 7 grams   5. Solder joints 15
3. Input power 0.75 watt!

FIG. 8.   Today's modern philosophy of circuits (light telemetering subsystem).

markedly reduced in the molecular configuration as in Fig. 9. The subsystem now has a volume of only 0.001 cubic inch, weighs just 0.02 gram, requires 0.06 watt input power, and has only 1 component and 2 soldered joints.

By the use of molectronics in the design of this device, its size is reduced by a factor of 4000, weight is reduced by a factor of 1300, and power consumption is reduced by a factor of 83. There has also been a decrease in the number of components and connections from 34 to 3, a factor of more than 10. This has been accomplished by looking at a function that needs to be performed and then designing a block of material to perform this function. Equally dramatic

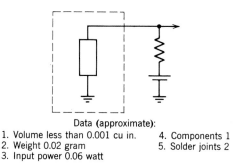

Data (approximate):
1. Volume less than 0.001 cu in.   4. Components 1
2. Weight 0.02 gram   5. Solder joints 2
3. Input power 0.06 watt

FIG. 9. Tomorrow's molectronic system concept (light telemetering subsystem).

reductions in size, weight, and number of components have resulted from designing functional blocks to perform certain amplifier, multivibrator, variable potentiometer, and switching functions. It is expected that, in time, an overwhelming majority of electronic functions can be performed with molectronic devices.

Before discussing the impact of this radical electronic design concept on the reliability prediction process, a qualitative examination will be made on the effect molectronics is likely to have on the over-all reliability problem. At the present time, our experience with the application of molectronic devices is still extremely limited. Although our basic understanding of the solid-state phenomena which are the basis of molectronics is relatively good, it is, as you would expect, incomplete. Further, many of the manufacturing and design problems which will no doubt arise in the future cannot now be predicted. As a result, much of the following discussion must be considered to be in the realm of speculation. As our experience with these devices grows, and data are accumulated, the present concepts will undoubtedly be somewhat altered.

Certain characteristics of molectronic devices will definitely affect the reliability problem. First, these devices operate at low power levels. In the past, high power requirements for conventional components, with the attendant heat dissipation problems, have decreased reliability. Second, molectronic devices have no mechanical moving parts, again eliminating an important source of part failures. Third, since molectronic devices to perform entire functions will be manufactured largely by automatic processes, a greater uniformity of product can be expected, which again should increase reliability. Fourth, the small size, weight, and power requirements of these devices makes the widespread use of redundant circuitry feasible.

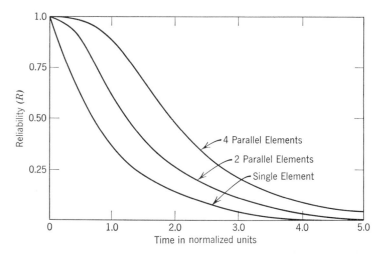

FIG. 10. Idealized reliability improvement with redundancy.

Let us consider this last point in more detail. Most present-day circuitry is of the series type: each component must operate if the entire circuit is to operate. This, it will be recalled, is the basis of the product-rule concept of reliability. Now, if parallel circuits or parallel functions can be used in the design, there will most certainly be a gain in over-all reliability. As the number of parallel circuits, components, or functions are increased, the reliability is increased significantly as shown in Fig. 10. Redundancy, however, has its limits. The reliability of the failure-detecting and switching devices must be considered in the calculation of the improvement redundancy yields. It has been found that this factor acts to place an upper limit on the reliability improvement that can be expected from the redundancy technique.

There is an additional advantage which may accrue as a result of the small size and weight characteristics of molectronics devices. It appears reasonable to expect that, as a result of their small size, it may be possible to control the ambient environment of molectronic systems more perfectly and more conveniently than is possible with present devices. From experience it is known that a controlled environment, such as is obtained by hermetic sealing or by maintenance of constant temperature, increases component life. It has not been practical, however, to provide widespread environmental control for the relatively large and bulky present-day devices. The small size of molectronic devices should make it possible to employ ambient environmental control as a routine design practice.

A fifth factor relating to the reliability improvement which may result from the use of molectronic devices is the expected decrease in catastrophic failures in systems composed of such devices. Our experience with transistors and diodes gives a basis for speculating about the life characteristics of future molectronic devices. Solid-state devices, as a general rule, are not subject to the catastrophic type of failure that is characteristic of vacuum tubes. Instead a gradual degradation in performance can be expected to occur as a function of component age. From a systems standpoint, this will mean that the system failure rate will not be constant across a significant length of time. This, it will be recalled, was assumed to be the case with conventional electronics. The impact of this fact is that, for the first time, preventative maintenance of electronic devices will begin to make some sense. With present systems, it has not been prudent to remove components from equipment according to a predetermined schedule. This, of course, is a result of the fact that present-day devices have essentially constant probabilities of failure with time and are generally subject primarily to chance or catastrophic failures. Molectronic devices, on the other hand, as a result of the gradual diffusion of impurities within the material, will deteriorate in performance. Once the rate of deterioration is learned, there will be a sound basis for preventative maintenance. Very likely, it should be possible to accomplish most of the preventative maintenance function automatically by redundancy switching devices, in which case essentially continuous operation of the system can be expected for extremely long periods, even considering the unreliability of the switch. Further, entire subsystems, e.g., amplifiers, will tend to be replaced at once in module form. This will expedite the maintenance process to a significant extent.

Another reliability advantage resulting from molectronics, which has been alluded to earlier, is the very sharp decrease in the number of soldered and mechanical connections required. Although there has been considerable progress in soldering techniques, the number of connections in a complex system is so great that even one defective joint out of 1000 is completely unsatisfactory. Molectronics, by its very nature, will largely eliminate this problem.

The final reliability factor which must be considered relates to the problem of manufacturing molectronic devices.

Molecular engineering probably has as serious a reliability problem as conventional systems if the problem of manufacturing yield is considered. Presently, the production of a transistor requires 10 to 15 operations. This process produces transistors which can be classified in perhaps 20 to 30 categories. Thus, in starting out to build a transistor of specified properties, our chances of succeeding are only 0.033. Fortunately, 40% of the classifications of transistors represent saleable devices. However, as complexity increases to multi-purpose molecular devices, two things may happen:

1. A much larger number of classifications will occur because many more operations are required to produce the device.

2. The saleable portion of the classification matrix will tend to decrease because the unit becomes more and more of a special-purpose device which must meet specific performance standards.

It is interesting, in this connection, to consider two probability figures. The first, P_1, can be defined as the probability of making a system that lives long enough to be shipped to the customer. The second, P_2, can be defined as the probability that the device operates over its expected period of use. Molectronics probably reduces P_1 while increasing P_2. Thus, even if we assume that the product P_1P_2 may be the same for conventional and molecular systems, the weak link in the molecular system occurs in the manufacturing shop where it is at least possible to contemplate doing something about it.

Let us, for the moment, speculate on the impact of molectronics on the reliability prediction process. There can be little doubt that the life characteristic of each individual molectronic device will be different from that of a conventional device, such as a vacuum tube. However, this may not invalidate the exponential reliability law as a representation of over-all system reliability. Statistically, it can be shown that exponential component life is not a necessary prerequisite for exponential system life. As long as there is a mixture of components with different life characteristics, the exponential may still be used as a description of system life. The product rule also can be retained as a representation of system reliability. However, the computation of system failure rate will not be as simple as it is for present devices. The widespread use of combinations of series and parallel circuits in the same equipment will require more sophistication in arriving at predicted system failure rates. Finally, the molectronic concept of replacing many components interconnected to perform a single function with a single functional block will outdate the expression of reliability in terms of component failure rates. Function reliabilities will be the single consideration. Thus, the question will be centered around the probability that this amplification or that switching function will be performed rather than the probability that this resistor or that capacitor will work. This should help a great deal in predesign reliability analysis.

In conclusion, molectronics, being in essence a means for designing unitized subsystems, provides an opportunity to apply the reliability systems concepts discussed earlier. Specifically, by employing sound systems thinking now, in the early days of molectronics, we may avoid the complexity pitfalls of the past. Well-conceived studies to trade off complexity and performance within each molectronic device will prevent us from attempting to build too much into each block and thus from canceling the reliability advantages of molectronics.

Only future experience will reveal all the phases and aspects of molectronics. However, I am very hopeful, based on what I have seen to date, that at long last a concept has been developed which has the potential of significantly decreasing our severe present-day reliability problem. I can only hope that my expectations are well founded.

CHAPTER 12

ON IDENTIFICATION
AND EVALUATION OF THE
TRANSFER DYNAMICS
OF PHYSICAL SYSTEMS

E. MISHKIN and J. G. TRUXAL

The electronic or control systems engineer is charged with the responsibility for the design of a system incorporating a variety of physical and human elements in an interconnection specifically planned to achieve the required over-all system dynamic characteristics. In the design of such a system, the focal problem is usually not one of analysis in the classical sense of electrical engineering, nor one of synthesis in the "modern" sense of electrical engineering, but rather one of identification—involving the determination of appropriate deterministic or probabilistic models for the components of the system.

These mathematical models must describe the dynamic transfer characteristics of the individual components, with the descriptions in a form from which the over-all system characteristics can be derived. Thus, the identification problem consists of, first, a determination of the appropriate form for the individual models; second, an evaluation of these models from analysis of the physical laws which underlie component behavior or from experimental measurement of the component characteristics; and finally, an insertion into the models of relevant characteristics to describe the statistical variation of the system components (i.e., the reliability features, manufacturing tolerances, variations in performance resulting from changing environmental conditions, etc.). The identification problem is completed only when the element is characterized mathematically in sufficient completeness to permit analysis of system behavior.

In this chapter, we consider the identification techniques of basic importance in the engineering of control and electronic systems.

A SIMPLE EXAMPLE OF IDENTIFICATION

Before the general techniques of identification are considered, we describe briefly a simple identification problem. A major problem of any university department arises as the faculty attempts to keep the curriculum abreast of the changing times. All professors preach the philosophy that we must be educating not for the scientific and engineering tasks of today, but rather for the demands of the future. Unable to foresee this future with any reasonable certainty, however, we are forced to teach a curriculum which is focused on the current areas of promise. The currency of the educational program is further emphasized by the demands imposed by a student body acutely aware of the current fields of glamor and exciting promise.

If any serious attempt is made to keep the program in line with the demands of the students and industry, the faculty is immediately faced with an *identification problem*. The signals available are measured by the faculty awareness of current trends in research, recent developments of apparent significance, and the current technical literature—both the periodicals of the professional societies and recent textbooks. On the basis of this information, the faculty must predict the important directions of curriculum emphasis three years hence (if we optimistically assume that a curriculum can be revised in approximately three years). Furthermore, intelligent planning requires a less specific prediction of the direction of the engineering field during the next decade, particularly if the staff is to be strengthened in areas of future importance and if research is to be initiated to assist in staff growth and development of the graduate and undergraduate educational programs.

The identification problem then involves a determination of the growth of individual areas of technology—the evaluation (based upon past experience) of mathematical models appropriate for prediction of the future growth pattern of the field. The problem is illustrated in detail by Fig. 1, which shows a group of curves which may be appropriate for a description of the history of the field of automatic feedback control theory.

We first plot curve 1, which represents the basic knowledge of the subject. Although feedback control systems have been utilized for centuries, there was very little known about the analysis of such systems until the 1920's, with the first rapid increase of knowledge occurring during World War II. During the period 1945–1955 there was a marked decrease in the slope of the curve (with slight increases resulting from the work on sampled-data systems and nonlinear systems, for example), but during the last few years the intensive research in connection with computer control, guidance systems, process control systems, and adaptive and optimizing systems has apparently resulted in a sharp increase in the slope of the curve.

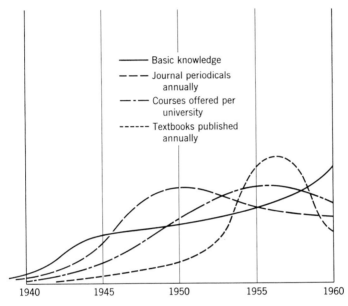

FIG. 1. Example of identification.

Obviously, the exact dimensions and shape of the curve are subject to individual evaluation, but control engineers seem to agree on the general form. Once this curve is determined, it is of interest to plot on the same time scale the rate of publication of articles by the professional societies, curve 2 of Fig. 1. The delay between the high rate of increase of basic knowledge (1943) and the peak of curve 2 (about 1950) is perhaps in part the result of wartime security restrictions, but to a much greater extent a reflection of the fact that most articles are detailed (and rather insignificant) slight extensions of a basic innovation of at least five years earlier.

Curve 3, representing the courses offered per university, demonstrates an even greater lag because of the time required for curriculum revision and the time lag while a few forward-looking schools are training the teachers of the new courses at the majority of the universities. Finally, curve 4 demonstrates that textbook publication is characterized by even a greater lag, with the peak textbook production occurring shortly after the courses are instituted in the universities throughout the country.

The importance of a faculty appreciation of the characteristics of Fig. 1 for each significant area of the departmental subject is perhaps apparent, at least for any school which seeks to lead educationally and to exert some influence on the course of engineering development. Once the characteristics of Fig. 1 are obtained and consideration is given to the influence of such special factors as security restrictions during wartime, an estimation (by the faculty) of the present nature of curve 1—basic knowledge—permits at least an approximate prediction of the future course of the other curves, even if the rate of change of basic knowledge cannot be predicted.

ROLE OF IDENTIFICATION

The importance of the identification problem is illustrated by the very elementary feedback control configuration of Fig. 2. The process to be controlled is specified at the outset of the problem; a transducer

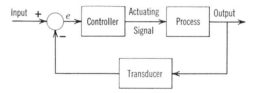

FIG. 2. Simple feedback configuration.

is used to measure the output and generate a feedback signal which is compared to the input to yield an error signal e. The system design problem is essentially that of determining appropriate characteristics for the controller element.

Before the system design problem can be considered, however, we must have an analytic or mathematical model for the process. In practical situations, the process of Fig. 2 frequently consists of a large number of input and output signals, with the controller designed to generate the entire set of actuating signals. In such circumstances, identification involves the determination of the matrix of dynamic relationships among each of the actuating signals and the outputs.

When we consider the design of automatically optimizing or adaptive controls in Fig. 3, the identification problem assumes a fundamental role in system operation. In the general configuration shown in the figure, the process to be controlled generates the output signal. An identifier block is added, fed by the actuating signal and the output signal, to measure continuously or at frequent intervals the transfer characteristics of the process. These transfer characteristics, along with the characteristics of the input signal, are fed to the decision computer, which then decides on the desirable characteristics for the controller (i.e., decides on the appropriate actuating signal). In this type of communication or control system, therefore, the identification problem is solved continuously in real time by the

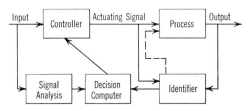

FIG. 3. Basic adaptive system.

identifier components, and the design of the system is automatically adjusted as the process characteristics vary (as a result, for example, of changes in environmental conditions).

In an adaptive system such as that depicted in Fig. 3, the identification problem is frequently simplified if a test signal is inserted (as shown by the dashed line) in order to excite the process even during periods when the normal actuating signal is small, or to excite the process with a signal possessing a waveform particularly selected to simplify identification. Regardless of whether a separate test signal or the normal actuating signal is utilized, however, the identification must be completed in a short interval of time (in order to permit the controller characteristics to track changes automatically in process characteristics), in contrast to identification in the more conventional system design problem depicted in Fig. 2, when the time required is of no importance and identification is a portion of the engineering of the system.

Thus, in electronic and control system design there are two essentially different forms of the identification problem:

1. Identification for design—in which case extensive measurements can be utilized as we seek to understand the details of process operation and we attempt to describe the process by a detailed and reasonably accurate model.

2. Identification during operation—when we measure salient features of process performance and, because of the time limitations, are content with a gross evaluation of process characteristics. Rather than a complete model for the process, our objective in identification is frequently only one or two parameters or measures of the general nature of the process dynamics (e.g., we might measure only the gain level).

In the next two sections, we consider the basic techniques of the electrical engineer in each of these aspects of the identification problem.

IDENTIFICATION IN SYSTEM DESIGN

The fundamental mathematical model of the electrical engineer is the set of simultaneous differential equations describing system dynamics, with each of the differential equations the mathematical manifestation of either a physical (or natural) law or an assumed behavior for an individual component of the system. The form of the model is essentially independent of the nature of the system, whether the nature be electrical, pneumatic, mechanical, thermal, acoustical, or otherwise. Even if the system involves a human being, our analysis of the interaction of the human element with the inanimate components requires, at least in simple situations, that we describe the transduction characteristics of the human being by an integro-differential difference equation.

The forms of the mathematical or analytic models frequently used by electrical engineers are described most readily in terms of a specific example.[1] An important component of numerous positioning control systems is the electromechanical element depicted in Fig. 4: a d-c electric motor driving, through a gear train, a load consisting of damping and inertia. The actuating signal (or input) of the system is the electric voltage e or the current i; the response or output signal is the angular displacement of the load θ_L.

Analysis or understanding of the method of operation of such a physical system is initiated by the writing of a set of simultaneous differential equations, with each equation describing the behavior of a separate portion of the over-all process. Each of the equations represents the mathematical expression of a law of physics or a definition of the operation of a component (such as the gear train).

Kirchhoff's law for the armature electric circuit

$$e = L\frac{di}{dt} + Ri + K_b\frac{d\theta_m}{dt}$$

Energy-conversion term

$$l_d = K_b i$$

D'Alembert's law at motor shaft

$$l_d = J_m\frac{d^2\theta_m}{dt^2} + B_m\frac{d\theta_m}{dt} + K_1(\theta_m - \theta_1)$$

Definition of the gear ratio

$$\theta_2 = \frac{1}{g}\theta_1 \qquad (1)$$

Torque transmitted through gears (Hooke's law)

$$gK_1(\theta_1 - \theta_m) = K_2(\theta_L - \theta_2)$$

D'Alembert's law at load

$$0 = J_L\frac{d^2\theta_L}{dt^2} + B_L\frac{d\theta_L}{dt} + K_2(\theta_L - \theta_2)$$

From this set of equations, we can determine, for example, any of the dependent variables (six in number: i, l_d, θ_m, θ_1, θ_2, θ_L) if the independent variable e is given as a function of time and the initial values of the various stored energies are known.

The differential equations constitute only a *model* of the physical system; the determination of these equations requires a large number of simplifying assumptions (primarily in connection with the linearity,

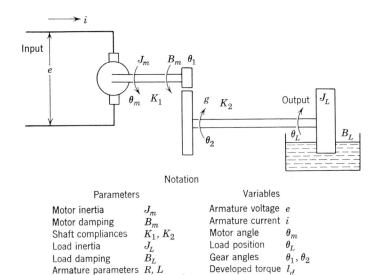

Notation

Parameters		Variables	
Motor inertia	J_m	Armature voltage	e
Motor damping	B_m	Armature current	i
Shaft compliances	K_1, K_2	Motor angle	θ_m
Load inertia	J_L	Load position	θ_L
Load damping	B_L	Gear angles	θ_1, θ_2
Armature parameters	R, L	Developed torque	l_d

FIG. 4. An electromechanical process.

but also in neglecting certain parameters which are of secondary importance). For example, eqs. 1 are based upon the linearity of the motor (no saturation, no static friction), idealness of the gears (no backlash, negligible inertia), representation of the shafts as purely compliant elements, and assumption that all damping is viscous. The extent to which such a model correctly represents the physical process depends not only on the particular process but also on the characteristics of the exciting signals and the operation of the over-all system within which the electromechanical system is only one component; these factors also determine whether further model simplifications are feasible—in many positioning systems, for example, it is permissible to assume the shafts are rigid, and eqs. 1 become considerably simpler.

If we continue to work with eqs. 1 as typical of the most common mathematical model for a process, there are several ways in which we can rewrite the equations to place the model in a more useful form. First, we might represent the model as a block diagram to show visually the way in which the variables are interrelated. There are numerous block diagrams which can be constructed, each representing the mathematical model. Indeed, there is usually no single diagram of maximum usefulness and, particularly in the analysis of more complex systems, it is helpful to be able to develop a variety of configurations. The commonest block diagram, however, is the one which presents, insofar as possible, a picture of the way we normally consider the signal to flow through the system, i.e., the diagram which emphasizes the cause-and-effect relationships which the engineer intuitively associates with the operation of the individual components. Our primary purpose in developing a block-diagram model is to emphasize these cause-and-effect relationships by a topological portrayal of the interaction of the various elements of the system, particularly with the hope that the visual representation will simplify the understanding of system operation.

The block diagram is derived from the differential equation in the following steps:

1. We first decide on the sequence or path by which signals flow from input e to output θ_L. In other words, we determine the successive cause-effect relations among the system variables. In the foregoing process, the applied voltage e causes a current i to flow in the armature; this i in turn gives rise to a developed torque l_d. The l_d causes a torque transmitted through the K_1 shaft, and then a torque amplified through the gear train. This torque flowing out of the gears causes

motion of the load. If this sequence of variables is assumed natural (and clearly there are other sequences equally "natural"), the block diagram should involve the succession of variables e, i, l_d, $K_1(\theta_m - \theta_1)$, $gK_1(\theta_m - \theta_1)$, and θ_L. The block diagram must take the rough form indicated in Fig. 5, with various blocks and adders to provide the interconnection of the variables.

$$\underline{e_a} \quad \underline{i} \quad \underline{l_d} \quad \underline{K_1(\theta_m - \theta_1)} \quad \underline{gK_1(\theta_m - \theta_1)} \quad \underline{\theta_L}$$

FIG. 5.   Initial form for the block diagram.

2. e is the independent variable; each of the other variables must be given in terms of e or the other dependent variables in order to complete the block diagram.   Again we have considerable freedom in deciding which equation (of set 1) is to be solved for which variable, but generally we would like to have each variable in the block diagram depend on the variable to its left, in order that the flow may be from left to right.   Thus, although the equation

$$l_d = K_b i \tag{2}$$

could be used to solve for i and represented as a block of gain $1/K_b$ from l_d to i, it is more natural to utilize the equation*

$$e = Lpi + Ri + K_b p\theta_m \tag{3}$$

written in the form

$$i = \frac{1}{Lp + R} (e - K_b p\theta_m) \tag{4}$$

Equation 4 is represented in the block diagram as a subtracting device fed by a block from e and one from θ_m and feeding another block, as in Fig. 6. We have now used the first relation of eqs. 1, and this

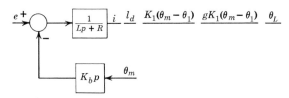

FIG. 6.   Block diagram including the first of eqs. 1.

* Throughout the remainder of this section, p is used to represent the operator d/dt. If we utilized the Laplace transformation, each p would be replaced by the complex frequency s.

equation alone must not be used again later to determine another variable or the block diagram will represent a nonindependent set of equations. One additional point is noteworthy: it has been necessary to introduce the added variable θ_m in the determination of i in this first stage. Although we would have liked to avoid this additional variable, above all we wish to retain a simple relation between the block diagram and the interaction of signals in the system. Equation 3, a simple and evident relation existing in the armature electric circuit, should appear directly in the block diagram.

3. We next determine l_d, preferably from i, the variable to the left. A possible relation is the second of eqs. 1,

$$l_d = K_b i \tag{5}$$

and we have the partial block diagram of Fig. 7.

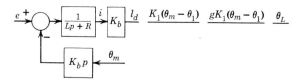

FIG. 7. Block diagram including eq. 5.

4. The next variable $K_1(\theta_m - \theta_1)$ is given in terms of l_d (and θ_m) by the third of eqs. 1:

$$l_d = J_m p^2 \theta_m + B_m p \theta_m + K_1(\theta_m - \theta_1) \tag{6}$$

or

$$K_1(\theta_m - \theta_1) = l_d - (J_m p^2 + B_m p)\theta_m \tag{7}$$

The fact that we are using, in order, the relations of eqs. 1 is not coincidental; these relations were written on the basis of our understanding of circuit operation, the same understanding which guided

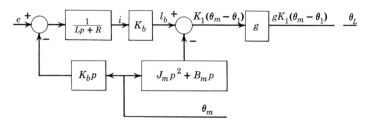

FIG. 8. Partial block diagram.

us in our choice of the sequence of variables for the block diagram. We can also, in this step, note that the variable $gK_1(\theta_m - \theta_1)$ is simply g times the variable $K_1(\theta_m - \theta_1)$, and the new partial block diagram takes the form shown in Fig. 8.

5. We still must determine θ_m and θ_L in terms of the other variables of the system. Combining the last two equations of set 1, we have

$$(J_Lp^2 + B_Lp)\theta_L + gK_1(\theta_1 - \theta_m) = 0 \tag{8}$$

or

$$\theta_L = \frac{gK_1(\theta_1 - \theta_m)}{J_Lp^2 + B_Lp} \tag{9}$$

which serves as the relation for θ_L and yields the block diagram of Fig. 9.

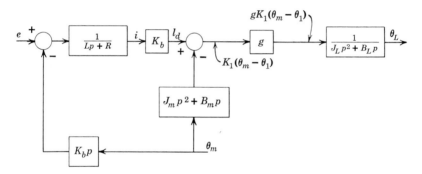

FIG. 9. Partial block diagram.

6. The final step in the construction of the block diagram requires the solution for the variable θ_m, which was introduced in the course of the foregoing derivation. Equations 4 and 5 of set 1 have not yet been used in the formulation of the partial block diagram of Fig. 6 and thus must be included at this point. The specific manner in which the equations are manipulated to obtain a relation for θ_m in terms of the other system variables is largely dependent upon our interests in a specific design problem; for example, if we wished to consider in detail variations of K_1 and K_2, we would want the remainder of the block diagram drawn in such a way that K_1 and K_2 appeared alone as the gains of individual blocks. Alternatively, we can write relation 5 of eqs. 1 as

$$\theta_m = g\theta_2 - \frac{K_2}{gK_1}(\theta_L - \theta_2) \tag{10}$$

by using relation 4 to eliminate θ_1. The new variable θ_2 is then given from the last relation of eqs. 1 as

$$\theta_2 = \frac{J_L p^2 + B_L p + K_2}{K_2} \theta_L \tag{11}$$

and we have the final block diagram of Fig. 10.

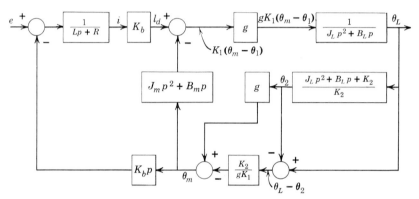

FIG. 10. One possible final block diagram.

The block diagram of Fig. 10 is, as noted frequently in the preceding derivation, only one of several possible configuration representations

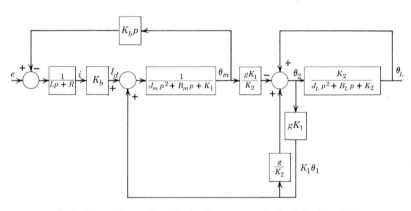

FIG. 11. Alternative block diagram equivalent to Fig. 10.

of the original set of six simultaneous equations. Other possibilities include the simpler configuration shown in Fig. 11, as well as the many possibilities which are characterized by the fact that a particular parameter which we wish to study in detail appears only once, and in a single location as the gain of a single block (e.g., Fig. 12 shows a configuration useful in the study of the effects of K_1). The derivation of any of these block diagrams follows the same pattern already described in detail. When we wish to focus attention on a single parameter, we merely modify the procedure by first rewriting the

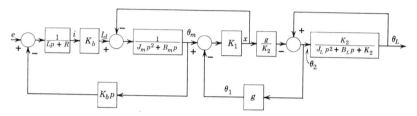

FIG. 12. Block diagram for detailed study of K_1.

equations so that the parameter appears only once and then as a multiplier. For example, the six relations of eqs. 1 can be rewritten as follows (to place K_1 under study):

1. Since K_1 appears only in the term $K_1(\theta_m - \theta_1)$ in our equations, we define a new variable x by the relation

$$x = K_1(\theta_m - \theta_1) \tag{12}$$

and rewrite the six equations as:

$$e = (Lp + R)i + K_b p\theta_m \tag{13}$$

$$l_d = K_b i \tag{14}$$

$$l_d = (J_m p^2 + B_m p)\theta_m + x \tag{15}$$

$$\theta_2 = \frac{1}{g}\theta_1 \tag{16}$$

$$gx = K_2(\theta_L - \theta_2) \tag{17}$$

$$0 = (J_m p^2 + B_m p + K_2)\theta_L - K_2\theta_2 \tag{18}$$

2. Equations 12 through 18 form the basis for a block diagram with the desired properties. *If the equations are written with a*

single different dependent variable appearing on the left of each,

$$x = K_1(\theta_m - \theta_1) \qquad i = \frac{1}{Lp + R}(e - K_b p \theta_m)$$

$$l_d = K_b i \qquad \theta_m = \frac{1}{J_m p^2 + B_m p}(l_d - x)$$

$$\theta_1 = g\theta_2 \qquad \theta_2 = \theta_L - \frac{g}{K_2}x \tag{19}$$

$$\theta_L = \frac{K_2}{J_L p^2 + B_L p + K_2}\theta_2$$

the block diagram of Fig. 12 is directly identified equation by equation.

Thus, the differential-equation model is exactly analogous to a block-diagram model for the process. Manipulation of the block diagram into various forms corresponds to rewriting the set of simultaneous differential equations by forming linear combinations of the original equations. The two forms of mathematical models place in evidence the interrelationship of the various system parameters.

In view of the equivalence of the two representations (the block diagram and the set of simultaneous differential equations), we might logically ask: What advantages are associated with the block-diagram model? What does the systems engineer gain by the utilization of such a topological representation of the interrelationship of system components and of the various signals existing throughout the system? These questions are particularly pertinent because the systems engineering techniques of the electrical engineer depend to a very marked extent on the manipulation and exploitation of the block-diagram models.

The primary advantages of the block-diagram or graphical representation are six in number:

1. If we desire to reduce eqs. 1 to a single relation between *one* output or response variable and the driving signal *e*, the block diagram permits a simple and direct reduction. In the application of the reduction formula, the over-all transmittance is written in terms of the various direct signal paths from input to output and the closed, feedback loops (around which signals may circulate, with the possibility of instability resulting). The form of the reduction is particularly convenient when we are concerned with the system stability,

and the manner in which the stability depends upon a specific parameter.

2. The block diagram may portray graphically the existence of isolation between two parts of the system. If, for example, the block diagram can be bisected in such a way that all paths flowing across the line of bisection are in the same direction, the over-all system can be represented as the tandem connection of two simpler systems: we are able to decompose one complex problem into two simpler problems, and frequently can thereby greatly simplify the over-all analysis, the stability study, and the determination of the dependence of system characteristics on a particular parameter.

3. The block diagram frequently indicates the possibility of eliminating certain of those dependent variables which are of no direct interest in the understanding of system performance. Just as we can establish rules and techniques for eliminating variables algebraically in the original set of equations, we can formulate rules for the simplification of the block diagram by the combination of parallel paths, the translation of the origin or termination of a specific path, or the elimination of feedback loops. Although these transformations are directly based on the validity of the corresponding algebraic manipulations, the visual portrayal of the block diagram frequently permits the engineer to deduce particularly simple procedures for the elimination of inconsequential dependent variables. Thus, the block-diagram representation essentially affords the analyst an alternative viewpoint, a different way of looking at the analysis problem; associated with this alternative approach is the possibility of greater circumspection, hence, improved analysis.

4. The block diagram is particularly useful when attention is to be focused on a single parameter, the relation of this parameter to system stability, and the sensitivity of over-all system characteristics to variations of this parameter. Both the system stability and the sensitivity depend upon the feedback "around" the particular parameter; i.e., the gain or transmittance from the output to the input of the parameter block, when the block diagram is constructed in such a way that the parameter under investigation appears only once and as the gain of a single block (e.g., as we have shown K_1 in Fig. 12). The entire subject of feedback theory is primarily concerned with the study of the significance of this loop transmittance around a specific parameter and the manner in which such loop transmittance should be controlled in feedback system design.

5. When we are interested primarily in the effects of one parameter, the block diagram indicates appropriate techniques for reduction of

the system complexity around this parameter, i.e., for combination and simplification of the other elements of the system.

6. The block diagram is an extremely useful starting point in the programming of the system for an analog or digital computer. For any system of interesting complexity, computer studies constitute an essential element in system analysis or design. Such a study program is required if for no other reason than simply to ascertain the effects which are to be anticipated from unavoidable nonlinearities which always exist in a physical system. By far the most difficult aspect of a computer study is the phrasing of questions to be posed to the computer; i.e., what information the designer should seek from the computer. For example, the existence of oscillations in a nonlinear system commonly depends upon the initial conditions (or initial energy storage, at the time excitation is applied). When a computer study is undertaken, the systems engineer must decide upon the ranges of initial conditions to be investigated, and then must interpret the computer results. Both of these tasks are enormously simplified if the engineer possesses a clear picture of the mode of operation of the system, the interrelation of the various signals, and the manner of interconnection of the individual components—exactly the information and insight provided by the block diagram. Intelligent utilization of the computer therefore demands, in most problems of significant complexity, an understanding of the block diagram and a programming of the computer so that individual sections of the computer retain a $1:1$ correspondence with the elements of the block diagram.

An alternative, important form of the block diagram for the representation of the simultaneous differential equations involves converting to a set of simultaneous first-order differential equations by the definition of additional variables. In order to illustrate the approach, we consider a somewhat simpler process described by the mathematical model

$$\frac{d^2y}{dt^2} + 3\frac{dy}{dt} + 2(y - x) = f_1(t) \tag{20}$$

$$\frac{d^2x}{dt^2} + 4\frac{dx}{dt} - 2\frac{dy}{dt} + 3x = f_2(t) \tag{21}$$

where x and y are the dependent variables, and f_1 and f_2 are the excitation functions. The process can be described directly by the block diagram of Fig. 13, if we utilize eq. 20 for the determination of y and eq. 21 for x. (It is noteworthy that Fig. 13 is essentially in an appropriate form for the immediate construction of an analog-computer simulation.)

Conversion of the mathematical model to a set of simultaneous first-order differential equations can be accomplished in a variety of

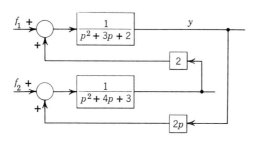

FIG. 13. Block diagram for eqs. 20 and 21.

ways. The simplest approach involves defining two new variables

$$u \equiv \frac{dy}{dt} \tag{22}$$

$$v \equiv \frac{dx}{dt} \tag{23}$$

in which case the four model equations are

$$\frac{dy}{dt} - u = 0$$

$$\frac{dx}{dt} - v = 0$$

$$\frac{du}{dt} + 3u + 2y - 2x = f_1 \tag{24}$$

$$\frac{dv}{dt} + 4v - 2u + 3x = f_2$$

(No additional complexity would be introduced if we were to choose to define u as

$$u = \frac{dy}{dt} + ax + by \tag{25}$$

where a and b can be selected arbitrarily.)   Regardless of the particular definition of u and v, however, the mathematical model in the form of eqs. 24 is directly recognizable as an analog-computer program involving only single integrators, adders, and sign changers.

On the basis of the models as described above (either in terms of the simultaneous linear differential equations or in the form of the block diagram), we can now consider the nature of the problem of model identification. The *complete* solution of the identification problem requires the evaluation of each of the parameters in the mathematical model of the process. Thus, in the relatively simple armature-controlled d-c motor and load, solution of the identification problem involves determination of all the parameters: L, R, K_b, B_m, J_m, K_1, K_2, g, J_L, and B_L. If the model adequately represents the process and if the parameters are known with reasonable accuracy, we are in a position to evaluate the performance of the process under all possible operating conditions and excitations, whether the evaluation be analytical or by a computer simulation.

Unfortunately, it is customarily impossible to obtain such extensive data with reasonable accuracy, at least within the lifetime of the project. For example, very often it is only after the airplane is flying (and the control system is operating at least semisatisfactorily) that certain important process parameters are known with any accuracy. Certain parameters can usually be determined with little difficulty or are already known as a result of the work of either the component manufacturer or the preliminary system designer. For example, again in the specific example of motor control of an inertial-damping load, the gear ratio, the motor inertia (and possibly also an average value of motor damping), the motor torque constant, and the shaft compliances are usually known with at least reasonable accuracy.

Evaluation of the other, unknown parameters can be effected in a variety of problems involving relatively simple processes. The appropriate tests for such an evaluation are selected from consideration of the differential equations, the block diagram, or the circuit diagram —the specific approach depending to a large extent on the engineering background of the control engineer.* The electric circuit diagram for our specific electromechanical example of a motor-driven load is shown in Fig. 14; the equations describing the circuit response to the excitation e are identically those of eqs. 1.

The determination of model parameters is essentially an art, rather than a completely logical procedure in which specific rules can be listed. If the circuit is sufficiently simple, the systems engineer is

---

* Electrical engineers usually think most clearly in terms of the circuit diagrams, whereas aeronautical engineers, for example, often prefer to work directly with the differential equations.

often able to deduce directly tests appropriate for the determination of model parameters. Our circuit diagram indicates directly, for example, the following aspects of the process dynamics: if a step input is applied as e,

(a) the final value of θ_L is determined by the three resistors in the voltage divider: R, $K_b{}^2/B_m$, and $g^2K_b{}^2/B_L$;

(b) the initial part of the response is determined by the two inductances $[L_a$ and $K_b{}^2(1/K_1 + g^2/K_2)]$ and two capacitances $(J_m/K_b{}^2$ and $J_L/g^2K_b{}^2)$;

(c) the resonances occur among the four reactive elements: the armature inductance, the two inertias, and the inductors representing the shaft compliances.

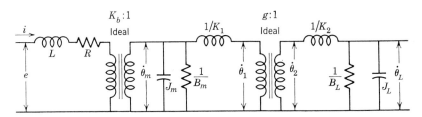

FIG. 14. Circuit diagram for Fig. 4 (values in ohms, farads, henrys).

Likewise, the circuit diagram indicates clearly the data which can be obtained by removing the load (B_L and J_L set to zero), by blocking the motor rotor (θ_m set equal to zero), or by removing the input and exciting the system from the mechanical side.

For example, with the rotor blocked, R and L can be determined by applying either step functions or sinusoidal signals as e. If a step function is applied, the current takes the form

$$i = \frac{E}{R}\left(1 - e^{-\frac{Rt}{L}}\right) \tag{26}$$

and R can be found from the final value, L from the time constant (L/R) of the exponential rise toward the final value. If sinusoidal signals of varying frequency are applied, R and L can be determined from the fact the driving-point admittance takes the form

$$\frac{I}{E} = \frac{1}{j\omega L + R} \tag{27}$$

(actually measurement of the complex value of the impedance at any single frequency in the neighborhood of R/L radians per second is sufficient for the determination of the two parameters). In a similar fashion, additional tests permit the evaluation of the parameters of the mechanical side of the system (although it is usually more troublesome to measure torque with a strain-gage bridge, for example, than to measure electric current with an ammeter).

Two features of such a one-by-one determination of model parameters are noteworthy. First, the evaluation we outlined is possible only when the systems engineer understands the detailed operation of the process, is able to write the differential equations from the fundamental laws of physics and chemistry, and is able to ascertain correctly which parameters are negligible and which important. Such an idyllic situation rarely exists except in relatively simple control or communications problems concerned with relatively trivial processes. Whereas redundancy in the measurements can often be used to establish (or refute) the validity of assumptions made concerning the negligibility of certain parameters, the interpretation of experimental results becomes a most difficult problem in complex situations. Even in the simple situation depicted in Fig. 14, the existence of a small but significant gear-train inertia (represented by a shunt capacitor between the two compliance inductors, to a first approximation) is exceedingly difficult to detect from the usual measurements of the over-all transfer characteristics or of the mechanical-system response with $e = 0$.

The second factor limiting the usefulness of this parameter-evaluation approach to the identification problem arises from the inherent nonlinearity of physical processes. If the linear model is to be useful, the parameters of the model must be determined at the proper operating point, or in the appropriate operating region. Thus, in the example just given, blocked-rotor tests may be useless even though the results are strikingly simple to correlate with the model, simply because the blocked-rotor condition corresponds to an operating condition radically different from any ever encountered in normal operation—i.e., the values of L and R under blocked-rotor conditions are just not applicable in normal operation. Such a situation is particularly common in the study of motors of all types, hydraulic and pneumatic as well as electric: as a result of the high power levels being processed by the transducer, the operating characteristics are severely nonlinear and parameters vary radically over the entire operating range (indeed, this parameter variation was our strongest motivation for the utilization of feedback originally).

As a result of these difficulties, we are usually forced in the identification problem to lower our sights. Rather than attempting to realize a complete description of the model of the physical process, we focus our attention on only those characteristics which we know to be directly of interest. In particular, rather than trying to determine the equivalent circuit or block diagram or differential equations, we concentrate on an evaluation of the transfer characteristics from the specific inputs to the outputs of primary interest. For example, in the electromechanical control system which has been used as the running illustration throughout this section, instead of attempting to evaluate each of the parameters of Fig. 14, we seek only the over-all transfer function θ_L/E, or (even more simply) only those characteristics of this transmittance which are essential in our design and evaluation of the over-all control system.

FIG. 15. Basic identification problem.

Once we restrict the identification problem by seeking not a detailed model for the process, but only the external (or terminal) characteristics, we are dealing with the same identification problem we encounter in the design of adaptive systems such as depicted in Fig. 3 (even though in engineering design the time required for the identification may be of no significance, whereas the successful operation of the adaptive controller depends upon the rapidity with which accurate, reliable identification can be accomplished). In either case, we are dealing with the problem of determining significant characteristics of the process g in Fig. 15 from the measured values of m and c. (In the figure, the input m and output c in general represent entire sets of signals; in the discussion to follow, we simplify the interpretation by considering a two-port process, with single input and output signals.)

IDENTIFICATION OF TRANSFER DYNAMICS

Even if we admit that in most engineering problems only the terminal characteristics are of interest and therefore we can restrict the scope of the identification problem, we are still left with several basic questions which can only be answered in terms of the specific system under consideration. For example:

1. Can we characterize the device as a linear element, or do the

nonlinearities play a fundamental role in determining the operation of the over-all system?

2. If the device is linear, is it time-invariant, or does the correct characterization depend on the time at which the device is to be used? For example, does the device incorporate learning, with the characteristics changing with age or amount of past experience?

3. If the device is linear and time-invariant, do we need a complete characterization of the transfer dynamics? If so, in what form would such a characterization be most useful for the design or evaluation of the remainder of the system? If not, what particular characteristics of the transfer dynamics are of major significance?

4. In any case, what are the requirements imposed on the time duration required for identification and on the accuracy of identification?

5. In almost every real-life problem, the systems engineer has certain a priori information about the process. For example, he may know that the process is adequately described by a third-order differential equation, or that the gain of the process inevitably falls off rapidly beyond a known frequency. The question arises: How can this information be utilized to simplify the solution of the identification problem and to assure that the solution obtained is compatible with the a priori knowledge?

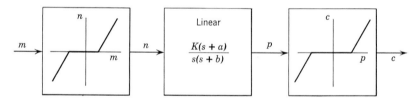

FIG. 16. Simple nonlinear system.

Unfortunately, we are able to do very little, in the present state of the art, with the identification of processes which are nonlinear or time-varying. The difficulty of the nonlinear problem is illustrated by the simple system of Fig. 16, consisting of two single-valued nonlinearities surrounding a linear block. In even this case (far simpler than the frequently typical problem involving a multiloop configuration including the interconnection of numerous linear and nonlinear blocks), we find that it is exceedingly difficult to perform identification with any generality because of the critical dependence of system performance on the nature or waveform of the input signals.

The problem is sufficiently complex even when we know the form of the system block diagram as a priori information; if identification is initiated with no a priori informaton, the situation is almost hopeless unless we can estimate the nature of the configuration on the basis of measurements. Once the configuration of Fig. 16 is known, actuating signals (m) can be selected which permit determination of both the frequency-dependent linear portion and the nonlinear sections. Such a fortuitous situation does not necessarily exist, however; for example, if the input nonlinearity were saturation, it might never be possible to drive the linear element with a high-frequency signal of sufficient amplitude to yield an output p which exceeded the dead-zone width of the output element, so that measurement of the high-frequency characteristics of the linear section would have to be accomplished essentially by highly precise evaluation of low-frequency performance. The resulting demands on the accuracy of the identification process may easily be beyond the capabilities of available measurement techniques.

In the absence of even a reasonably useful theory for the identification of nonlinear processes, we focus our attention in this section on the rather extensive theory associated with the study of linear systems. A linear time-invariant transmission process or system can be described in a variety of equivalent mathematical forms, each of which is of interest in the automatic solution of the identification process. Although the specific forms are many in number, the basically different representations are: (a) the differential equation, (b) the frequency response, and (c) the impulse response.

In this section, we consider useful techniques for evaluating the parameters in each of these mathematical models, and the relationships which exist among the three representations. Figure 15 shows the notation to be used throughout the section and indicates the simplifying restriction of consideration to the evaluation of a system with only one input $m(t)$ and a single output $c(t)$. Clearly, m and c can be variables in any physical system (electrical, mechanical, pneumatic, hydraulic, acoustical, etc.), and they need not be in the same units; the only restriction is that the process be linear and time-invariant (i.e., the process dynamics do not change significantly over the interval required for the measurement).

Evaluation of the Differential Equation
The differential equation for the process of Fig. 15 assumes the form of a linear relation among the derivatives of c and m. For example, if the system is third order (i.e., the highest derivative of c is the third when the lowest derivative of c is the zero order), the

equation can be written as*

$$\frac{d^3c}{dt_3} + a_2 \frac{d^2c}{dt^2} + a_1 \frac{dc}{dt} + a_0c = b_2 \frac{d^2m}{dt^2} + b_1 \frac{dm}{dt} + b_0m \qquad (28)$$

Evaluation of the coefficients of the differential equation is conveniently broken into two parts: evaluation of the a's and of the b's. For several reasons, the former is by far the more important and difficult aspect. Very often, the form of the right side of the differential equation is known from an understanding of the physics of the process; for example, in the electromechanical system of Fig. 4, the form of the equivalent circuit indicates that the right-hand side of the differential equation is simply a single term.† More significantly, once the a's are known, calculation of the b's is a relatively straightforward task since the b's determine only the relative amplitudes of the terms in the system response whereas the a's determine the natural frequencies or the forms of the time variations; accordingly, we first turn our attention to the evaluation of the left-hand side of the differential equation.

As indicated in the preceding footnote, the a's are the coefficients in the characteristic polynomial of the process system function; the zeros of the polynomial

$$s^3 + a_2s^2 + a_1s + a_0$$

are the natural frequencies of the process. If these zeros are denoted as s_1, s_2, and s_3, the transient response of the process contains terms of the form e^{s_1t}, e^{s_2t}, and e^{s_3t}. (For example, if the process is unstable, at least one of the s_1, s_2, or s_3 must possess a positive real part so that the corresponding term grows without bound).‡ Consequently, one method

---

* In the usual physical system, the order of the highest derivative of m is less than that of c because the output cannot follow immediately a discontinuous jump in the input: for example, in a mechanical system, inertia prevents, with finite torque available, an instantaneous jump in the load velocity. In certain idealized systems, where such inertia is neglected in order to simplify analysis and obtain a gross understanding of system behavior, higher order derivatives of m may be present, but this situation is unusual and of secondary interest.

† The existence of additional terms on the right-hand side of the differential equation corresponds to a zero of transmission for at least one value of the complex frequency s, since the transfer function for eq. 28 is

$$\frac{C}{M} = \frac{b_2s^2 + b_1s + b_0}{s^3 + a_2s^2 + a_1s + a_0}$$

‡ In general, instability may also arise when there are multiple zeros of the polynomial for purely imaginary values of s, but this case is of little practical importance.

for determining the characteristic polynomial involves evaluation of the natural frequencies present in the transient response. This method is discussed in more detail later in connection with the measurement of impulse response.

If the order of the differential equation and the nature of the right-hand side are known, it is possible to carry out an evaluation of the coefficient a's by the procedure outlined in Fig. 17 for this specific equation:[1]

$$\frac{d^3c}{dt^3} + a_2 \frac{d^2c}{dt^2} + a_1 \frac{dc}{dt} + a_0c = b_0m \tag{29}$$

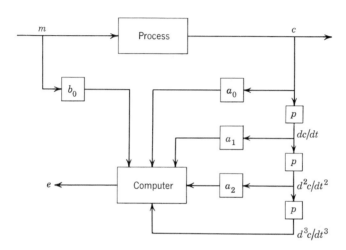

FIG. 17. Analytical evaluation of characteristic polynomial ($p = d/dt$).

If the system is stable, a_0 is determined by the steady-state response with a step-function input: if the input amplitude is M, the steady-state c is b_0M/a_0. Actually, a_0 is frequently known from an understanding of process operation and the fact the zero-frequency gain is b_0/a_0.

a_1 and a_2 are evaluated by generation of the signals dc/dt, d^2c/dt^2, and d^3c/dt^3 by successive differentiations of the response, and determination of a_1 and a_2 in such a way as to minimize the deviation from satisfaction of the differential equation. For example, if m is a step function, a_2 and a_1 can be evaluated to minimize the semi-infinite integral of the square of the error e, defined as

$$e = \frac{d^3c}{dt^3} + a_2 \frac{d^2c}{dt^2} + a_1 \frac{dc}{dt} + a_0c - b_0m \tag{30}$$

There are several difficulties which arise in implementing such an approach. First, the adjustment of a_1 and a_2 automatically to realize the minimum of $\int_0^\infty e^2\,dt$ ordinarily involves the searching over a two-dimensional space for an absolute minimum and the avoidance of the system settling at a local minimum. In the case of much higher order systems, such an approach involves extensive and tedious calculations. Such a difficulty is of somewhat reduced importance in the design of most adaptive control systems, however, because of the nature of the automatic measurement: once the system is operating properly, if the process characteristics change gradually, we are regularly requiring only slight changes in the values of a_1 and a_2, hence only seeking a nearby minimum.

Second, if the order of the system has been incorrectly estimated, the characteristic polynomial derived often bears little apparent relation to the actual polynomial. The problem of approximating one characteristic polynomial by another of different order is exceedingly difficult, and several current research efforts are directed toward increasing our scant knowledge of this particular aspect.

Thus, the approach to identification of attempting to evaluate the differential equation describing process dynamics is primarily confined (in the design of adaptive control systems) to problems in which:

1. The order of the differential equation is known a priori and is reasonably low.

2. The process dynamics (i.e., the coefficients of the differential equation) never change radically in a time interval short with respect to the measurement time (or in a time interval of the order of 10 times the response time of the control system).

Evaluation of the Frequency Response

The most common method of identifying the transmittance dynamics of the process in electrical engineering entails measurement of the frequency response of the process: the gain and phase characteristics of the transfer function

$$T(j\omega) \equiv \frac{C}{M}(j\omega) \tag{31}$$

as a function of the angular frequency ω, measured in radians per second. A constant-amplitude sinusoidal signal is applied as $m(t)$ and the relative amplitude and phase of the resulting $c(t)$ are measured. If the system is linear and stable and the input has been applied long enough to permit essentially complete decay of the transient response, $c(t)$ is sinusoidal at the same angular frequency as $m(t)$. The ratio of the amplitudes of c and m is $|T(j\omega)|$, and the angle $T(j\omega)$ measures the phase of c with respect to m. As the frequency of m is varied from very low to very high values, we obtain gain and phase characteristics: curves of $|T|$ and angle T as a function of ω, which might assume the form shown in Fig. 18.

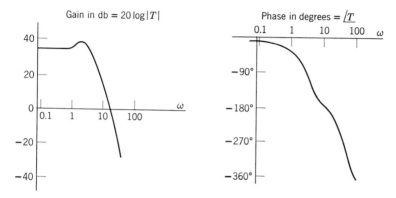

FIG. 18.   Possible form of gain and phase curves.

In the testing of complex systems, it is important to monitor, if possible, by variables within the process to detect internal nonlinearities which might invalidate the results even though the output waveform is nearly sinusoidal.   For example, in the system shown in

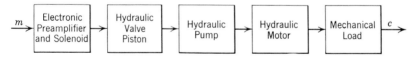

FIG. 19.   Electrohydraulic process.

diagrammatic form in Fig. 19, nonlinearity in the operation of the hydraulic pump may not be noticeable in the waveform of the output c because of the filtering of the harmonics (introduced at the pump) by the transfer characteristics of the motor and mechanical load, yet this nonlinearity may seriously affect the operation of the over-all system with step-function inputs.   In the presence of such a nonlinearity, the measured C/M transfer function is a describing function and must be measured not only as a function of ω but also as a function of the input amplitude.

Although this measurement of frequency response is extremely important in the general area of control system design, it is appreciably less useful in the solution of the identification problem in adaptive or computer-controlled systems because of the extensive time required for the determination of the gain (and/or phase) characteristic. By their very nature, adaptive systems must involve continuing and repeated solution of the identification problem, and it is seldom permissible to consume long intervals of time in amassing data or to drive the system with large, lengthy test signals merely inserted for identification. Consequently, almost all proposed adaptive systems are based upon impulse-response determination for the solution of the identification problem.

Evaluation of the Impulse Response

A linear, time-invariant two-port transducer can be completely characterized by the impulse response—the time response $c(t)$ when the excitation $m(t)$ is an impulse of known area. More generally, the process is characterized by the response to any known aperiodic signal, although interest is usually confined to impulses (or pulses so much shorter than the response time of the system that they can be represented as impulses) or step functions, the integrals of impulses.

There are basically four ways in which the impulse response can be measured experimentally. The first, and most natural, way is to excite the system with an impulse and measure directly the response. Secondly, we can excite the system with any known signal $m(t)$, starting at a specified time (denoted $t = 0$), and determine the response $c(t)$. If the system is inert at $t = 0$ (i.e., there is no energy stored in the process just prior to the application of the impulse), the impulse response $g(t)$ is given mathematically in terms of m and c by the convolution integral

$$c(t) = \int_0^t g(x)m(t - x)\, dx \qquad (32)$$

Thirdly, the impulse response can be measured by application of a small random signal to the process. Fourthly, a sequence of impulses can be applied and the output sampled, so that we obtain the sampled transfer function $C^*(z)/M^*(z)$—the ratio of the z transforms of the output and input signals. Each of these four methods is important in the design of adaptive control systems.

Before considering further the details of the foregoing measurement techniques, we should note that, particularly in the consideration of adaptive control, it is not possible to separate the measurement of the impulse response from the consideration of the application to be made of this measurement. In an adaptive system, the impulse response of the process is, in itself, of little direct use, but rather represents an intermediate step in the control or compensation of the over-all system. In other words, in system design even after we know the impulse response, we must decide how to utilize this response as a basis for the design of the controller. In the design of a conventional control system, the control engineer frequently uses the impulse response as a means of evaluating the transfer function of the process, which then serves as a basis for an intelligent design of the remainder of the system; in adaptive systems, the automatization of such a step frequently involves far too much equipment, and we may be interested not in the complete impulse response, but rather in perhaps just one aspect—such as some quantitative measure of the oscillatory tendency. Thus, in our consideration of the techniques for measuring $g(t)$, it is essential also to consider the use which will be made of the measured function.

One other aspect of the measurement problem is noteworthy. We have indicated that the single response $g(t)$ (or the step response) essentially contains all the information derivable from the gain and phase characteristics; in other words, a single measurement in the time domain is equivalent to lengthy, extended measurements in the frequency domain. Although time-domain measurement certainly is more economical in many ways, there clearly are disadvantages to the characterization in terms of transient response. First of all, the impulse response measurement does not include the redundancy inherent in the gain and phase measurements. Slight errors in the measurement of $g(t)$ in general lead to relatively significant changes in the corresponding transfer function, whereas small errors in the gain and phase characteristics have relatively little effect on the $T(s)$ which can be determined from these data. Another way of viewing this situation is to note that rather major changes in the pole-zero pattern of $T(s)$ may have little effect on $T(j\omega)$ (unless the poles are close to the axis), but a much larger effect on the corresponding impulse response $g(t)$. Likewise, the gain and phase measurements usually portray the nature of small, but not insignificant, nonlinearities much more graphically than $g(t)$. Finally, the simplicity of the transient-response measurement compared to the frequency-response measurement is to some extent de-emphasized by the fact that usually repeated transient measurements are required to average out the effects of noise, whereas random noise has only a very secondary effect in the frequency-domain measurements.

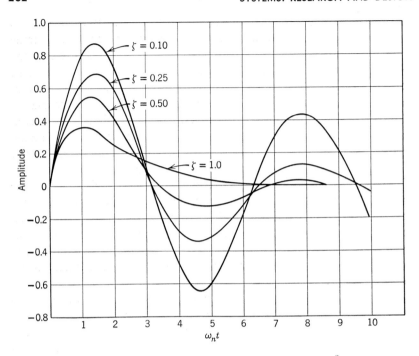

FIG. 20. Impulse response for transfer function $\dfrac{\omega_n^2}{s^2 + 2\zeta\omega_n s + \omega_n^2}$.

With these comments as background, we now consider the various methods of measuring the impulse response. The most direct method is to apply an impulse to the process, after which $g(t)$ can be measured directly. The form of $g(t)$ depends, of course, on the nature of the particular process under test, but the response when the system is second-order is of particular interest. In this case

$$\frac{C}{M}(s) = \frac{\omega_n^2}{s^2 + 2\zeta\omega_n s + \omega_n^2} \tag{33}$$

or

$$\frac{d^2c}{dt^2} + 2\zeta\omega_n \frac{dc}{dt} + \omega_n^2 c = \omega_n^2 m \tag{34}$$

and the impulse response (as a function of the relative damping ratio ζ) is shown in Fig. 20.

This second-order case is not only important because of the direct application to a wide variety of physical situations (e.g., the piloted-aircraft motion in the longitudinal axis is to a first approximation described by a second-order system), but also because many more complex systems are *approximately* described by a second-order differential equation.

The measured impulse response can be utilized to guide the automatic (adaptive) design of the controller in a variety of ways. For example, the Aeronutronics Systems Division of Ford Motor Company adaptive system compares the positive and negative areas of the response and utilizes the ratio as a measure of the relative damping; the Sperry Gyroscope Company adaptive autopilot measures the relative amplitude of successive peaks of the ringing oscillation as an indication of ζ. Clearly, both approaches are predicated upon the assumption that the process is second-order, or at least that $g(t)$ has the same form as for a second-order system. In terms of the transfer function, the only poles of primary importance in determining the transient response are a single, conjugate complex pair at $-\zeta\omega_n \pm j\omega_n\sqrt{1 - \zeta^2}$; any other poles, if the system is of order greater than 2, must lie near zeros or far to the left in the complex plane.

Alternatively, rather than focusing on a single numerical characteristic of the impulse response, we can attempt to utilize the entire, measured response as a basis for the design of the remainder of the adaptive control system. One effective means of utilizing the complete impulse response is to determine the coefficients of the expansion of $g(t)$ in a series of orthonormal functions. If the set of functions is selected so that the Laplace transforms of the component functions are realizable as the transfer functions of simple RC-active networks, we can use the coefficients of the expansion to control the gains in a set of variable-gain amplifiers and thus construct automatically a low-power model of the process under observation.

In the preceding discussion, we have completely avoided the questions raised by the possibility of initial energy storage. If there is energy stored in the process at the time the impulse is applied, the measured output is the sum of the impulse response and the response to this stored energy. Such a problem arises particularly in an adaptive control system design, since the impulses are injected into the process ordinarily during normal operation and the response is then the sum of $g(t)$, the response to initial energy storage, and the response to the normal excitation during the interval in which $g(t)$ is being measured. If the $g(t)$ term is (during this interval) significantly larger than the other two terms, an accurate evaluation can be made. If, however, the process is normally being driven to an appreciable fraction of its saturation level, the only satisfactory way to measure $g(t)$ by directly applying impulses is to turn off the normal process input during the measurement and allow sufficient time for the energy-storage transient to decay. Fortunately, if the normal operating signal is large, it is frequently possible to measure $g(t)$ by appropriate data processing of the normal process input and output.

The impulse response of the system can also be measured by exciting the process with arbitrary, aperiodic inputs, in which case the convolution integral, eq. 32, must be solved for $g(t)$ from the known $m(t)$ and the measured $c(t)$. Again in this evaluation, the relation assumes no initial energy storage at $t = 0$; if the system is not at rest at $t = 0$, $c(t)$ contains additional terms confusing the evaluation. In the design of ordinary control systems, eq. 32 is usually solved by approximating both $c(t)$ and $m(t)$ by a sequence of impulses, steps, or ramps occurring at regular intervals, after which the integral equation becomes a set of difference equations which can be solved numerically for $g(t)$.

The impulse response of the process can be measured approximately by evaluation of the sampled-data transfer function. Instead of applying the signal $m(t)$, we first generate the sampled signal $m^*(t)$: a sequence of regularly spaced impulses (every T seconds), with the area of each impulse representing the value of $m(t)$ at the corresponding sampling time. Thus, $m^*(t)$ is described by a sequence of numbers (the areas of successive impulses); the Laplace transform of $m^*(t)$ is denoted $M^*(z)$ and is simply

$$M^*(z) = m_0 + m_1 \frac{1}{z} + m_2 \frac{1}{z^2} + \cdots + m_n \frac{1}{z^n} + \cdots \qquad (35)$$

where m is the value of $m(t)$ at $t = nT$, and $1/z$ is a delay operator equal to ϵ^{-Ts} (where s is the Laplace transform variable).

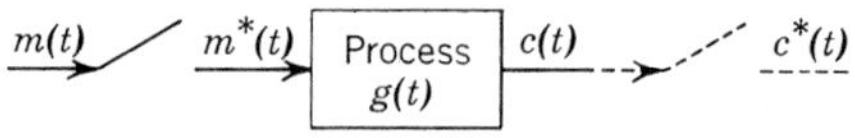

FIG. 21. The sampled-data transfer function.

If we assume a sampler at the output, as shown by the dashed lines in Fig. 21, to generate the sampled $c^*(t)$, the ratio of $C^*(z)$ to $M^*(z)$ is known as the sampled transfer function of the process:

$$G^*(z) = \frac{C^*(z)}{M^*(z)} \qquad (36)$$

Since the over-all system is linear, the transfer function possesses the same significance as for conventional linear systems.

In any actual measurement, we are unable to utilize the infinite sequence of pulses for either $c(t)$ or $m(t)$, but are instead restricted to sequences of finite duration. Such a restriction corresponds to multiplying $c^*(t)$ [or the corresponding $m^*(t)$] by a time function of the form shown in Fig. 22, which is equivalent to convolution of

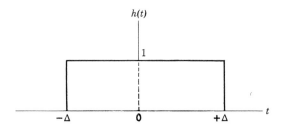

FIG. 22. Artificial time function.

the transform $C^*(z)$ with an $H(\omega) = (\sin k\omega)/k\omega$ function—the transform of our function of Fig. 22. The dimensions of $H(\omega)$, directly related to the duration of the width of the $h(t)$ pulse, indicate the extent to which the actual $C^*(z)$ is adequately approximated by the spectrum function which is actually measured with a finite sequence of samples. Furthermore, we can distort the $h(t)$ function of Fig. 22 in the interval from $-\Delta$ to $+\Delta$ in order to improve the quality of our measurement [we simply select the distortion to make $H(\omega)$ become more nearly the ideal, unit impulse at $\omega = 0$].

Thus, when the identification problem is solved with a finite sequence of impulses, we possess a direct means for determining the permissible sampling period T and the required period of observation 2Δ, in both cases if the measured $C^*(z)$ is to approximate the actual $C^*(z)$ within a specified accuracy. In the utilization of $G^*(z)$ as a means for the characterization of a process which does not actually involve the sampling operation, we are still left with the difficult problem of evaluating the differences in the relative performances of $G^*(z)$ and $G(s)$; however, if the sampling period is selected appreciably less than the significant time constants of $g(t)$, the sampled representation is ordinarily adequate. If the process is actually actuated by a digital controller (so that the actuating signal is either sampled or piecewise-constant), the $G^*(z)$ representation is directly appropriate.

Finally, the impulse response $g(t)$ can be determined from excitation of the process by an $m(t)$ which is a random noise signal. In such a case, the cross-correlation function between $c(t)$ and the noise input is simply the response $c(t)$ which would be obtained if the process were excited by an input signal which was the autocorrelation function of the input noise. In other words, if white noise is used as the input (with a power density spectrum flat over a bandwidth much wider than the process bandwidth), the cross-correlation function between $c(t)$ and the noise is the impulse response. Such an approach has the advantage that $g(t)$ can be evaluated without disturbing significantly the normal operation of the system, since only small-amplitude noise need be employed, but the disadvantage that rather elaborate electronic equipment is required to perform the cross-correlation operations in a short interval of time (usually we need a separate channel for each point to be measured on the impulse-response characteristic).

CONCLUDING COMMENT

In this chapter we have attempted to summarize the basic techniques which the electrical engineer has found most useful in the approach to the identification problem for linear systems. Unfortunately, the major research effort in both control and electronic systems engineering during the past decade has been focused on techniques for the design and evaluation of the system once the identification problem is solved. As systems engineering encounters problems with increasingly stringent specifications (so that increased demands are imposed on the accuracy of identification) and problems of rapidly increasing breadth, encompassing situations in which the pertinent physical laws are unknown, the systems engineer devotes an increasing portion of his effort to identification.

In this chapter we have restricted consideration not only to linear systems but, even further, to models which are analytic and deterministic in nature. If we further introduce the problems of reliability and consistency (in the presence of manufacturing tolerances), the models must be probabilistic (e.g., containing random-signal generators to represent the effects of variations of component values).

Thus, we have indicated only the fundamental and most widely used techniques of the electrical engineer, and focused particular attention on those approaches which are most useful in the construction of adaptive systems, in which the equipment is asked to perform a continuing, automatic self-design.

REFERENCE

1. E. Mishkin and L. Braun, Jr., *Adaptive Control Systems,* McGraw-Hill Book Co., New York, 1960, Chap. 3.

CHAPTER 13

ON THE INTERRELATIONSHIPS OF SYSTEMS SCIENCE AND SYSTEMS ENGINEERING IN THE PROCESSING INDUSTRIES

A. R. AIKMAN

The practice of engineering is based partly on science, partly on art. The branch of engineering with which this chapter is concerned, namely process control engineering, has been developed in a short time to a surprisingly sophisticated and successful level with very little aid from engineering science. Until very recently, it was based almost entirely on art.

These statements in no way minimize the massive contribution of the physical sciences to the design of instruments for measurement— a contribution satisfying a need. Rather, they are intended to imply that control instruments have been and are commercially available with intrinsic performance characteristics beyond the capability of most users to exploit to the full. They are also intended to imply that only within the last few years has there been any economic need for the application of scientific system design methods.

In order to appreciate fully the situation which exists in this not unimportant section of the economy, it is necessary to trace the salient points in the evolution of process control instruments and their applications before attempting to assess the contribution of systems science.

ON SYSTEMS ENGINEERING

Control of a manufacturing process, in the normal sense of the words, means coordinated actions based on the feedback of information about measured variables, to achieve a given objective most economically. Since processing companies are in business to make a profit (within defined legal boundaries), the criteria for acceptance of new control equipment or methods are rather simple: will they help the company make money, and if so how much? As an expression of the acceptance of instrumentation by process management, installed instrument costs in new plants generally run from 5% to 10% of total capital costs, which is by no means insignificant. Instruments are selected on the basis of accuracy, maintainability, dynamics characteristics (sometimes), and general suitability; this work is the province of the applications engineer.

Systems engineering does not start until a functional analysis of the system objective, and of each component of the control loop (especially including the process itself), has been carried out. The systems engineer may utilize all the pertinent scientific disciplines, and all the arts of application engineering. In this sense the systems engineer is still a *rara avis* in industry, because acceptance of his methods by the processing industry has been slow, although the "tools" have been available for rather a long time.

One of the basic reasons for the slow acceptance of systems engineering may be the way in which process plants are designed, i.e., with considerable reserve capacity for safety and for maximum flexibility in operation. If a plant were designed with large enough capacities to run for long periods at steady rates, it would require the very minimum of unsophisticated controls. At the other extreme, minimization of capacities in large interconnected systems tends to maximize the amount and complexity of controls and computers, especially in processes with fast kinetics. It is now generally realized that somewhere in this spectrum of alternative system designs is the economically optimum design for a given process; this optimum can only be arrived at by systems engineering studies.

ON PROCESS CONTROL

The closed loop of an automatic control system, shown in Fig. 1, has a behavior pattern which indicates that it is more than the sum of its parts, because of the ever-circulating information content of the loop. The blocks in this diagram will be familiar, in function and sequence, to all readers. Stress is laid on the "disturbance" signals which impinge on the loop, for without disturbances no controls would be needed. On occasion the "set-point" signal itself may rank as a disturbance, deliberately injected by the operator.

Real processing systems are composed of a multiplicity of such

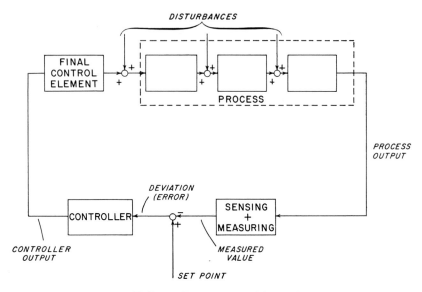

FIG. 1. Process control loop.

loops, which may interact each with the other in any degree. At least 95% of the control instruments today are applied to the automatic control of environmental conditions such as flow, pressure, temperature, and level, although the continuous measurement of composition is becoming feasible on an ever-broadening front.

The design problems in these systems may be ranked in three major categories: stability, controllability, and operability. I shall briefly examine these general problems in order, before considering details of instrumentation.

ON STABILITY

A linear closed-loop control system will be stable if the open-loop gain is less than unity over an appropriate frequency range and if there is adequate phase margin. Most systems are linear within the range of small excursions. Stability is not difficult to comprehend or to achieve. Modern standard controllers, either pneumatic or electronic, have only three adjustable parameters—proportional band, reset rate, and rate (or derivative) time. Each of these parameters is variable over a range of 100 : 1 or more. Thus it is normally a very easy matter to "turn on the air (or electricity)," adjust the knobs, and achieve some stability. Exceptions occur, as would be expected, in the presence of marked nonlinearities or strong interloop coupling.

ON CONTROLLABILITY

Controllability is a concept which signifies the amount of useful work that the controller is doing for the user. Many quantitative measures of controllability have been proposed in the literature.

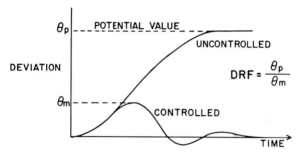

FIG. 2. Deviation reduction factor.

Among the simplest measures are the frequency of damped oscillation of the loop and the deviation reduction factor or DRF.[1] The DRF, in a process with self-regulation, is the ratio of the potential value of deviation without control θp to the maximum value of deviation when under control θm when a sudden disturbance is injected into the system, as shown in Fig. 2. Obviously, the higher the value of DRF, the more controllable is the system.

The controllability of a system depends on the location of the disturbance and on the topology of the process elements. The smaller the distance between disturbance and sensing element, the less effective will be the efforts of the controller to reduce the effects of the disturbance. Also, the type of energy storage in the process has a major influence on controllability; two extreme categories of process lag are generally recognized, dead-time (or transport) lag and capacity (or transfer) lag, both shown in Fig. 3. Dead time, with its inherently low controllability, may be experienced in the domestic shower. The

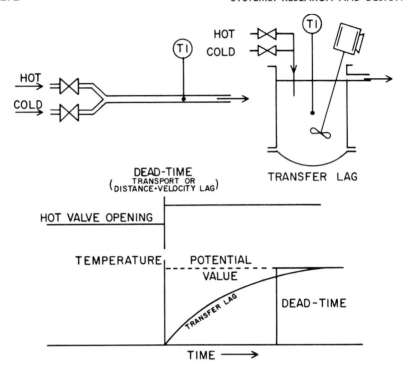

FIG. 3. Transient behavior of process lags.

well-agitated tub (whose controllability would satisfy the most fastidious) typifies the capacity lag. All real processes partake of the character of each of these types of lag in varying proportion. The effect of changing the proportion of each, in a given total, is illustrated in Fig. 4. When the process is all dead time, the DRF is at the irreducible minimum of unity, and as the dead time decreases the DRF tends toward infinity.

Most continuous reaction processes take place most efficiently under conditions of piston flow,[2] where each element of fluid resides in the reactor for the same length of time. In the more easily controlled agitated vessels[3] there may be a distribution of residence times which is unfavorable for reactor efficiency; this is a major problem for the systems engineer. Meaningful quantitative measures of controllability can only be derived from dynamic analysis of the process itself.

A number of methods have been used for the experimental determination of process transfer functions, most of these methods requiring the deliberate injection into the process of a signal of known form (such as a pulse, step, or sinusoid). One method[4] is based on the statistical correlation of input and output data and has the advantage that it does not require any active interference with the process. The limited studies reported in the literature suggest that the frequency-response method, see Fig. 5, is the most accurate even in the presence

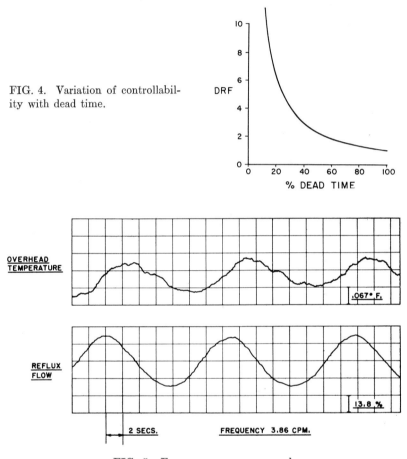

FIG. 4. Variation of controllability with dead time.

FIG. 5. Frequency-response record.

of noise;[5, 6] can often be carried out with very small signals;[5] and has the great advantage that the data can be rapidly reduced to usable form without machine computation unless the noise is excessive. On the other hand, the demand on the investigator's time may be quite considerable.

It must be reported that the correlation of measured transfer functions with the same calculated from basic process parameters is lagging the field; one reason for this may be that most real processes of economic interest have distributed parameters and must be represented by rather intractable partial differential equations.[7]

ON OPERABILITY

The control of processing operations is generally exercised by a human operator, through the instruments. Operability of the processes

FIG. 6. Circular chart recorder-controller. (Courtesy Foxboro Company.)

depends on the design of the physical plant and on the means by which information is conveyed to the operator for logical deductions which will result in useful action. An examination of instruments and instrument arrays will point up the main system design problems.

FIG. 7. Circular chart recorder-controller: internals. (Courtesy Foxboro Company.)

ON THE EVOLUTION OF CONTROL INSTRUMENTS

Pneumatic instrument systems, in which information is carried on an air pressure signal, came into general use in the 1920's and still have the major share of the market. Compressed air as a medium for power and information transfer combines the qualities of great power amplification, very low cost, and high reliability; furthermore, it is not under any circumstances a fire or explosion hazard. Instruments of the general type shown in Figs. 6 and 7 (with mechanical input, pneumatic output) tended to dominate the scene until the 1940's, when it became technically possible to divorce the sensing, recording, and controlling functions through the application of plant-mounted feedback transmitters such as those shown in Figs. 8 and 9.

The simultaneous evolution of pneumatic controllers separable from the recorders permitted the application engineers very considerable flexibility, as illustrated by such instrument systems as Fig. 10; it became possible to separate the control from the point of supervision by distances of hundreds of feet. Research studies on pneumatic

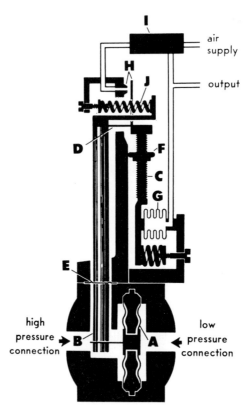

FIG. 8.   Differential-pressure   transmitter,   schematic.   (Courtesy   Foxboro Company.)

transmission[8-10] disclosed the ultimate limitations of pneumatic controls, in particular their peculiar impedance-matching problems. Since the 1950's, as would be expected, all-electronic measurement and control systems have been developed to an acceptable level of reliability and are now making a significant dent in the market.

A control room, or area of centralized supervision, built in the early 1940's would look like the one shown in Fig. 11. The module is about 2 feet in dimension; recorder-controllers are stacked two-high; there-

FIG. 9.   Differential-pressure transmitter, installation.   (Courtesy Foxboro Company.)

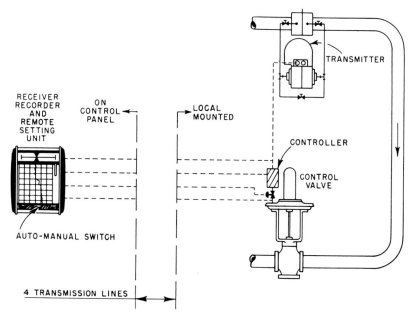

FIG. 10.   Flow control: controller on control valve.   (Courtesy Foxboro
Company.)

FIG. 11.   Control room.   (Courtesy Foxboro Company.)

fore the instrument packing density is about one per lineal foot. In large integrated refineries producing a variety of products simultaneously, from aviation gasoline to lubricating oil, the control panel would be hundreds of feet long to accommodate all the necessary recorder-controllers. Since one operator could only supervise a very limited length of panel, a great many operators were required and the problems of interhuman communication could become acute.

FIG. 12. Graphic control panel. (Courtesy Foxboro Company.)

A great advance in the utilization of information was made in 1948 with the invention of the "graphic panel,"[11] an example of which is shown in Fig. 12. Using the new generation of recorders which require only 5 or 6 inches of lineal panel space, not only could a greater packing density be achieved but the operator could be given a graphic image of the process itself. Packing densities of up to four instruments per lineal foot have recently become practicable and fairly common, as illustrated in Fig. 13.

With these developments in instrumentation, plus the introduction of analytical instrumentation and digital data-loggers,[12] the operator's job has assumed new dimensions. The motive for further progress in process automation is not reduction in labor—for the irreducible minimum compatible with safety has been reached already—but in allowing machines to make more lower level decisions with greater efficiency and economy. The human operator excels in his ability to:

1. Sense minimum amounts of visual and acoustic energy.
2. Perceive visual patterns.
3. Improvise, use imagination, and exercise judgment.

The basic problem in the design of information systems for process

FIG. 13.   Semigraphic panel.   (Courtesy Foxboro Company.)

control has been, and still is, the presentation of meaningful information to the operator in such a way as to make full use of these special abilities. The design of a process control room is a complex problem in man-machine interfaces. Little scientific effort has been made to define or improve the efficiency of this interface, and the solutions we have today are the results of 30 years' empirical experience.

ON ANALYTICAL INSTRUMENTATION

A profound change in process control, which results in even further demands on the operator, is taking place owing to the increasing availability of reliable instruments which yield rapid data on quality and composition, thus eliminating the long and variable dead times which take place in laboratory analysis. The installation of an automatic analyzer shortens this dead time in the information feedback from hours to minutes or seconds, and makes the information more valuable in nonlinear proportion (if it is interpreted and used correctly). However, for a good return on investment, analytical instrumentation demands good systems engineering because of some inherent peculiarities:

1. The raw data may require computation to make them rapidly intelligible; furthermore, data may be sampled.
2. Good sample-handling systems are of paramount importance.
3. Composition may not be a simple function of one manipulated variable.

ON THE EVOLUTION OF SYSTEMS SCIENCE

A chronology of important developments in process systems engineering and systems science has been constructed in a subjective (and perhaps arbitrary) fashion by the writer, and is presented in Fig. 14. Most of the developments in engineering have been touched on, if lightly, and details are available in manufacturers' catalogs. As to the relevant developments in systems science, these are embodied in the literature and some attempt will be made to disentangle the skein of some of these theoretical developments and illustrate their influence on engineering:

1. *Nonlinear theory.* Stemming from the early work of Minorsky and others, a flood of papers has appeared during the last five years.

It cannot be maintained that nonlinear theory has had any practical influence on process control; the trend in engineering has been to linearize gross nonlinearities, and to eliminate by better instrument design the small-signal nonlinearities. No attempt has yet been made to exploit some of the advantages of deliberately nonlinear controllers, probably because linear ones are so inexpensive.

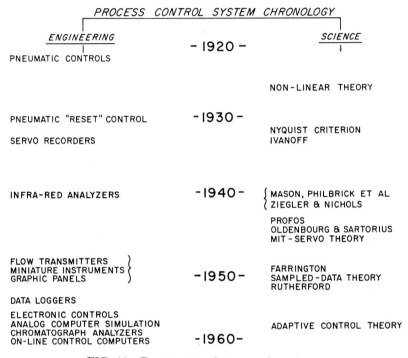

FIG. 14. Process control system chronology.

2. *Frequency-response theory*. Although the use of sinusoids in network stability analysis has been familiar to electrical engineers since the propounding of the Nyquist criterion, and although the practicality of this tool in process control was suggested by Ivanoff in 1934,[13] it was not until about 1950 that it was forged into a simple, usable engineers' aid by Farrington[14] and Rutherford[1] both for stability and controllability analysis, despite the massive contribution of MIT writers in the middle 1940's. Today, it is fairly generally accepted and used.

3. *Sampled-data theory*. The output of theoretical papers during the last 10 years has been very considerable (perhaps spurred on by military needs). Only a few writers[15] have attempted to translate

this body of material into terms able to be used by process systems engineers, although the explosive development of analytical instruments such as the chromatograph now demands the use of such tools. Here is a fine field for exploitation by those engineers with a taste for simplification.

4. *Differential equations.* Mason, Philbrick, Ziegler, Nichols, and also Oldenbourg and Sartorius[16] attempted to apply the methods of differential equations to process control around 1940. Little of practical significance has appeared since, but a resurgence of interest is now noted owing to the spreading use of analog computers for process simulation.

5. *Human factors and operations research.* The systematic application of these powerful new disciplines (or interdisciplines) to process control is lagging, except for the design of dials and pointers.

6. *Transfer function analysis.* In any attempt to analyze the controllability of a process yet in the design stage, accurate means for calculating the transfer functions from design data are a necessity. Although mathematical methods for deriving the transfer functions of heat exchangers (with distributed parameters) have been published by Profos,[7] Takahashi,[17] and others, much simplification remains to be done before these methods can become widely useful in engineering.

7. *Adaptive control theory.* This is a relatively new science,[18, 19] with great potential applications in the engineering of computer-directed control systems.

This list could be extended, but the general picture that emerges is that systems science has had little direct influence on process system engineering. In those few cases where there has been a direct influence, frequently decades have elapsed between the first publication of a new concept of methodology and its general acceptance into the body of engineering practice. In many instances, of course, instrument technology has not been of a high enough standard to enable the system designer to avail himself of the scientific tools, but it is believed that this phase is passing or has already passed. The very recent development of computers suitable for on-line control is proving to be a powerful stimulus for systems engineering.[20]

ON COMPUTERS AND OPTIMIZING CONTROL

By "computer" is meant a calculating machine which continually and automatically receives measured data from several points in the process, makes computations of an arithmetic or integrodifferential nature using these data, makes decisions, and causes manipulation of dependent variables.

As has already been described, there is a rapid trend now in progress to "move the lab into the plant" by using more analytical instruments on-stream. Another trend is just beginning: to mechanize the operations of process management, and to make more higher level decisions on rates of output, process coordination, and profit maximization automatically and with less lag. This is what the control computer is intended to do.

For a computer to pay out the investment rapidly enough, at least three conditions must be satisfied:

1. There must be adequate, reliable measuring instrumentation.

2. There must be control systems which will respond to instructions quickly and accurately.

3. There must be a "model" of the process, containing criteria of some sort for the optimum conditions.

A model of a process is quite necessary. It may be as simple as a cam or a graph, but more typically it will be sets of equations which define relationships between input and output variables, define restraints, and express the profit or performance being derived from the process.

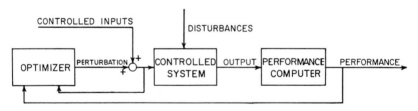

FIG. 15. Direct optimization.

Direct optimization without a model has been used in a scheme such as Fig. 15, in which a periodic perturbation is employed to initiate changes in inputs. Direct optimizaton is exploratory and sequential in nature, in that the result of each perturbation is assessed before the next is injected, and is sometimes described as "peak-searching optimization." The sequencing and strategy of perturbation became unduly complex for more than two inputs, and the usefulness of this approach may be limited.

Schemes such as Fig. 16, repetitive computed optimization,[21] are of more general application. By repetitive feedback of output information, and by reference to a model of some kind, the system tends to force the process to the desired performance despite inadequacies of the model. In real systems, which are incompletely deterministic, the

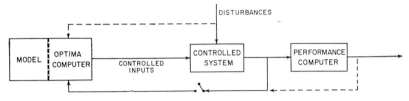

FIG. 16. Repetitive computed optimization.

model will always be inadequate to some degree, and these inadequacies limit the length of time for which an accurate prediction can be made by the computer in repetitive optimization schemes.

As the process continues to operate, with the passage of time more information becomes available to the computer, and it is possible to postulate a control system, Fig. 17, which can "learn" to improve its

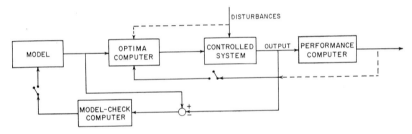

FIG. 17. Adaptive optimization.

performance based on experience. This is the conceptual basis for the recent development of adaptive control theory. Theoretically at least, a computer can learn to modify its behavior, or whole policies of behavior, by taking cognizance of changes in inputs or process characteristics.

In the development of kinetic and dynamic models descriptive of the process, the most important step is the correlation of the model with data observed and recorded, e.g., by a digital logger. This procedure almost inevitably demands the solution of partial differential equations, for which analog or digital computers may be used. In the past, conventional analog computers, in spite of their relatively high speed and low cost, have been almost excluded from this type of operation because of excessive component requirements. However, recent developments in reliable dynamic memory and high-speed repetitive operation in analog computers have made it possible to evaluate the required functions in a rapid, accurate, and economical manner, either on a simulation or control basis. It may be that these new techniques will give a new dimension to the ancient art of analog computation.

It must be noted that many schemes for computer control amount to the mechanization of statistical methods for evolutionary control which have been successfully used in industry for some time.[22, 23]

ON RELIABILITY AND COSTS
OF COMPUTER CONTROL

Reliability of a control computer—or of any other on-line control device—is of course of paramount importance. Complete fail-safe protection can be built into the computer, to avoid disaster, but of course excessive downtime breeds an unfavorable psychological attitude in the operator which will tend to negate the expected benefits.

The cost of a control computer may run from a few thousand dollars to $100,000. To this must be added the cost of special facilities to match the computer to the other instrumentation and the costs of system analysis and programming; the total may approach $250,000. To justify such an expenditure it is necessary to estimate the dollar benefits before installation. Estimation of the possible payout requires an unusually searching analysis of the process and associated control systems, during the course of which much will be learned about the instruments, the process, and the process operability. It has been stated recently[24] that this type of analysis is usually highly profitable, whether or not a computer is ultimately required.

At the time of writing, one may receive the impression from some of the published literature that there are more manufacturers of control computers (one estimate is 15) than customers. However, from the first installation in 1959, expected 1960 sales may be over $10 million, and the market can be expected to grow exponentially for a few years. This will not be an insignificant portion of the total market for instruments and controls, currently estimated at $4 billion per annum. In brief, computers are setting the pattern of control for tomorrow.

REFERENCES

1. C. I. Rutherford, The Practical Application of Frequency Response Analysis to Automatic Process Control, *Proceedings of the Institution of Mechanical Engineers (London)*, vol. 162, 1950, p. 334.
2. P. V. Danckwerts, Continuous Flow Systems, *Chemical Engineering Science*, vol. 2, no. 1, 1953, p. 1.
3. O. A. Solheim, A Guide to Controlling Continuous-Flow Chemical Reactors, *Control Engineering*, Apr. 1960, vol. 7, p. 107.
4. T. P. Goodman and J. B. Reswick, Determination of System Characteristics from Normal Operating Records, *Transactions of the American Society of Mechanical Engineers*, vol. 78, 1956, p. 259.
5. A. R. Aikman, Frequency Response Analysis of a Fractionating Column, *Proceedings of the Instrument Society of America*, vol. 11, 1956, Paper 56-28-3.
6. P. Cowley, The Application of an Analog Computer to the Measurement of Process Dynamics, *Transactions of the American Society of Mechanical Engineers*, vol. 77, 1957, p. 823.
7. P. Profos, *Die Behandlung von Regelproblemen vermittels des Frequenzganges des Regelkreises*, Leemann, Zurich, 1943.
8. M. Bradner, Pneumatic Transmission Lag, *Instruments*, vol. 22, no. 7, 1949, p. 618.
9. J. E. Samson, Dynamic Characteristics of Pneumatic Transmission, *Transactions of Society of Instrument Technology*, vol. 10, no. 3, 1958, p. 117.
10. W. H. Howe, "Some Recent Developments in Process Control," in *Automatic and Manual Control*, A. Tustin, ed., Butterworths, 1952.
11. D. M. Boyd, Process Control by Graphic Panel, *Oil and Gas Journal*, vol. 48, Sept. 15, 1949, p. 86.
12. E. J. Schubert, Statistical Computers Can Really Reduce Data, *Control Engineering*, Apr. 1960, vol. 7, p. 146.
13. A. Ivanoff, Theoretical Foundations of the Automatic Regulation of Temperature, *Journal of the Institute of Fuel*, vol. 7, 1934, p. 117.
14. G. H. Farrington, Theoretical Foundations of Process Control, *Journal of the Institution of Electrical Engineers (London)*, vol. 94, 1947, p. 23.
15. Gene F. Franklin, Introduction to Sampled Data Systems, *Proceedings of the Instrument Society of America*, vol. 11, 1956, Paper 56-6-3.
16. R. C. Oldenbourg and H. Sartorius, *Dynamik Selbststatiger Regelungen*, Verlag Oldenbourg, Munich, 1944.
17. Y. Takahashi, "Transfer Function Analysis of Heat Exchange Processes," in *Automatic and Manual Control*, A. Tustin, ed., Butterworths, 1952.
18. J. A. Aseltine, et al., A Survey of Adaptive Control Systems, *IRE Transactions on Automatic Control*, vol. PGAC-6, Dec. 1958, p. 102.
19. R. Bellman, and R. Kalaba, On Adaptive Control Processes, *IRE Transactions on Automatic Control*, vol. PGAC-4, no. 2, 1959, p. 1.
20. M. Phister, Jr., Digital Control Systems—Present and Future, *IRE Transactions on Industrial Electronics*, vol. PGIE-11, 1959, p. 44.
21. I. Lefkowitz, and D. P. Eckman, Optimizing Control by Model Methods, *Journal of the Instrument Society of America*, vol. 6, no. 7, 1959, p. 74.
22. O. L. Davies, (ed.), *Statistical Methods in Research and Production*, Hafner, New York, 1957.

23. W. J. Youden, Evolutionary Operation, *Industrial and Engineering Chemistry,* June 1959, vol. 51, p. 79A.
24. C. R. Hall, Computer Control of Processes: Is it worth the cost? *Chemical Engineering Progress,* vol. 56, no. 2, 1960, p. 62.

CHAPTER 14

SYSTEMS ENGINEERING FROM AN INDUSTRIAL VIEWPOINT

H. CHESTNUT

The importance of engineering is generally recognized in an industrial manufacturing organization; however, the particular systems engineering task is frequently not so explicitly identified. To present the systems engineering problem from an industrial viewpoint, the nature of the industrial process will be described and the environment in which its products operate will be discussed. With the problem thus stated, consideration will be given to the definition of systems engineering, including the objectives and restraints of the system.

Because systems engineering problems frequently do not follow a prescribed design procedure, the general approach to be used in the solution of systems engineering will next be outlined. This general approach can then be set forth in a mathematical formulation which shows the multiloop, multivariable, nonlinear nature of the systems engineering problem and points to the direction of its control. Finally, because the present state of the systems engineering art is somewhat remote from the ideal that has been described, some of the steps that lie ahead in bringing the ideal closer to reality are outlined.

THE INDUSTRIAL PROCESS
AND THE ENVIRONMENT FOR ITS SYSTEMS

The industrial process consists of the conception, design, and manufacture of products, a number of which work together as systems. These systems are installed and operated in a customer's environment that includes the natural phenomena of temperature, humidity, shock, vibration, etc., as well as the external sources of power and the human environment of maintenance and service. These relationships are shown in a simple schematic fashion in Fig. 1, which also indicates the effect of the materials and inspection prior to the production and the quality control, test, packing and shipping following it. As is evident from this diagram, the engineering of a system of the sort being considered here is one which provides for the compatible operation of the equipment under the "operate" and "maintain and service" phases as well as the ability to accomplish the design and production of the equipment. The large arrow pointing from left to right serves to emphasize the fact that the systems engineering problem is spread out in time and space over a number of locations.

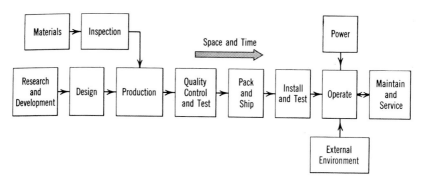

FIG. 1. Industrial process and the environment for its products.

Because many of the large systems being engineered these days are sufficiently small in number or perhaps are a sufficiently small part of the total equipment operated by the user, it is highly desirable from the manufacturer's and from the user's points of view that the system components be somewhat compatible with other equipments that are similar in function. Figure 2 illustrates the fact that whereas one system (no. 1) may be manufactured for customer A with his personnel, environment, and operating conditions, the next system (no. 2) may be developed, designed, produced, and tested in essentially the same place at a later time for customer B with another set of personnel, environment, and operating conditions. To the extent that it is possible to use facilities, training, and procedures for more than one system, the manufacturer is able to spread some of his overhead expenses over a broader base and reduce this item of cost. To the extent that it is possible for a user to be able to operate and maintain systems from different manufacturers, he is able to buy in a market with more suppliers with a better possibility of a lower price being realized. Thus, the systems engineering approach involves a consideration of more than one set of choices in which the effect of

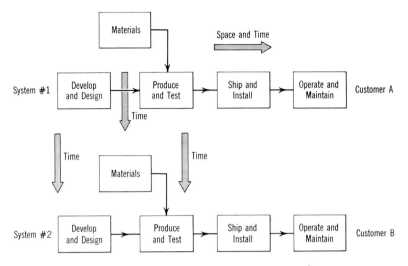

FIG. 2. Relationship of one system to another.

neighboring systems in time and space can have a bearing on the cost and value of a system over a period of time.

In judging a system, the customer weighs it on a number of different scales to determine its over-all worth to him and therefore its value to him. These standards of judgment include:

1. Performance.
2. Cost.
3. Reliability.
4. Time (to build and install, life of system).
5. Serviceability.

Thus the system engineer has a number of different criteria that his design must meet. Although the engineer in considering system design traditionally places paramount emphasis on performance and/or cost, this may not be the same basis on which the customer weighs his decision as to the value of the system to him. It is of great importance to the systems engineer that he appreciate the relative utility of these customer value standards and that he be successful in providing that system which most nearly meets in the over-all sense the customer's desires.

The foregoing illustrations serve to indicate the nature of the systems engineering problem as viewed from industry and to provide a starting point on which a more thorough investigation of systems engineering may be based.

WHAT IS SYSTEMS ENGINEERING?

Systems engineering has a large number of definitions and meanings to the increasing number of people who are getting interested in it. My description of the term will emphasize what seem to be the central themes common to these many definitions, rather than stress the inherent merit of one particular definition.

Systems engineering involves the over-all consideration of various methods of accomplishing a desired result. The result is considered as an integrated whole which may include a number of subsidiary parts or functions. The selection of these parts includes a series of choices in which the characteristics of the parts are judged in terms of their ability to contribute to the optimum weighted result for the whole.

To provide a concrete statement with which to explain the various facets of systems engineering, use will be made of the definition set forth by J. A. Morton, Vice President of the Bell Telephone Laboratories.[1] This quotation presents a reasonable basis for bringing out the concept of systems engineering without introducing still another definition in a field where so many already exist.

The Systems Engineering method recognizes that each system is *an integrated whole* even though composed of *diverse, specialized structures and sub-functions*. It further recognizes that *any system has a number of objectives* and that the *balance between them may differ widely from system to system*. The methods seek to *optimize the overall system functions according to the weighted objectives* and to achieve maximum compatibility of its parts.

In order to clarify this definition, it is worthwhile to consider the italicized terms in somewhat greater detail.

An Integrated Whole

The nature of the whole is in no way limited in terms of the size, the nature of physical problem, or the manner in which the whole is subdivided. The system may be an economic, social, or political system or it may, as in the cases of the systems we are considering, be an engineering system for the design and manufacture and operation of a particular product. The success of the system, rather than whether each part functions in an optimum fashion of itself, is the primary objective. The system may be made up of existing parts and the problem may be one of how to use most effectively these parts in conjunction with new portions, or the problem may be one of determining the best equipment to be used independent of existing devices.

Furthermore, the particular system involved with its inputs and outputs may itself either serve as a part of a larger "supersystem" or the various subsystems making up this present system may themselves be considered from the systems approach. Thus, a radar system may form a part of a National Missile Defense System and in turn the radar system may have, as part of its own system, an antenna drive system which again can be treated in the same systems fashion. Although the requirements placed on each of these different systems are not the same, the general methods used in arriving at the systems solution are similar.

Diversed, Specialized Structures and Subfunctions

There is no particular a priori way in which the parts making up the whole are chosen. The needs and objectives of the whole influence the structures and subfunctions which contribute to the over-all whole. The subfunctions are chosen in such a way as to make possible the over-all operation and contribute to the success of the whole. The choice of the individual parts may be greatly influenced by the availability of certain equipment or facilities that represent the current "state of the art."

Any System has a Number of Objectives

These objectives can be related to the objectives of the individual subfunctions which may be objectives of the whole system or may merely be a way of contributing to the operation of the whole system. These objectives may be such things as simplicity, ease of maintenance, cost, life, performance, or other factors, all of which may be required to be present simultaneously or at different times. Thus, a jet engine may have as its objective to produce a certain maximum thrust. However, under some limited number of conditions, the attainment of this maximum thrust might require excess temperatures that would reduce the life of the engine or might require a prohibitive increase in weight. Under these conditions the maximum thrust requirement may be waived in favor of some of the other objectives.

Balance Between Them may Differ Widely from System to System

Some systems stress precision of performance and relegate cost to a minor role. Some are extremely cost-sensitive and are less responsive to reliability or other factors. Because of these differences in balance, it is necessary that each system be considered on its own basis and the relative merits of the different objectives be considered in their proper order of importance.

Optimize the Over-all System Functions According to the Weighted Objectives

In effect, the over-all system functions are optimized by combining in a weighted fashion the many subsidiary objectives in their proper value. Rather than operating each part at its individual optimum, the weighted average of each of the objectives is given suitable consideration to achieve the optimum for the over-all system functions. In many systems the nature of the weighting functions which describe the value of the various functions is but vaguely known and it is necessary to study in considerable detail the true nature of the process so as to be able to properly weight the contribution of each function.

SYSTEMS ENGINEERING OBJECTIVES AND RESTRAINTS

To further illuminate the definition of the system problem, it is important to note that in addition to the many objectives set forth for the system there are also a number of restraints which are present and that these may vary from system to system. This section will indicate more specifically the nature of some of these objectives and restraints.

One of the objectives of a system is that it accomplish a desired level of performance. In general, the many desired objectives are frequently stated as the minimum acceptable or the maximum allowable. Frequently, more favorable results than are asked for in the requirements are welcomed, but the value of these better results may not be proportionate to the effort required to obtain them. On the other hand, the required level of performance may not be known precisely since the operation has been under manual control with only meager instrumentation or data logging. As examples of certain end results we have such factors as speed, accuracy, size of equipment, efficiency, gross output, weight, or other similar considerations.

Another objective is that the desired performance be obtained within an acceptable cost goal. The specific cost goal must be clearly stated because cost is influenced markedly by the nature of the type of cost being considered. For example, the cost may be that for one unit, or the cost may be that for a number of units. Furthermore, the cost of interest is probably the cost over a period of time, e.g., a year, five years, or perhaps 2000 operating hours. The cost over this period of time is a function of a particular kind of maintenance, downtime, or service given the equipment. Costs include the purchased cost of the equipment, the cost of installation, the cost of maintenance, the cost of operation, etc.

Another factor involved in the cost picture is the loss incurred by the system or equipment not functioning properly. This factor must be considered during the system investigation. For example, if a given relay is an essential portion of the particular system being considered, the cost of the relay must be balanced against the cost of having the system not operate owing to the failure of the relay to perform satisfactorily.

This matter of cost immediately brings out the importance of reliability as a factor which affects both performance and cost. Reliability is "the probability that the system of subsystems operate in the manner intended when operated in the environment encountered." Reliability is related to systems performance because if certain parts of the system fail the designed performance is not obtained. Degradation may be partial, in which event there is only partial performance, or the degradation may be total, in which event entirely unsatisfactory performance may be obtained unless fail-safe features are employed.

Reliability is also related to cost because reduced performance resulting from low reliability involves added cost factors. There are charges for repairing the failure and for spoiling the product. There is a loss of return on investment because the capital required for the purchase of the system fails to yield satisfactory returns.

The time required to accomplish the objectives also affects cost. Since the improved system represents a more effective way of doing the job, the sooner it is available the sooner will the increased return on the money invested be realized. A further benefit of a shorter time to accomplish an end result is that being first or early with a new product is definitely advantageous. As such, there is a premium placed on accomplishing the end result more quickly.

On the other hand, if the time required to do the job is so short that much premium pay or extraordinary effort is needed to realize the system, the costs tend to increase. Contrarily, a job which is performed too slowly costs more than if it were done more rapidly. This follows from the fact that a person must devote a certain percentage of his efforts to a given undertaking simply to understand it and be able to contribute to it. If half or less of a person's time is required, it is still necessary to hire one person and the additional costs tend to mount up.

Influencing the decisions of a system are the restraints placed on it in addition to its objectives. These restraints may include external environments or inputs to the system, and in addition they may include internal conditions which are limited by the inherent capabilities of the equipment or system being employed.

Included in the external environments may be such factors as the following:

1. Power sources, i.e., the nature of the power source, be it electrical, hydraulic, mechanical, pneumatic.

2. Signal characteristics, whether the signal is a relatively clear one, whether it is analog or digital in form, whether it is a-c or d-c, and other such considerations.

3. Temperature, whether the temperature is the over-all outside ambient temperature or a localized environment generated as a result of the equipment itself.

4. Humidity, whether this is the local humidity or the broader over-all ambient humidity.

5. Vibration, shock, and disturbances, either internally or externally caused, and other factors, such as, e.g., the radiation exposure.

Other conditions serving as restraints to the solution of a systems problem might include the following:

6. Use of specific material or components required. Under these conditions systems engineering may involve a determination of the best method of operating specific equipment or components, with a limitation in terms of the kind and number of additional devices that may be used in conjunction with the specific equipment.

7. Union or management manpower rules. These may also serve as restraints in terms of what can be accomplished or what can be considered. The capabilities of the people involved are likewise an additional constraint. This matter will influence the degree of maintenance, servicing, and installation judgment. A decision is necessary as to the part of the work left to the operator and the part achieved by the system designer.

Additional restraints include such things as the capabilities of the people involved, the state of the art of manufacturing equipment available, the state of the art as far as engineering knowledge and resources are concerned, and last, but by no means least, the lack of exact data on which to base judgment. A significant area in this regard is the matter of having inexact or questionable data on which to base the weighting and relative importance of the various portions of the system.

APPROACH USED IN SOLVING SYSTEMS ENGINEERING PROBLEMS

Characteristic of the systems engineering problem are the facts that the exact nature of the results sought may not be known and that many alternative ways exist for accomplishing the over-all result. Hence, the successful solution of systems engineering problems tends to follow certain general approaches in which an iterative method is employed to refine the results as the initial hypotheses are compared with actual facts. The following outline follows the suggestions of Morton in the solution of systems engineering problems.[1]

Formulation of Problem

Determine requirements, establish the objectives, goals, and restraints, and determine the weighting functions to place the proper emphasis on the various system requirements.

The system requirements are determined from a consideration of the users' stated needs, as, e.g., from specifications or previous experience, or from a general knowledge of the same or similar processes. These include the answers to such questions as:

What is the system to do in terms of
    performance (size, weight, efficiency, appearance, etc.)
    cost (absolute, relative, or competitive situations)
    time (when is product wanted, time required to produce)
    reliability (life, failure rate, etc.)
What environment does it have to operate it
    home, commercial, military
    power supply, variations
    maintenance, service
What environment is the product to be made in
    engineering skills and facilities
    manufacturing skills and facilities
    what other products are being engineered and built
    what materials are available

The relative weighting factors to be used with the information gained from the answers to the foregoing questions should be determined as well as possible.

Synthesize System to Meet Performance Requirements

A number of alternative solutions which appear possible of success should be considered. From these a limited number should be chosen which appear to have the most likelihood of being successful. A range of values should be used for the various parameters and configurations, and a region of acceptable solutions can be determined. These data frequently point up what information is needed to make further decisions. Furthermore, from such analysis the critical assumptions are indicated and one is most able to make decisions as to which solutions appear most probable of meeting systems requirements.

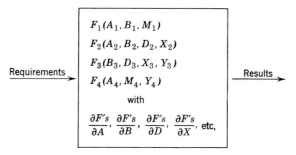

Requirements →

$$F_1(A_1, B_1, M_1)$$
$$F_2(A_2, B_2, D_2, X_2)$$
$$F_3(B_3, D_3, X_3, Y_3)$$
$$F_4(A_4, M_4, Y_4)$$

with

$$\frac{\partial F's}{\partial A}, \frac{\partial F's}{\partial B}, \frac{\partial F's}{\partial D}, \frac{\partial F's}{\partial X}, \text{etc,}$$

Results →

FIG. 3. Consider alternative basic configurations for structuring the system by means of equations, models, block diagrams for alternative configurations.

Each of the alternative configurations is described by means of equations, models, block diagrams, or any other method by which the requirements can be physically realized in an acceptable solution. As shown in Fig. 3, each of the basic configurations is expressed in terms of the significant parameters that effect the end product or result. Not only are the direct functional relationships required but also the rates of change of these functions with changes in the various parameters. From this sort of information it is possible to establish what particular parameters are the most significant ones and what ones are less important for initial consideration.

Those parameters, portions of parameters, or groups of parameters which are found to be most significant are the ones which should be considered for the major functional elements or portions of the system. It is around the major elements that produce the significant parameters that the system structure should logically be built. The basis for determining the significant parameters is that these are the quantities that can influence most markedly the resultant system characteristics with changes in their values.

The system requirements tend to emphasize different aspects of the problem which have to be satisfied. In most cases they do not impose a firm need for a particular kind of hardware or equipment to perform these functions. Thus, a number of separate subsystems tend to be

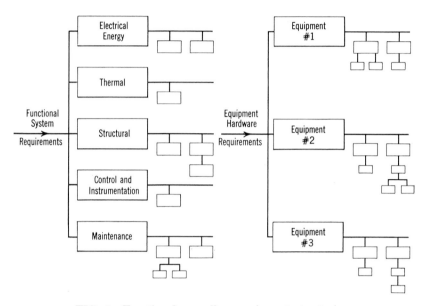

FIG. 4. Functional as well as equipment structuring.

generated, e.g., electrical energy, thermal, structural, controls, and instrumentation, and maintenance and service, with more than one of such subsystems in each area being needed when there are a multiplicity of requirements.

Figure 4 illustrates this situation pictorially. More detailed descriptions of each subsystem such as these are useful in conveying information and later in educating others involved in manufacture, test, installation, and operation about the system.

Find Ways to Construct System

The design process involved is an iterative one of repeatedly trying to obtain improved solutions. Initially when the input data are not well known, approximate methods, calculations, and tests are indicated.

As the sensitivity of the variables becomes apparent the second-order effects should first be neglected. Later, as the first-order effects are understood, it will be essential to include the second-order effects to be sure no obvious obstacles will appear later and that the most satisfactory over-all results will be obtained.

It is now necessary to focus attention on the functional equipment that will most effectively group together the physical parts that will accomplish the systems requirements. By grouping together the necessary hardware in this fashion, a structure of subsystems is created which must be responsive to the system requirements on one hand and to the manufacturing and operational needs on the other.

Figure 4 indicates the nature of the structural configuration that is formed and is purposefully drawn to show schematically all the subassemblies on one sheet. In presenting the information in this way, the effect of different individual items on each other and on the over-all system is emphasized. By referring back to the systems requirements, one is able to weigh the relative effects of various part locations on such factors as performance, cost, reliability, and time.

It is now necessary to relate back the significant decisions to see what effect they have on other portions of the system. When the system structure is well chosen, changes in one part tend to have small, or simply described, effects on the other parts. Included in the interrelationships being considered should be the information and communication problems among individuals working on different parts of the system. As a case in point, some systems structuring methods lead to simple and easily understood interconnecting of elements and others, such as consecutive ones, may lead to great complexity or time-consuming procedures.

Measure Performance and Compare with Objectives

The process of solution of systems engineering problems is an evolutionary one of gradual transition from a statement of the problem in operational terms to a description of the physical equipment that makes up the system in terms of its capabilities. Initially there is a strong emphasis on mathematical equations and model representations. The performance of these representations is compared with the requirements. As the program proceeds the number of physical models and their characteristics increase, with less emphasis on the mathematical representations. Finally, the measured experimental data as represented by the production system must be compared with the original objectives.

Use Performance Error to Refine Formulation, Design, and Construction

As more and more data are available, the ways of converting error information into appropriate changes increase. The refinement and changes in the steps should take place all the way from the problem formulation to the measurement of results. As time proceeds, a higher degree of certainty exists in the knowledge of the system and what it will do. Because of the inherent uncertainty of the data and the requirements, a strong statistical treatment of the problem is required throughout. From consideration of the statistical factors, the effect of small changes in the requirements or the performance of the various parts can be determined and any inherent criticality of these requirements can be established.

NATURE OF THE SYSTEMS ENGINEERING PROBLEM

The existence of many objectives for the systems engineering problem means that the problem is indeed a multivariable, multiloop one. System parameters and decisions made on the basis of their effect on one objective also have effects on the other objectives. The systems engineering problem is one of so arranging the treatment of the system that these interactions are minimized or hopefully made to be most favorable for each of the systems.

Figure 5 is a block diagram indicating the interrelationship of performance, cost, reliability, and statistical parts of a problem. As is indicated, there exist a number of performance loops in which the desired performance is compared with the system performance and the difference is used either to choose a new set of functions and/or equations to describe the performance or to choose some different parameters. In similar fashion there are one or more cost loops in which the desired cost is compared with the system cost and the difference used to modify the functions or parameters of the performance loops so that the cost as well as performance loops can be brought more closely into correspondence with the desired value. Also, there exist one or more reliability loops in which the desired reliability is compared to the system reliability and the difference is used to modify the basic parameters for the circuit if this is required. Other factors influencing the reliability include materials and environment and the probability of each. As can be seen, there are portions

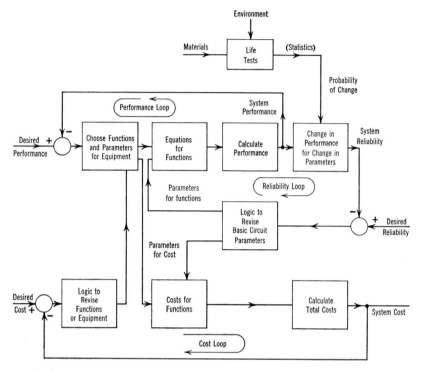

FIG. 5. Interrelationship of performance, reliability, and cost loops.

and values of the reliability and performance loops which are common; hence changes in one are reflected in the other.

Frequently, the problem is a nonlinear one in which the effects of changes in a parameter are not the same in various portions of its operating range, or as a function of other parameters. Because of the presence of nonlinearities it is more desirable for the system to operate in one structural arrangement or configuration than another. Thus, nonlinearities provide significant indicators on which systems design may be based.

Another factor which may be found in systems problems is the presence of discontinuities or discrete size changes or steps. These steps provide nonlinearities and boundaries which may make it markedly more advantageous to operate with one set of values for a given parameter than with a neighboring but different set of values.

In summary, the solution to the systems engineering problem is one of successive approximations. The system requirements are established. One or more systems capable of meeting these requirements are postulated; the most favorable are considered further. These systems are compared with the system objectives and are modified in the light of their inability to meet the initial requirements or to produce the most favorable results. The modified system is again compared and again changed as required by performance data and system requirements.

A MATHEMATICAL FORMULATION
OF THE PROBLEM

The preceding sections of this chapter have tended to stress the qualitative aspects of the systems engineering problem. To emphasize more the quantitative nature of the real problem, a hypothetical case will be considered in this section. A number of objectives will be placed on performance (P_1, P_2, and P_3), on reliability (R_1 and R_2), and on cost (C_1, C_2, and C_3). These are essentially limits, upper or lower as the case may be, for these objectives. Certain critical factors, represented symbolically by A, B, X, Y, and Z will be independent variables whose values may cover a range of values. The over-all utility of the system, U_T, is judged on the basis of a weighted average of the performance, reliability, and cost of the system.

Thus, let the significant performance objectives be represented, as an example, by

$$P_1\text{—the maximum speed}$$
$$P_2\text{—the efficiency} \tag{1}$$
$$P_3\text{—the maximum voltage}$$

Let the reliability objectives be stated as

$$R_1\text{—mean time to failure} \tag{2}$$
$$R_2\text{—mean downtime after failure}$$

Let the cost objectives be stated as

$$C_1\text{—total initial cost of one unit}$$
$$C_2\text{—cost for maintenance} \tag{3}$$
$$C_3\text{—cost of complete unit over a five-year life}$$

The critical factors, represented by A, B, X, Y, and Z, have been greatly reduced in number for purposes of simplicity and might represent

$$A\text{—over-all external dimensions}$$
$$B\text{—closest tolerance to be observed}$$
$$X\text{—quality of mechanical properties used} \tag{4}$$
$$Y\text{—quality of magnetic properties used}$$
$$Z\text{—quality of insulation properties used}$$

Combining expression 4 in expressions 1, 2, and 3, we may write

$$P_1 = f_{P1}(A, B, X, Y, Z)$$
$$P_2 = f_{P2}(A, B, X, Y, Z) \tag{5}$$
$$P_3 = f_{P3}(A, B, X, Y, Z)$$

$$R_1 = f_{R1}(A, B, X, Y, Z)$$
$$R_2 = f_{R2}(A, B, X, Y, Z) \tag{6}$$

$$C_1 = f_{C1}(A, B, X, Y, Z)$$
$$C_2 = f_{C2}(A, B, X, Y, Z) \tag{7}$$
$$C_3 = f_{C3}(A, B, X, Y, Z)$$

Now separating out the f's and replacing them with functional coefficients which may be nonlinear and also functions of other variables, eqs. 5, 6, and 7 may be written as

$$P_1 = M_{P1A}A + M_{P1B}B + M_{P1X}X + M_{P1Y}Y + M_{P1Z}Z$$
$$P_2 = M_{P2A}A + M_{P2B}B + M_{P2X}X + M_{P2Y}Y + M_{P2Z}Z \tag{8}$$
$$P_3 = M_{P3A}A + M_{P3B}B + M_{P3X}X + M_{P3Y}Y + M_{P3Z}Z$$

$$R_1 = M_{R1A}A + M_{R1B}B + M_{R1X}X + M_{R1Y}Y + M_{R1Z}Z$$
$$R_2 = M_{R2A}A + M_{R2B}B + M_{R2X}X + M_{R2Y}Y + M_{R2Z}Z \tag{9}$$

$$C_1 = M_{C1A}A + M_{C1B}B + M_{C1X}X + M_{C1Y}Y + M_{C1Z}Z$$
$$C_2 = M_{C2A}A + M_{C2B}B + M_{C2X}X + M_{C2Y}Y + M_{C2Z}Z \tag{10}$$
$$C_3 = M_{C3A}A + M_{C3B}B + M_{C3X}X + M_{C3Y}Y + M_{C3Z}Z$$

The M coefficients, as indicated, may themselves be related to more than one variable and in fact may be nonlinear functions of the variable of which they are the coefficient. Equations 8, 9, and 10 are ones in which small changes are considered from nominal operating points although the M_{ANB} coefficients may change from nominal operating point to nominal operating point.

In addition the over-all utility, U_T, of the system in total is a weighted function of all the objectives which might in its simpler form have a simple additive relationship like the following:

$$U_T = W_{P1}P_1 + W_{P2}P_2 + W_{P3}P_3 +$$
$$W_{R1}R_1 + W_{R2}R_2 + \tag{11}$$
$$W_{C1}C_1 + W_{C2}C_2 + W_{C3}C_3$$

where W_{P1}, W_{P2}, and W_{P3} are the weighting factors assigned to the value of P_1, P_2, and P_3 to the customer. In similar fashion W_{R1}, W_{R2} are the reliability weighting factors; and W_{C1}, W_{C2}, and W_{C3} are the cost weighting factors. It may well be that the W_P's and the W_R's can all be expressed in dollars so that all the utility terms will end up in dollars. In actuality the problem of getting a clear-cut definition in numerical form of what constitutes the expression for over-all utility may be a difficult one to obtain. Suffice to say, this relationship may be one which will have to be refined with time and further data.

Since from eqs. 8, 9, and 10 the P's, R's, and C's are all functions of A, B, X, Y, and Z, eq. 11 may be rewritten as

$$
\begin{aligned}
U_T = &\left[\begin{array}{l} W_{P1}M_{P1A} + W_{P2}M_{P2A} + W_{P3}M_{P3A} + W_{R1}M_{R1A} + \\ W_{R2}M_{R2A} + W_{C1}M_{C1A} + W_{C2}M_{C2A} + W_{C3}M_{C3A} \end{array} \right] A \\
&+ \left[\begin{array}{l} W_{P1}M_{P1B} + W_{P2}M_{P2B} + W_{P3}M_{P3B} + W_{R1}M_{R1B} + \\ W_{R2}M_{R2B} + W_{C1}M_{C1B} + W_{C2}M_{C2B} + W_{C3}M_{C3B} \end{array} \right] B \\
&+ \left[\begin{array}{l} W_{P1}M_{P1X} + W_{P2}M_{P2X} + W_{P3}M_{P3X} + W_{R1}M_{R1X} + \\ W_{R2}M_{R2X} + W_{C1}M_{C1X} + W_{C2}M_{C2X} + W_{C3}M_{C3X} \end{array} \right] X \quad (12) \\
&+ \left[\begin{array}{l} W_{P1}M_{P1Y} + W_{P2}M_{P2Y} + W_{P3}M_{P3Y} + W_{R1}M_{R1Y} + \\ W_{R2}M_{R2Y} + W_{C1}M_{C1Y} + W_{C2}M_{C2Y} + W_{C3}M_{C3Y} \end{array} \right] Y \\
&+ \left[\begin{array}{l} W_{P1}M_{P1Z} + W_{P2}M_{P2Z} + W_{P3}M_{P3Z} + W_{R1}M_{R1Z} + \\ W_{R2}M_{R2Z} + W_{C1}M_{C1Z} + W_{C2}M_{C2Z} + W_{C3}M_{C3Z} \end{array} \right] Z
\end{aligned}
$$

An electrical analog equivalent of the sort of relationships expressed in eq. 12 in an abbreviated form is shown in Fig. 6. Each of the critical factors A, B, X, Y, and Z through the various M coefficients make up the quantities P_1, P_2, R_1, C_1, C_2 which are combined through the weighting functions W_{P1}, W_{P2}, W_{R1}, W_{C1}, and W_{C2} to the sum, U_T. Since the coefficients and weighting functions may be nonlinear or, discontinuous, the problem of optimizing the result U_T is not a simple one.

From a control point of view, a logical approach to this situation is to feed back the resulting value, U_T, through some process control logic back to the factors A, B, X, Y, and Z, as indicated symbolically in Fig. 7.

The design of the process control logic appears to be different from the customary sort in that only one signal from U_T is available to generate five outputs to A, B, X, Y, and Z. Upon further consideration, one realizes that there is contained in the design process information the design process gradients related to the effect of changes in U_T with each of the factors. Hence, the design of the process control logic appears to be amenable to solution. However, this problem of designing the logic to optimize the design does represent a major area where work is required.

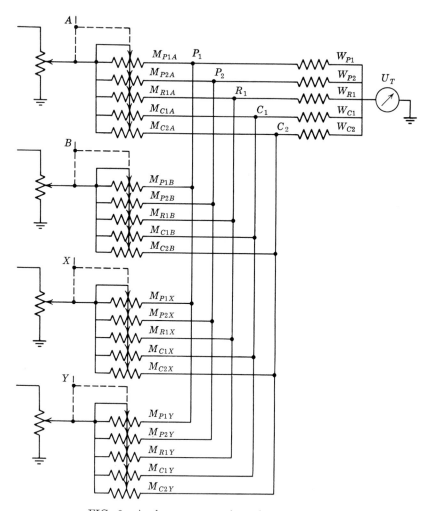

FIG. 6. Analog representation of system utility.

Although an analog interpretation has been placed on the fore-going method of solution, it is evident that the design optimization is ideally fitted for digital solution methods.

The preceding mathematical formulation of the systems engineering problem is useful in serving to identify and describe the process whereby the systems objectives can be related to systems parameters. Furthermore, it serves to point the way toward which a process control logic can be developed which will work toward self-optimizing the design to obtain the greatest over-all utility for the system.

From this simplified description it is evident that a number of areas exist for further effort to be exerted, such as:

1. Development of more exact mathematical models of relationships for performance, reliability, and cost in terms of parameters as given in eqs. 5, 6, and 7. Especially in the fields of cost and reliability is it apt to be particularly difficult to obtain good model relationships.

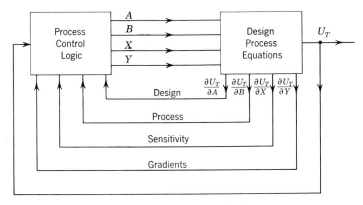

FIG. 7. Logic for controlling design process.

2. Exploration of various ways for performing the quasi-linearization process of eqs. 8, 9, and 10 to obtain a relatively simple relationship between changes in the parameters and in the system's objectives. It is quite evident that the ways for handling product, quotient, and other nonlinear combinations of terms must be given consideration.

3. Development of more exact mathematical models for the over-all utility of a system in terms of its appropriate significant objectives as described in eq. 11. Although this procedure will differ from system to system, the general form for the method to be employed may be one that lends itself to a reasonably standardized approach.

4. Development of process control logic design methods to facilitate the ready optimization of the design process subject to the process relationships that are said to exist for the objectives, restraints, and over-all utility factors.

CONCLUSIONS

The engineering of large and comprehensive industrial systems has been handled successfully in a number of fields. Increased emphasis and interest in such systems is being brought about by the advent of more and better information-gathering equipment to learn more of the nature of the system and by the necessity of optimizing the proper balance between such diverse factors as performance, cost, reliability, and time. Although the basic approach for handling the solution of the general systems engineering problem has been set forth, the need remains for obtaining more information on the quantitative relationships which exist between the desired end results and the parameters producing them. In addition, there is also need for further work on the development of more advanced control logic to permit more speedy optimization of the over-all system design.

The rapid and automatic optimization of industrial systems has been under way for some time now. The opportunity now exists for more extensive exploitation of these systems engineering ideas on a broader basis. Although much more work remains to be done, the direction has been indicated and the benefits to be gained warrant the effort.

REFERENCE

1. J. A. Morton, Integration of Systems Engineering with Component Development, *Electrical Manufacturing*, vol. 64, Aug. 1959, p. 85.

INDEX